MARY ANN CROSS, "GEORGE ELIOT."

(An Hitherto Unpublished Portrait from a Drawing by Mrs. Charles Bray.)

The Personal Edition of
GEORGE ELIOT'S WORKS

Miscellaneous Essays
Impressions of Theophrastus Such

THE VEIL LIFTED
BROTHER JACOB

Biographical Introduction
BY
ESTHER WOOD

Doubleday, Page & Co.
NEW YORK

Press of J. J. Little & Co.
Astor Place, New York

MISCELLANEOUS ESSAYS.

It was as an essayist, in the pages of the *Westminster Review*, that George Eliot made her entry into English literature,—or into the journalism that was nearer to literature than any journalism of to-day. It was as an essayist that she said her last words to us, in the *Impressions of Theophrastus Such*. Nearly thirty years—twenty of which were spent in novel-writing—separated the *Westminster* article on " Worldliness and Other-Worldliness " from the last of the *Impressions*. To turn back to the first essay is to call up in our minds the figure of the young authoress, brought suddenly into the best literary circle that the London of the fifties knew. In *Theophrastus Such* we meet the writer crowned with years and fame ; secure of her audience, and yielding, not unworthily, to the temptation to use up a little accumulated material.

The most surprising characteristic of these miscellanies is their uniformity of style and temper from first to last. The knowledge, the information of the writer keep pace with the years ; the point of view is not shifted by a hair's-breadth. Her art matures, grows from point to point, in many directions, between *Clerical Scenes* and *Silas Marner, Romola* and *The Mill on the Floss.* Her philosophy is already mature before the *Clerical Scenes* are written.

We have hinted that the gulf between journalism and literature in the fifties was bridged over by work of George Eliot's kind. Rather, the old-fashioned ideal of journalism was that of the essayist ;—a definition which makes it the more difficult to classify George Eliot's essays on the one side or the other. In subject-matter the majority of them are journalism merely, the treatment of one or two—the *Heine* particularly—sustains them under the tests of literature. "Reviewing" in those days was a weighty business ; press notices were not dashed off in a night ; space meted out to them by the thousand words, or much less generously. It was in 1850, on her return from the continent, where she spent the autumn after her father's death, that the way gradually opened up for a literary career. Her sole work of this nature hitherto had been her translations of Strauss's *Leben Jesu* and Spinoza's *De Deo*, which had come to her hand through her friendship with the Brays at Coventry. Already, during the last months spent at Foleshill with her father, her diaries and letters have given suggestive glimpses of the growth of her mind, and the spiritual struggles through which she was brought to reject many of those Christian doctrines which she had formerly held dear, and to lay hold of what she fully believed to be a truer, broader, and deeper religious life. " I say it now and I say it once for all," she declares passionately when the crisis is over, " that I am influenced in my own conduct at the present time by far higher considerations, and by a nobler ideal of duty, than I ever was while I held the evangelical beliefs." Another passage is admirably typical of that keener insight into the highest meaning of the gospel stories which came to her, as to many of us, as the reward of intellectual honesty. " I have been thinking of that most beautiful passage in Luke's gospel, the appearance of Jesus to the disciples at Emmaus. How universal in its significance ! The soul that has hopelessly followed its Jesus—its impersonation of the highest and best —all in despondency ; its thoughts all refuted, its dreams all dissipated ! Then comes another Jesus—another, but the same—the same highest and best, only chastened—crucified instead of triumphant—and the soul learns that this is the true way to conquest and glory. And then there is the burning of the heart which assures us that ' this was the Lord ! '—that this is the inspiration from above ; the true Comforter that leads unto truth." The translation of some of the more destructive parts of Strauss had been so painful to her that she confessed she could hardly have got through it but for the consoling image of the Risen Christ—a cast from Thorwaldsen's sculpture—which was ever before her in her little study at Foleshill. Yet all this time she was eagerly craving more activity for her whole nature. " I have a profound faith that the serpent's head will be bruised," she says. " This conscious kind of false life that is ever endeavoring to form itself within us, and eat away our true life, will be overcome by continued accession of vitality, by our perpetual increase in ' quantity of existence ' as Foster calls it. Creation is the super-added life of the intellect : sympathy, all-embracing love, the superadded moral life."

The visit to Geneva, where she made lifelong friends of M. and Mme. D'Albert, her host and hostess, formed a sort of rallying-point in the young writer's career. She returned home in March, 1850, having written a short time before : " I can only think with a shudder of returning to England. It looks to me like a land of gloom, of *ennui*, of platitude, but in the midst of all this it is the land of duty and affection, and the only ardent hope I have for my future life is to have given to me some woman's duty,—some possibility of devoting myself where I may see a daily result of pure calm blessedness in the life of another."

The circle of friends to whom she returned from Geneva was small indeed. Her brother and sister were both married. The trio formed by Mr. and Mrs. Charles Bray and Miss Sara Hennell made a real "home," however, and with them she stayed the spring and summer. Mr. Chapman, the publisher, and other literary visitors came frequently to Rosehill, and evidently fired " Miss Evans," as she was then, with ambitions towards London. " Will you send me," she writes to a friend, before she has been home many weeks, " an account of Mr. Chapman's prices for lodgers, and if you know anything of other boarding-houses, etc., in London ? Will you tell me what you can ? I am not asking you merely for the sake of giving you trouble. I am really anxious to know." Her review of Mackay's " Progress of the Intellect," which she wrote in the autumn of the same year, probably helped a good deal towards the carrying out of the London plan, by commending her to Mr. Chapman as a writer of a scholarly type. At the end of September she went to stay with the Chapmans at 142 Strand, as a boarder, and as assistant editor of the *Westminster Review*. . . . Miss Frederica Bremer was also boarding with the Chapmans at this time."

Her letters of the next four years are full of interest, both for the glimpses they give us of her own life, and for the light they throw on well-known figures in the literary circle to which she was now introduced. Froude she already knew ; an article of hers in the *Coventry Herald* in 1849—a review of his "Nemesis of Faith"—in which he thought he recognized her hand, had made him seek her acquaintance. A close and lifelong friendship with Herbert Spencer soon began. With Lewes she by no means fell in love at first sight. "I was introduced to Lewes the other day in Jeff's shop—a sort of miniature Mirabeau in appearance," she writes at the end of September (1851) ; but Mr. Cross adds that no friendship ensued until Herbert Spencer took Lewes to call upon George Eliot later in the year. Thenceforward the records become more cordial :—" Lewes as always, genial and amusing. He has quite won my liking in spite of myself. . . . He was describing ' Currer Bell ' to me yesterday as a little plain, provincial, sickly-looking old maid. Yet what passion, what fire in her ! "—" People are very good to me. Mr. Lewes especially is kind and attentive, and has quite won my regard, after having had a good deal of my vituperation. Like a few other people in the world, he is much better than he seems. A man of heart and conscience wearing a mask of flippancy."

Of the staff of the *Westminster Review*, and her editorial labors and anxieties, she writes with delightful humor and spontaneity to her old Coventry friends. "Carlyle," she says, "was very amusing the other morning to Mr. Chapman about the exhibition (1851). He has no patience with the Prince and ' that Cole ' assembling Sawneys from all parts of the land till you can't get along Piccadilly. . . . On Saturday afternoon came Mr. Spencer to ask Mr. Chapman and me to go to the theater ; so I ended the day in a godless manner seeing the 'Merry Wives of Windsor.' You must read Carlyle's denunciation of the opera, published in the *Keepsake*. He is a naughty fellow to write in the *Keepsake* and not for us, after I wrote him the most insinuating letter offering him three glorious subjects. . . . Carlyle called the other day, strongly recommending Browning the poet as a writer for the *Review*, and saying ' We shall see' about himself. Lewes says his article on ' Julia von Krudener' will be glorious. He sat in the same box with us at the ' Merry Wives of Windsor,' and helped to carry off the dolorousness of the play. . . . Harriet Martineau called on Monday morning with Mr. Atkinson. Very kind and cordial. Last Monday I was talking and listening for two hours to Pierre Laroux—a dreamy genius. George Sand has dedicated some of her books to him. . . . We are trying to get Mazzini to write on ' Freedom versus Despotism.' I must tell you a bit of Louis Blanc's English which Mr. Spencer was reciting the other night. The *petit homme* called on some one and said, ' I come to tell you how you are. I was at you the other day, but you were not.' "

Her review of Carlyle's " Life of Sterling " appeared in 1852. Her translation of Ludwig Feuerbach's *Essence of Christianity* was published in July, 1854, in Chapman's Quarterly Series, with her name on the title-page. This was the first and only time her maiden name of Mary Ann Evans appeared in print. She exchanged it a few weeks later for that of Lewes, and went with her husband to Weimar ; a happy sojourn which yielded an article, though not a very distinctive one, for the *Westminster Review*, and another for *Frazer's Magazine*. In October of the same year she contributed an essay on " Women in France : Madame de Sable." This was followed by " Evangelical Teaching : Dr. Cumming," in October, 1855 ; " German Wit : Heinrich Heine," January, 1856 ; " The Natural History of German Life : a review of Riehl," July, 1856 ; " Silly Novels by Lady Novelists," October, 1856 ; and " Worldliness and Other-Worldliness," " The Poet Young," January, 1857. Several of these are referred to in her letters :—" I have just

finished a long article on Heine which none of you will like."
(This was to the Brays and Miss Hennell.) "Since you
have found out the 'Cumming,' I write by to-day's post just
to say that it *is* mine, but also to beg that you will not mention it as such to any one likely to transmit the information
to London, as we are keeping the authorship a secret. The
article appears to have produced a strong impression, and
that impression would be a little counteracted if the author
were known to be a *woman.*" In after years her stepson,
Mr. Charles Lewes, tells Mr. Cross that he remembers it was
after reading this article that his father was prompted to
say to George Eliot, whilst walking one day with her in
Richmond Park, that it convinced him of the true genius in
her writing. Up to this time he had not been quite sure of
anything beyond great talent in her productions. In addition to these articles she was writing frequently for Mr.
Lewes's paper, *The Leader*, and pursuing the weighty task of
translating Spinoza's *Ethics* in what might almost ironically
be called spare hours. In 1856 she gradually withdrew from
the *Westminster*, and settled down with her husband to a
quieter life in their new home at 8 Park Shot, Richmond.

Yet those were rare Bohemian times in the early fifties at
Chapman's in the Strand ! Very often the young sub-editor
(for a journalist was still young at thirty in those palmy
days !) had to take her share in entertaining the literary lions
of the season, and being entertained in her turn with
theater, flower-shows, concerts, and fashionable festivals of
various kinds. "I had an invitation to the Parkes's to meet
Cobden," she writes, "one Saturday night. Heaven send
some lions to-night to meet Fox, who is coming." Again,—
"I *did* go to the Conversazione ; but you have less to regret
than you think. Mazzini's speeches are better read than
heard. . . . Grote is very friendly, and has propitiated J. S.
Mill, who will write for us when we want him . . . Harriet
Martineau's article on 'Niebuhr' will not go in the July
number. I am sorry for it,—it is admirable. After all, she
is a *trump*,—the only Englishwoman who possesses thoroughly the art of writing. . . . I had a pleasant talk with

Greg and Forster. Greg was 'much pleased to have made my acquaintance.' Forster, on the whole, appeared to think that people should be glad to make *his* acquaintance. . . . The opinions on the articles in the *Review* are, as before, ridiculously various. Greg says the article on India is ' very masterly,' while he calls Mazzini's ' sad stuff, mere verbiage.' Dickens is to preside at a meeting (of authors against the Booksellers' Association) in this house some day next week."

An amusing account of this meeting follows in another letter, describing "Dickens in the chair, preserving a courteous neutrality of eyebrows, and speaking with clearness and decision,"—Professor Owen with his " tremendous head" and his "silvery bland way" of speaking,—and George Cruikshank, " the most homely genuine-looking man, not unlike the pictures of Captain Cuttle." " The meeting," she says, " went off triumphantly, and I saluted Mr. Chapman with ' See the conquering Hero comes ' on the piano at 12 o'clock, for not till then was the last magnate, except Herbert Spencer, out of the house."

Very different is the picture we get of the George Eliot of twenty-five years later ; the author of the *Impressions of Theophrastus Such*. That early ardor and vivacity which her letters alone, of all her writings, ever show, are almost quenched by years of ill-health and a deepening sense of the responsibilities of authorship. Freshness of sentiment she never lost ; but it was with labor and tribulation that she "swept to her goal."

The writing of the Essays which comprise *Theophrastus Such* occupied the summer of 1878—the last summer that George Eliot and her husband spent together—at their beautiful country home, " The Heights," Witley, Surrey—only a few months before Lewes's death. Miss Betham-Edwards's description of her in her mature age corroborates that of Mr. Cross and other lovingly prejudiced admirers, when she says :—" Some people have talked of the ugliness of this great woman . . . because, forsooth, she lacked dimpled cheeks, round eyes, and pretty mouth ! If hers was ugliness, would we had more of it in the world ! When, in speaking, her large, usually solemn features lighted up, a positive light would flash from them, a luminosity irradiate not her own person only, but her surroundings. A sovereign nature, an august intellect, had transported us into its own atmosphere."

In October, 1878, there was an interesting meeting between George Eliot and Tourguénieff, at the house of a friend at Six-Mile-Bottom, near Newmarket. At dinner, Lewes proposed the health of the Russian guest, who gracefully repudiated the title of "the greatest living novelist" and transferred it to George Eliot. On the 28th of November George Henry Lewes died, and George Eliot wrote to her publisher, —"Pray do not announce 'Theophrastus' in any way. It would be intolerable to my feelings to have a book of my writings brought out for a long while to come." When she recovered enough to see visitors, her old friend Madame Bodichon came to call on her, and made this record of her visit :—"I spent an hour with Marian. She was more delightful than I can say, and left me in good spirits for her,— though she is wretchedly thin and looks in her long, loose, black dress like the black shadow of herself. She said she had so much to do that she must keep well,—' the world was so *intensely interesting.*' . . . We both agreed in the great love we had for life. In fact, I think she will do more for us than ever."

But George Eliot did no more,—save consenting to the publication of *Theophrastus* in the following May. Thus closed, with the death of Lewes, the chapter that had opened for her with his comradeship in the pages of the *Westminster Review.*

ESTHER WOOD.

PREFACE.

WISHES have often been expressed that the articles known to have been written by George Eliot in the *Westminster Review* before she had become famous under that pseudonyme, should be republished. Those wishes are now gratified — as far, at any rate, as it is possible to gratify them. For it was not George Eliot's desire that the whole of those articles should be rescued from oblivion. And in order that there might be no doubt on the subject, she made, some time before her death, a collection of such of her fugitive writings as she considered deserving of a permanent form, carefully revised them for the press, and left them in the order in which they here appear, with written injunctions that no other pieces written by her, of date prior to 1857, should be republished.

It will thus be seen that the present collection of Essays has the weight of her sanction, and has had, moreover, the advantage of such corrections and alterations as a revision long subsequent to the period of writing may have suggested to her.

The opportunity afforded by this republication seemed a suitable one for giving to the world some " notes," as George Eliot simply called them, which belong to a much later period, and which have not been previously published. The exact date of their writing cannot be fixed with any certainty, but it must have been some time between the appearan e of "Middlemarch" and that of "Theophrastus Such." They were probably written without any distinct view to publication, — some of them for the satisfaction of her own mind; others perhaps as memoranda, and with an idea of working them out more fully at some later time. It may be of interest to know that, besides the "notes" here given, the note-book contains four which appeared in "Theophrastus Such," three of them practically as they there stand; and it is not impossible that some of those in the present volume might also have been so utilized had they not happened to fall outside the general scope of the work. The marginal titles are George Eliot's own, but for the general title, "Leaves from a Note-book," I am responsible.

I need only add that, in publishing these notes, I have the complete concurrence of my friend, Mr. Cross.

CHARLES LEE LEWES.

HIGHGATE, *December,* 1883.

TABLE OF CONTENTS.

ESSAYS.

PAGE

WORLDLINESS AND OTHER-WORLDLINESS: THE POET YOUNG . . 9
(Westminster Review, 1857.)

GERMAN WIT: HEINRICH HEINE 63
(Westminster Review, 1856.)

EVANGELICAL TEACHING: DR. CUMMING 105
(Westminster Review, 1855.)

THE INFLUENCE OF RATIONALISM: LECKY'S HISTORY 139
(Fortnightly Review, 1865.)

THE NATURAL HISTORY OF GERMAN LIFE: RIEHL 157
(Westminster Review, 1856.)

THREE MONTHS IN WEIMAR 194
(Fraser's Magazine, 1855.)

ADDRESS TO WORKING MEN, BY FELIX HOLT 214
(Blackwood's Magazine, 1868.)

LEAVES FROM A NOTE-BOOK.

AUTHORSHIP 233
JUDGMENTS ON AUTHORS 238
STORY-TELLING 240
HISTORIC IMAGINATION 243
VALUE IN ORIGINALITY 245
TO THE PROSAIC ALL THINGS ARE PROSAIC 245

PAGE

"Dear Religious Love" 245

We make our own Precedents 246

Birth of Tolerance 246

Felix qui non potuit 247

Divine Grace a Real Emanation 247

"A Fine Excess." Feeling is Energy 248

IMPRESSIONS OF THEOPHRASTUS SUCH.

Looking Inward 253

Looking Backward 265

How we encourage Research 279

A man surprised at his Originality 293

A too Deferential Man 301

Only Temper 309

A Political Molecule 316

The Watch-Dog of Knowledge 320

A Half-Breed 327

Debasing the Moral Currency 334

The Wasp credited with the Honey-Comb 341

"So Young!" 353

How we come to give ourselves false Testimonials, and
   believe in them 359

The too Ready Writer 368

Diseases of Small Authorship 377

Moral Swindlers 386

Shadows of the Coming Race 395

The Modern Hep! Hep! Hep! 401

The Lifted Veil 427

Brother Jacob 475

GEORGE ELIOT'S ESSAYS.

FACING PAGE

FRONTISPIECE—MARY ANN CROSS, " GEORGE ELIOT." .

GRIFF HOUSE, WHERE GEORGE ELIOT LIVED AS A CHILD 194

" MELROSE," RICHMOND, SURREY, WHERE GEORGE ELIOT
LIVED 395

GEORGE ELIOT'S ESSAYS.

FACING PAGE

FRONTISPIECE—MARY ANN CROSS, " GEORGE ELIOT." .

GRIFF HOUSE, WHERE GEORGE ELIOT LIVED AS A CHILD   194

"MELROSE," RICHMOND, SURREY, WHERE GEORGE ELIOT
    LIVED   395

ESSAYS OF GEORGE ELIOT.

WORLDLINESS AND OTHER-WORLDLINESS: THE POET YOUNG.

THE study of men, as they have appeared in different ages and under various social conditions, may be considered as the natural history of the race. Let us, then, for a moment imagine ourselves as students of this natural history, dredging the first half of the eighteenth century in search of specimens. About the year 1730 we have hauled up a remarkable individual of the species *divine* — a surprising name, considering the nature of the animal before us, but we are used to unsuitable names in natural history. Let us examine this individual at our leisure. He is on the verge of fifty, and has recently undergone his metamorphosis into the clerical form. Rather a parodoxical specimen, if you observe him narrowly: a sort of cross between a sycophant and a psalmist; a poet whose imagination is alternately fired by the Last Day and by a creation of peers, who fluctuates between rhapsodic applause of King George and rhapsodic applause of Jehovah. After spending " a foolish youth, the sport of peers and poets," after being a hanger-on of the profligate Duke of Wharton, after aiming in vain at a parliamentary career, and angling for pensions and preferment with fulsome dedications and fustian odes, he is a little disgusted with his imperfect success, and has determined to retire from the general mendicancy business to a particular branch; in other words, he has determined on that renunciation of the world implied in " taking orders," with the prospect of a good living and an advantageous matrimonial connection. And no man can be better fitted for an Established Church.

He personifies completely her nice balance of temporalities and spiritualities. He is equally impressed with the momentousness of death and of burial fees ; he languishes at once for immortal life and for "livings ;" he has a fervid attachment to patrons in general, but on the whole prefers the Almighty. He will teach, with something more than official conviction, the nothingness of earthly things ; and he will feel something more than private disgust if his meritorious efforts in directing men's attention to another world are not rewarded by substantial preferment in this. His secular man believes in cambric bands and silk stockings as characteristic attire for "an ornament of religion and virtue," hopes courtiers will never forget to copy Sir Robert Walpole, and writes begging-letters to the King's mistress. His spiritual man recognizes no motives more familiar than Golgotha and "the skies ;" it walks in graveyards, or it soars among the stars. His religion exhausts itself in ejaculations and rebukes, and knows no medium between the ecstatic and the sententious. If it were not for the prospect of immortality, he considers, it would be wise and agreeable to be indecent, or to murder one's father ; and, heaven apart, it would be extremely irrational in any man not to be a knave. Man, he thinks, is a compound of the angel and the brute : the brute is to be humbled by being reminded of its "relation to the stalls," and frightened into moderation by the contemplation of death-beds and skulls ; the angel is to be developed by vituperating this world and exalting the next ; and by this double process you get the Christian, "the highest style of man." With all this, our new-made divine is an unmistakable poet. To a clay, compounded chiefly of the worldling and the rhetorician, there is added a real spark of Promethean fire. He will one day clothe his apostrophes and objurgations, his astronomical religion and his charnel-house morality, in lasting verse, which will stand, like a Juggernaut made of gold and jewels, at once magnificent and repulsive ; for this divine is Edward Young, the future author of the "Night Thoughts."

It would be extremely ill-bred in us to suppose that our readers are not acquainted with the facts of Young's life; they are amongst the things that "every one knows;" but we have observed that, with regard to these universally known matters, the majority of readers like to be treated after the plan suggested by Monsieur Jourdain. When that distinguished *bourgeois* was asked if he knew Latin, he replied, "Oui, mais faîtes comme si je ne le savais pas." Assuming, then, as a polite writer should, that our readers know everything about Young, it will be a direct *sequitur* from that assumption that we should proceed as if they knew nothing, and recall the incidents of his biography with as much particularity as we may, without trenching on the space we shall need for our main purpose — the reconsideration of his character as a moral and religious poet.

Judging from Young's works, one might imagine that the preacher had been organized in him by hereditary transmission through a long line of clerical forefathers, that the diamonds of the "Night Thoughts" had been slowly condensed from the charcoal of ancestral sermons. Yet it was not so. His grandfather, apparently, wrote himself *gentleman*, not *clerk;* and there is no evidence that preaching had run in the family blood before it took that turn in the person of the poet's father, who was quadruply clerical, being at once rector, prebendary, Court chaplain, and dean. Young was born at his father's rectory of Upham, in 1681. We may confidently assume that even the author of the "Night Thoughts" came into the world without a wig; but, apart from Dr. Doran's authority, we should not have ventured to state that the excellent rector "kissed, *with dignified emotion,* his only son and intended namesake." Dr. Doran doubtless knows this, from his intimate acquaintance with clerical physiology and psychology. He has ascertained that the paternal emotions of prebendaries have a sacerdotal quality, and that the very chyme and chyle of a rector are conscious of the gown and band.

In due time the boy went to Winchester College, and subsequently, though not till he was twenty-two, to Oxford, where, for his father's sake, he was befriended by the wardens of two colleges, and in 1708, three years after his father's death, nominated by Archbishop Tenison to a law-fellowship at All Souls. Of Young's life at Oxford in these years, hardly anything is known. His biographer, Croft, has nothing to tell us but the vague report that, when " Young found himself independent and his own master at All Souls, he was not the ornament to religion and morality that he afterwards became," and the perhaps apocryphal anecdote, that Tindal, the atheist, confessed himself embarrassed by the originality of Young's arguments. Both the report and the anecdote, however, are borne out by indirect evidence. As to the latter, Young has left us sufficient proof that he was fond of arguing on the theological side, and that he had his own way of treating old subjects. As to the former, we learn that Pope, after saying other things which we know to be true of Young, added, that he passed "a foolish youth, the sport of peers and poets ; " and, from all the indications we possess of his career till he was nearly fifty, we are inclined to think that Pope's statement only errs by defect, and that he should rather have said, "a foolish youth and middle age." It is not likely that Young was a very hard student, for he impressed Johnson, who saw him in his old age, as "not a great scholar," and as surprisingly ignorant of what Johnson thought " quite common maxims " in literature ; and there is no evidence that he filled either his leisure or his purse by taking pupils. His career as an author did not commence till he was nearly thirty, even dating from the publication of a portion of the "Last Day," in the "Tatler ; " so that he could hardly have been absorbed in composition. But where the fully developed insect is parasitic, we believe the larva is usually parasitic also, and we shall probably not be far wrong in supposing that Young at Oxford, as elsewhere, spent a good deal of his time in hanging about possible and actual patrons, and accommodating himself to their habits with considerable flexibility of conscience and of tongue ; being none

the less ready, upon occasion, to present himself as the cham-
pion of theology, and to rhapsodize at convenient moments
in the company of the skies or of skulls.   That brilliant profligate, the Duke of Wharton, to whom Young afterwards clung
as his chief patron, was at this time a mere boy; and, though
it is probable that their intimacy had commenced, since the
Duke's father and mother were friends of the old Dean, that
intimacy ought not to aggravate any unfavorable inference as
to Young's Oxford life.   It is less likely that he fell into any
exceptional vice, than that he differed from the men around
him chiefly in his episodes of theological advocacy and rhapsodic solemnity.   He probably sowed his wild oats after the
coarse fashion of his times, for he has left us sufficient evidence that his moral sense was not delicate; but his companions, who were occupied in sowing their own oats, perhaps
took it as a matter of course that he should be a rake, and
were only struck with the exceptional circumstance that he
was a pious and moralizing rake.

There is some irony in the fact that the two first poetical
productions of Young, published in the same year, were his
"Epistle to Lord Lansdowne," celebrating the recent creation
of peers, — Lord Lansdowne's creation in particular, — and the
"Last Day." Other poets, besides Young, found the device
for obtaining a Tory majority — by turning twelve insignificant
commoners into insignificant lords — an irresistible stimulus
to verse; but no other poet showed so versatile an enthusiasm, so nearly equal an ardor for the honor of the new
baron and the honor of the Deity.   But the twofold nature
of the sycophant and the psalmist is not more strikingly
shown in the contrasted themes of the two poems, than in
the transitions from bombast about monarchs to bombast
about the resurrection, in the "Last Day" itself.   The dedication of the poem to Queen Anne, Young afterwards suppressed, for he was always ashamed of having flattered a
dead patron.   In this dedication, Croft tells us, "he gives
her Majesty praise indeed for her victories, but says that the
author is more pleased to see her rise from this lower world,

soaring above the clouds, passing the first and second heavens, and leaving the fixed stars behind her ; nor will he lose her there, he says, but keep her still in view through the boundless spaces on the other side of creation, in her journey towards eternal bliss, till he behold the heaven of heavens open, and angels receiving and conveying her still onward from the stretch of his imagination, which tires in her pursuit, and falls back again to earth."

The self-criticism which prompted the suppression of the dedication, did not, however, lead him to improve either the rhyme or the reason of the unfortunate couplet —

> "When other Bourbons reign in other lands,
> And, if men's sins forbid not, other Annes."

In the "Epistle to Lord Lansdowne," Young indicates his taste for the drama ; and there is evidence that his tragedy of "Busiris" was "in the theatre" as early as this very year, 1713, though it was not brought on the stage till nearly six years later; so that Young was now very decidedly bent on authorship, for which his degree of B. C. L., taken in this year, was doubtless a magical equipment. Another poem, "The Force of Religion ; or, Vanquished Love," founded on the execution of Lady Jane Grey and her husband, quickly followed, showing fertility in feeble and tasteless verse ; and on the Queen's death, in 1714, Young lost no time in making a poetical lament for a departed patron a vehicle for extravagant laudation of the new monarch. No further literary production of his appeared until 1716, when a Latin oration, which he delivered on the foundation of the Codrington Library at All Souls, gave him a new opportunity for displaying his alacrity in inflated panegyric.

In 1717 it is probable that Young accompanied the Duke of Wharton to Ireland, though so slender are the materials for his biography, that the chief basis for this supposition is a passage in his "Conjectures on Original Composition," written when he was nearly eighty, in which he intimates that he had once been in that country. But there are many

facts surviving to indicate that for the next eight or nine
years, Young was a sort of *attaché* of Wharton's. In 1719,
according to legal records, the Duke granted him an annuity,
in consideration of his having relinquished the office of tutor
to Lord Burleigh, with a life annuity of £100 a year, on his
Grace's assurances that he would provide for him in a much
more ample manner. And again, from the same evidence, it
appears that in 1721 Young received from Wharton a bond
for £600, in compensation of expenses incurred in standing
for Parliament at the Duke's desire, and as an earnest of
greater services which his Grace had promised him on his
refraining from the spiritual and temporal advantages of
taking orders, with a certainty of two livings in the gift of
his college. It is clear, therefore, that lay advancement, as
long as there was any chance of it, had more attractions for
Young than clerical preferment; and that at this time he
accepted the Duke of Wharton as the pilot of his career.

A more creditable relation of Young's was his friendship
with Tickell, with whom he was in the habit of interchanging
criticisms, and to whom in 1719 — the same year, let us note,
in which he took his doctor's degree — he addressed his
"Lines on the Death of Addison." Close upon these followed
his "Paraphrase of part of the Book of Job," with a dedication to Parker, recently made Lord Chancellor, showing that
the possession of Wharton's patronage did not prevent Young
from fishing in other waters. He knew nothing of Parker,
but that did not prevent him from magnifying the new
Chancellor's merits; on the other hand, he *did* know Wharton, but this again did not prevent him from prefixing to his
tragedy, "The Revenge," which appeared in 1721, a dedication
attributing to the Duke all virtues as well as all accomplishments. In the concluding sentence of this dedication Young
naïvely indicates that a considerable ingredient in his gratitude was a lively sense of anticipated favors. "My present
fortune is his bounty, and my future his care, — which I will
venture to say will always be remembered to his honor; since
he, I know, intended his generosity as an encouragement to

merit, though, through his very pardonable partiality to one who bears him so sincere a duty and respect, I happen to receive the benefit of it." Young was economical with his ideas and images ; he was rarely satisfied with using a clever thing once, and this bit of ingenious humility was afterwards made to do duty in the "Instalment," a poem addressed to Walpole : —

> " Be this thy partial smile, from censure free ;
> 'T was meant for merit, though it fell on me."

It was probably "The Revenge," that Young was writing when, as we learn from Spence's anecdotes, the Duke of Wharton gave him a skull with a candle fixed in it, as the most appropriate lamp by which to write tragedy. According to Young's dedication, the Duke was "accessary" to the scenes of this tragedy in a more important way. "not only by suggesting the most beautiful incident in them, but by making all possible provision for the success of the whole." A statement which is credible, not indeed on the ground of Young's dedicatory assertion, but from the known ability of the Duke, who, as Pope tells us, possessed

> " each gift of Nature and of Art,
> And wanted nothing but an honest heart."

The year 1722 seems to have been the period of a visit to Mr. Dodington, of Eastbury, in Dorsetshire, — the " pure Dorsetian downs," celebrated by Thomson, — in which Young made the acquaintance of Voltaire; for in the subsequent dedication of his "Sea Piece" to "Mr. Voltaire," he recalls their meeting on "Dorset Downs ; " and it was in this year that Christopher Pitt, a gentleman-poet of those days, addressed an "Epistle to Dr. Edward Young, at Eastbury, in Dorsetshire," which has at least the merit of this biographical couplet —

> · " While with your Dodington retired you sit,
> Charmed with his flowing Burgundy and wit."

Dodington, apparently, was charmed in his turn, for he told Dr. Wharton that Young was "far superior to the French

poet in the variety and novelty of his *bon-mots* and repartees."
Unfortunately, the only specimen of Young's wit on this
occasion, that has been preserved to us, is the epigram represented as an extempore retort (spoken aside, surely) to
Voltaire's criticism of Milton's episode of sin and death : —

> " Thou art so witty, profligate, and thin,
>   At once we think thee Milton, Death, and Sin ; "

an epigram which, in the absence of " flowing Burgundy,"
does not strike us as remarkably brilliant.   Let us give Young
the benefit of the doubt thrown on the genuineness of this
epigram by his own poetical dedication, in which he represents himself as having " soothed " Voltaire's " rage " against
Milton " with gentle rhymes ; " though in other respects that
dedication is anything but favorable to a high estimate of
Young's wit.   Other evidence apart, we should not be eager
for the after-dinner conversation of the man who wrote, —

> " Thine is the Drama, how renowned !
>   Thine Epic's loftier trump to sound ;
>   *But let Arion's sea-strung harp be mine :*
>   *But where 's his dolphin ?   Know'st thou where ?*
>   *May that be found in thee, Voltaire !* "

The " Satires " appeared in 1725 and 1726, each, of course,
with its laudatory dedication and its compliments insinuated
amongst the rhymes.   The seventh and last is dedicated to
Sir Robert Walpole, is very short, and contains nothing in
particular except lunatic flattery of George the First and his
prime minister, attributing that royal hog's late escape from
a storm at sea to the miraculous influence of his grand and
virtuous soul ; for George, he says, rivals the angels : —

> " George, who in foes can soft affections raise,
>   And charm envenomed satire into praise.
>   Nor human rage alone his power perceives,
>   But the mad winds and the tumultuous waves,
>   E'en storms (Death's fiercest ministers !) forbear,
>   And in their own wild empire learn to spare.
>   Thus, Nature's self, supporting Man's decree,
>   Styles Britain's sovereign, sovereign of the sea."

As for Walpole, what *he* felt at this tremendous crisis —

> " No powers of language, but his own, can tell ;
> His own, which Nature and the Graces form,
> At will to raise, or hush, the civil storm."

It is a coincidence worth noticing, that this Seventh Satire was published in 1726, and that the warrant of George the First, granting Young a pension of £200 a year from Lady-day, 1725, is dated May 3, 1726. The gratitude exhibited in this Satire may have been chiefly prospective, but the " Instalment," a poem inspired by the thrilling event of Walpole's installation as Knight of the Garter, was clearly written with the double ardor of a man who has got a pension, and hopes for something more. His emotion about Walpole is precisely at the same pitch as his subsequent emotion about the Second Advent. In the " Instalment " he says, —

> " With invocations some their hearts inflame ;
> *I need no muse, a Walpole is my theme.*"

And of God coming to Judgment, he says, in the " Night Thoughts : " —

> " I find my inspiration is my theme ;
> *The grandeur of my subject is my muse.*"

Nothing can be feebler than this " Instalment," except in the strength of impudence with which the writer professes to scorn the prostitution of fair fame, the " profanation of celestial fire."

Herbert Croft tells us that Young made more than three thousand pounds by his " Satires," — a surprising statement, taken in connection with the reasonable doubt he throws on the story related in Spence's " Anecdotes," that the Duke of Wharton gave Young £2,000 for this work. Young, however, seems to have been tolerably fortunate in the pecuniary results of his publications ; and with his literary profits, his annuity from Wharton, his fellowship, and his pension, not to mention other bounties which may be inferred from the high merits he discovers in many men of wealth and position, we may fairly suppose that he now laid the foundation of the considerable fortune he left at his death.

It is probable that the Duke of Wharton's final departure for the Continent and disgrace at Court in 1726, and the consequent cessation of Young's reliance on his patronage, tended not only to heighten the temperature of his poetical enthusiasm for Sir Robert Walpole, but also to turn his thoughts towards the Church again, as the second-best means of rising in the world. On the accession of George the Second, Young found the same transcendent merits in him as in his predecessor, and celebrated them in a style of poetry previously unattempted by him — the Pindaric ode, a poetic form which helped him to surpass himself in furious bombast. " Ocean, an Ode : concluding with a Wish," was the title of this piece. He afterwards pruned it, and cut off, amongst other things, the concluding Wish, expressing the yearning for humble retirement which, of course, had prompted him to the effusion ; but we may judge of the rejected stanzas by the quality of those he has allowed to remain. For example, calling on Britain's dead mariners to rise and meet their " country's full-blown glory," in the person of the new King, he says : —

> " What powerful charm
> Can Death disarm ?
> Your long, your iron slumbers break ?
> *By Jove, by Fame,*
> *By George's name,*
> Awake ! awake ! awake ! awake ! "

Soon after this notable production, which was written with the ripe folly of forty-seven, Young took orders, and was presently appointed chaplain to the King. "The Brothers," his third and last tragedy, which was already in rehearsal, he now withdrew from the stage, and sought reputation in a way more accordant with the decorum of his new profession, by turning prose writer. But after publishing " A True Estimate of Human Life," with a dedication to the Queen, as one of the " most shining representatives " of God on earth, and a sermon, entitled " An Apology for Princes ; or, the Reverence due to Government," preached before the House of Commons, his Pindaric ambition again seized him, and he matched his former ode by another, called " Imperium Pelagi ; a Naval Lyric ; written in imitation of Pindar's spirit, occasioned by his Majesty's return from Hanover, 1729, and the succeeding Peace." Since he afterwards suppressed this second ode, we must suppose that it was rather worse than the first. Next came his two " Epistles to Pope, concerning the Authors of the Age," remarkable for nothing but the audacity of affectation with which the most servile of poets professes to despise servility.

In 1730 Young was presented by his college with the rectory of Welwyn, in Hertfordshire, and, in the following year, when he was just fifty, he married Lady Elizabeth Lee, a widow with two children, who seems to have been in favor with Queen Caroline, and who probably had an income — two attractions which doubtless enhanced the power of her other charms. Pastoral duties and domesticity probably cured Young of some bad habits ; but, unhappily, they did not cure him either of flattery or of fustian. Three more odes followed, quite as bad as those of his bachelorhood, except that in the third he announced the wise resolution of never writing another. It must have been about this time, since Young was now " turned of fifty," that he wrote the letter to Mrs. Howard (afterwards Lady Suffolk), George the Second's mistress, which proves that he used other engines, besides Pindaric ones, in " besieging Court favor." The letter is too characteristic to be omitted : —

MONDAY MORNING.

MADAM, — I know his majesty's goodness to his servants, and his love of justice in general, so well, that I am confident, if His Majesty knew my case, I should not have any cause to despair of his gracious favor to me.

Abilities.	Want.	
Good Manners.	Sufferings	
Service.	and	} for his majesty.
Age.	Zeal	

These, madam, are the proper points of consideration in the person that humbly hopes his majesty's favor.

As to *Abilities*, all I can presume to say is, I have done the best I could to improve them.

As to *Good manners*, I desire no favor, if any just objection lies against them.

As for *Service*, I have been near seven years in his majesty's, and never omitted any duty in it, which few can say.

As for *Age*, I am turned of fifty.

As for *Want*, I have no manner of preferment.

As for *Sufferings*, I have lost £300 per ann. by being in his majesty's service; as I have shown in a *Representation* which his majesty has been so good as to read and consider.

As for *Zeal*, I have written nothing without showing my duty to their majesties, and some pieces are dedicated to them.

This, madam, is the short and true state of my case.   They that make their court to the ministers, and not their majesties, succeed better.   If my case deserves some consideration, and you can serve me in it, I humbly hope and believe you will: I shall, therefore, trouble you no farther ; but beg leave to subscribe myself, with truest respect and gratitude,

Yours, &c.,

EDWARD YOUNG.

P. S.   I have some hope that my Lord Townshend is my friend ; if therefore soon, and before he leaves the court, you had an opportunity of mentioning me, with that favor you have been so good to show, I think it would not fail of success; and, if not, I shall owe you more than any. (*Suffolk Letters*, vol. i. p. 285.)

Young's wife died in 1741, leaving him one son, born in 1733.   That he had attached himself strongly to her two daughters by her former marriage, there is better evidence in the report, mentioned by Mrs. Montagu, of his practical kindness and liberality to the younger, than in his lamentations over the elder as the Narcissa of the "Night Thoughts." Narcissa had died in 1735, shortly after marriage to Mr. Temple, the son of Lord Palmerston ; and Mr. Temple himself, after a second marriage, died in 1740, a year before Lady Elizabeth Young.   These, then, are the three deaths supposed to have inspired "The Complaint," which forms the three first books of the "Night Thoughts : " —

> "Insatiate archer, could not one suffice ?
> Thy shaft flew thrice : and thrice my peace was slain :
> And thrice, ere thrice yon moon had filled her horn."

Since we find Young departing from the truth of dates, in order to heighten the effect of his calamity, or at least of his climax, we need not be surprised that he allowed his imagination great freedom in other matters besides chronology, and that the character of Philander can, by no process, be made to fit Mr. Temple. The supposition that the much-lectured Lorenzo, of the "Night Thoughts," was Young's own son, is hardly rendered more absurd by the fact that the poem was written when that son was a boy, than by the obvious artificiality of the characters Young introduces as targets for his arguments and rebukes. Among all the trivial efforts of conjectured criticism, there can hardly be one more futile than the attempt to discover the original of those pitiable lay-figures, the Lorenzos and Altamonts of Young's didactic prose and poetry. His muse never stood face to face with a genuine, living human being ; she would have been as much startled by such an encounter as a necromancer whose incantations and blue fire had actually conjured up a demon.

The "Night Thoughts" appeared between 1741 and 1745. Although he declares in them that he has chosen God for his "patron" henceforth, this is not at all to the prejudice of some half-dozen lords, duchesses, and right honorables, who have the privilege of sharing finely turned compliments with their co-patron. The line which closed the Second Night in the earlier editions —

> "Wits spare not Heaven, O Wilmington ! — nor thee " —

is an intense specimen of that perilous juxtaposition of ideas by which Young, in his incessant search after point and novelty, unconsciously converts his compliments into sarcasms ; and his apostrophe to the moon, as more likely to be favorable to his song if he calls her "fair Portland of the

skies," is worthy even of his Pindaric ravings. His ostentatious renunciation of worldly schemes, and especially of his
twenty years' siege of Court favor, are in the tone of one who
retains some hope, in the midst of his querulousness.

He descended from the astronomical rhapsodies of his
Ninth Night, published in 1745, to more terrestrial strains,
in his "Reflections on the Public Situation of the Kingdom,"
dedicated to the Duke of Newcastle; but in this critical year
we get a glimpse of him through a more prosaic and less re-
fracting medium. He spent a part of the year at Tunbridge
Wells; and Mrs. Montagu, who was there too, gives a very
lively picture of the "divine doctor," in her letters to the
Duchess of Portland, on whom Young had bestowed the superlative bombast to which we have recently alluded. We
shall borrow the quotations from Dr. Doran, in spite of their
length, because, to our mind, they present the most agreeable
portrait we possess of Young:—

"I have great joy in Dr. Young, whom I disturbed in a reverie.
At first he started, then bowed, then fell back into a surprise; then
began a speech, relapsed into his astonishment two or three times,
forgot what he had been saying; began a new subject, and so went on.
I told him your grace desired he would write longer letters; to which
he cried ' Ha!' most emphatically, and I leave you to interpret what
it meant. He has made a friendship with one person here, whom I
believe you would not imagine to have been made for his bosom friend.
You would, perhaps, suppose it was a bishop or dean, a prebend, a
pious preacher, a clergyman of exemplary life, or, if a layman, of most
virtuous conversation, one that had paraphrased St. Matthew, or wrote
comments on St. Paul. . . . You would not guess that this asso-
ciate of the doctor's was — old Cibber! Certainly in their religious,
moral, and civil character, there is no relation; but in their dramatic
capacity there is some." — [Mrs. Montagu was not aware that Cibber,
whom Young had named not disparagingly in his Satires, was the
brother of his old schoolfellow ; but to return to our hero.] "The
waters," says Mrs. Montagu, " have raised his spirits to a fine pitch, as
your grace will imagine, when I tell you how sublime an answer he
made to a very vulgar question. I asked him how long he stayed at
the Wells: he said, ' As long as my rival stayed ; — as long as the sun

did.' Among the visitors at the Wells were Lady Sunderland (wife
of Sir Robert Sutton) and her sister, Mrs. Tichborne. He did an
admirable thing to Lady Sunderland: on her mentioning Sir Robert
Sutton, he asked her where Sir Robert's lady was ; on which we all
laughed very heartily, and I brought him off, half ashamed, to my
lodgings, where, during breakfast, he assured me he had asked after
Lady Sunderland, because he had a great honor for her ; and that,
having a respect for her sister, he designed to have inquired after her,
if we had not put it out of his head by laughing at him. You must
know Mrs. Tichborne sat next to Lady Sunderland. It would have
been admirable to have had him finish his compliment in that manner. . . . His expressions all bear the stamp of novelty, and his
thoughts of sterling sense. He practises a kind of philosophical ab-
stinence. . . . He carried Mrs. Rolt and myself to Tunbridge, five
miles from hence, where we were to see some fine old ruins. . . .
First rode the doctor on a tall steed, decently caparisoned in dark
gray; next, ambled Mrs. Rolt on a hackney horse ; . . . then followed your humble servant on a milk-white palfrey. I rode on in
safety, and at leisure to observe the company, especially the two
figures that brought up the rear. The first was my servant, valiantly
armed with two uncharged pistols; the last was the doctor's man,
whose uncombed hair so resembled the mane of the horse he rode, one
could not help imagining they were of kin, and wishing, for the honor
of the family, that they had had one comb betwixt them. On his
head was a velvet cap, much resembling a black saucepan, and on his
side hung a little basket. At last we arrived at the King's Head,
where the loyalty of the doctor induced him to alight ; and then,
knight-errant-like, he took his damsels from off their palfreys, and
courteously handed us into the inn. . . . The party returned to
the Wells; and 'the silver Cynthia held up her lamp in the heavens'
the while. The night silenced all but our divine doctor, who sometimes uttered things fit to be spoken in a season when all nature seems
to be hushed and hearkening. I followed, gathering wisdom as I went,
till I found, by my horse's stumbling, that I was in a bad road, and
that the blind was leading the blind. So I placed my servant between
the doctor and myself; which he not perceiving, went on in a most
philosophical strain, to the great admiration of my poor clown of a
servant, who, not being wrought up to any pitch of enthusiasm, nor
making any answer to all the fine things he heard, the doctor, wondering I was dumb, and grieving I was so stupid, looked round and
declared his surprise."

Young's oddity and absence of mind are gathered from other sources besides these stories of Mrs. Montagu's, and gave rise to the report that he was the original of Fielding's "Parson Adams;" but this Croft denies, and mentions another Young, who really sat for the portrait, and who, we imagine, had both more Greek and more genuine simplicity than the poet. His love of chatting with Colley Cibber was an indication that the old predilection for the stage survived, in spite of his emphatic contempt for "all joys but joys that never can expire;" and the production of "The Brothers," at Drury Lane in 1753, after a suppression of fifteen years, was perhaps not entirely due to the expressed desire to give the proceeds to the Society for the Propagation of the Gospel. The author's profits were not more than £400, — in those days a disappointing sum; and Young, as we learn from his friend Richardson, did not make this the limit of his donation, but gave a thousand guineas to the Society. "I had some talk with him," says Richardson in one of his letters, "about this great action. 'I always,' said he, 'intended to do something handsome for the Society. Had I deferred it to my demise, I should have given away my son's money. All the world are inclined to pleasure; could I have given myself a greater by disposing of the sum to a different use, I should have done it.'" Surely he took his old friend Richardson for Lorenzo!

His next work was "The Centaur not Fabulous; in Six Letters to a Friend, on the Life in Vogue," which reads very much like the most objurgatory parts of the "Night Thoughts" reduced to prose. It is preceded by a preface which, though addressed to a lady, is, in its denunciations of vice, as grossly indecent and almost as flippant as the epilogues written by "friends," which he allowed to be reprinted after his tragedies in the latest edition of his works. We like much better than "The Centaur," "Conjectures on Original Composition," written in 1759, for the sake, he says, of communicating to the world the well-known anecdote about Addison's death-bed, and, with the exception of his poem on Resignation, the last thing he ever published.

The estrangement from his son which must have embittered the later years of his life, appears to have begun not many years after the mother's death. On the marriage of her second daughter, who had previously presided over Young's household, a Mrs. Hallows, understood to be a woman of discreet age, and the daughter (or widow) of a clergyman who was an old friend of Young's, became housekeeper at Welwyn. Opinions about ladies are apt to differ. "Mrs. Hallows was a woman of piety, improved by reading," says one witness. "She was a very coarse woman," says Dr. Johnson; and we shall presently find some indirect evidence that her temper was perhaps not quite so much improved as her piety. Servants, it seems, were not fond of remaining long in the house with her; a satirical curate, named Kidgell, hints at "drops of juniper" taken as a cordial (but perhaps he was spiteful, and a teetotaler); and Young's son is said to have told his father that "an old man should not resign himself to the management of anybody." The result was, that the son was banished from home for the rest of his father's lifetime, though Young seems never to have thought of disinheriting him.

Our latest glimpses of the aged poet are derived from certain letters of Mr. Jones, his curate, — letters preserved in the British Museum, and happily made accessible to common mortals in Nichols's "Anecdotes." Mr. Jones was a man of some literary activity and ambition, — a collector of interesting documents, and one of those concerned in the "Free and Candid Disquisitions," the design of which was "to point out such things in our ecclesiastical establishment as want to be reviewed and amended." On these and kindred subjects he corresponded with Dr. Birch, occasionally troubling him with queries and manuscripts. We have a respect for Mr. Jones. Unlike any person who ever troubled *us* with queries or manuscripts, he mitigates the infliction by such gifts as "a fat pullet," wishing he "had anything better to send; but this depauperizing vicarage [of Alconbury] too often checks the freedom and forwardness of my mind." Another day

comes a "pound canister of tea;" another, a "young fatted
goose." Clearly, Mr. Jones was entirely unlike your literary
correspondents of the present day; he forwarded manuscripts,
but he had "bowels," and forwarded poultry too. His first
letter from Welwyn is dated June, 1759, not quite six years
before Young's death. In June, 1762, he expresses a wish
to go to London "this summer. But," he continues, —

"My time and pains are almost continually taken up here, and . . .
I have been, I now find, a considerable loser, upon the whole, by continuing here so long. The consideration of this, and the inconveniences I sustained, and do still experience, from my late illness,
obliged me at last to acquaint the Doctor [Young] with my case, and
to assure him that I plainly perceived the duty and confinement here
to be too much for me; for which reason I must, I said, beg to be at
liberty to resign my charge at Michaelmas. I began to give him these
notices in February, when I was very ill; and now I perceive, by
what he told me the other day, that he is in some difficulty : for which
reason he is at last, he says, resolved to advertise, *and even, which
is much wondered at, to raise the salary considerably higher*. (What
he allowed my predecessors was £20 per annum ; and now he proposes
£50, as he tells me.) I never asked him to raise it for me, though I
well knew it was not equal to the duty ; nor did I say a word about
myself when he lately suggested to me his intentions upon this
subject."

In a postscript to this letter, he says : —

"I may mention to you farther, as a friend that may be trusted,
that, in all likelihood, the poor old gentleman will not find it a very
easy matter, unless by dint of money, *and force upon himself*, to procure a man that he can like for his next curate, *nor one that will stay
with him so long as I have done*. Then, his great age will recur to
people's thoughts; and if he has any foibles, either in temper or conduct, they will be sure not to be forgotten on this occasion by those
who know him; and those who do not, will probably be on their
guard. On these and the like considerations, it is by no means an
eligible office to be seeking out for a curate for him, as he has several
times wished me to do ; and would, if he knew that I am now writing
to you, wish your assistance also. But my best friends here, *who well
foresee the probable consequences*, and wish me well, earnestly dissuade

me from complying: and I will decline the office with as much decency as I can: but high salary will, I suppose, fetch in somebody or other, soon."

In the following July he writes: —

"The old gentleman here (I may venture to tell you freely) seems to me to be in a pretty odd way of late, — moping, dejected, self-willed, and as if surrounded with some perplexing circumstances. Though I visit him pretty frequently for short intervals, I say very little to his affairs, not choosing to be a party concerned, especially in cases of so critical and tender a nature. There is much mystery in almost all his temporal affairs, as well as in many of his speculative theories. Whoever lives in this neighborhood to see his exit, will probably see and hear some very strange things. Time will show, — I am afraid, not greatly to his credit. There is thought to be *an irremovable obstruction to his happiness within his walls, as well as another without them;* but the former is the more powerful, and like to continue so. He has this day been trying anew to engage me to stay with him. No lucrative views can tempt me to sacrifice my liberty or my health, to such measures as are proposed here. *Nor do I like to have to do with persons whose word and honor cannot be depended on.* So much for this very odd and unhappy topic."

In August, Mr. Jones's tone is slightly modified. Earnest entreaties, not lucrative considerations, have induced him to cheer the Doctor's dejected heart by remaining at Welwyn some time longer. The Doctor is, "in various respects, a very unhappy man," and few know so much of these respects as Mr. Jones. In September he recurs to the subject: —

"My ancient gentleman here is still full of trouble: which moves my concern, though it moves only the secret laughter of many, and some untoward surmises in disfavor of him and his household. The loss of a very large sum of money (about £200) is talked of; whereof this vill and neighborhood is full. Some disbelieve; others say, '*It is no wonder, where about eighteen or more servants are sometimes taken and dismissed in the course of a year.*' The gentleman himself is allowed by all to be far more harmless and easy in his family than some one else who hath too much the lead in it. This, among others, was one reason for my late motion to quit."

No other mention of Young's affairs occurs until April 2, 1765, when he says that Dr. Young is very ill, attended by two physicians.

"Having mentioned this young gentleman [Dr. Young's son], I would acquaint you next, that he came hither this morning, having been sent for, as I am told, by the direction of Mrs. Hallows. Indeed, she intimated to me as much herself. And, if this be so, I must say that it is one of the most prudent acts she ever did, or could have done in such a case as this; as it may prove a means of preventing much confusion after the death of the Doctor. I have had some little discourse with the son: he seems much affected, and I believe really is so. He earnestly wishes his father might be pleased to ask after him; for you must know he has not yet done this, nor is, in my opinion, like to do it. And it has been said, farther, that upon a late application made to him on the behalf of his son, he desired that no more might be said to him about it. How true this may be I cannot as yet be certain; all I shall say is, it seems not improbable . . . I heartily wish the ancient man's heart may prove tender towards his son; *though, knowing him so well, I can scarce hope to hear such desirable news.*"

Eleven days later he writes : —

"I have now the pleasure to acquaint you that the late Dr. Young, though he had for many years kept his son at a distance from him, yet has now at last left him all his possessions, after the payment of certain legacies; so that the young gentleman, who bears a fair character and behaves well, as far as I can hear or see, will, I hope, soon enjoy and make a prudent use of a handsome fortune. The father, on his death-bed, and since my return from London, was applied to in the tenderest manner, by one of his physicians and by another person, to admit the son into his presence, — to make submission, intreat forgiveness, and obtain his blessing. As to an interview with his son, he intimated that he chose to decline it, as his spirits were then low and his nerves weak. With regard to the next particular, he said, 'I *heartily forgive him;*' and upon mention of this last, he gently lifted up his hand, and letting it gently fall, pronounced these words, '*God bless him!*' . . . I know it will give you pleasure to be farther informed that he was pleased to make respectful mention of me in his will, — expressing his satisfaction in my care of his parish, *bequeathing to me a handsome legacy,* and appointing me to be one of his executors."

So far Mr. Jones, in his confidential correspondence with a "friend who may be trusted." In a letter communicated apparently by him to the "Gentleman's Magazine," seven years later, — namely, in 1782, — on the appearance of Croft's biography of Young, we find him speaking of "the ancient gentleman," in a tone of reverential eulogy, quite at variance with the free comments we have just quoted. But the Rev. John Jones was probably of opinion with Mrs. Montagu, whose contemporary and retrospective letters are also set in a different key, that "the interests of religion were connected with the character of a man so distinguished for piety as Dr. Young." At all events, a subsequent quasi-official statement weighs nothing as evidence against contemporary, spontaneous, and confidential hints.

To Mrs. Hallows, Young left a legacy of £1,000, with the request that she would destroy all his manuscripts. This final request, from some unknown cause, was not complied with, and among the papers he left behind him was the following letter from Archbishop Secker, which probably marks the date of his latest effort after preferment.

DEANERY OF ST. PAUL'S, July 8, 1758.

GOOD DR. YOUNG, — I have long wondered that more suitable notice of your great merit hath not been taken by persons in power. But how to remedy the omission I see not. No encouragement hath ever been given me to mention things of this nature to his Majesty. And therefore, in all likelihood, the only consequence of doing it would be weakening the little influence which else I may possibly have on some other occasions. *Your fortune and your reputation set you above the need of advancement; and your sentiments above that concern for it, on your own account,* which, on that of the public, is sincerely felt by

Your loving Brother,

THO. CANT.

The "loving Brother's" irony is severe!

Perhaps the least questionable testimony to the better side of Young's character, is that of Bishop Hildesley, who, as the vicar of a parish near Welwyn, had been Young's neigh-

bor for upwards of twenty years. The affection of the clergy
for each other, we have observed, is, like that of the fair sex,
not at all of a blind and infatuated kind; and we may therefore the rather believe them when they give each other
any extra-official praise. Bishop Hildesley, then writing of
Young to Richardson, says : —

> "The impertinence of my frequent visits to him was amply re-
> warded; forasmuch as, I can truly say, he never received me but
> with agreeable open complacency; and I never left him but with
> profitable pleasure and improvement. He was one or other, the most
> modest, the most patient of contradiction, and the most informing and
> entertaining I ever conversed with — at least, of any man who had so
> just pretensions to pertinacity and reserve."

Mr. Langton, however, who was also a frequent visitor of
Young's, informed Boswell —

> "That there was an air of benevolence in his manner; but that he
> could obtain from him less information than he had hoped to receive
> from one who had lived so much in intercourse with the brightest
> men of what had been called the Augustan Age of England; and that
> he showed a degree of eager curiosity concerning the common occur-
> rences that were then passing, which appeared somewhat remarkable
> in a man of such intellectual stores, of such an advanced age,
> and who had retired from life with declared disappointment in his
> expectations."

The same substance, we know, will exhibit different qualities under different tests; and, after all, imperfect reports of
individual impressions, whether immediate or traditional,
are a very frail basis on which to build our opinion of a man.
One's character may be very indifferently mirrored in the
mind of the most intimate neighbor; it all depends on the
quality of that gentleman's reflecting surface.

But, discarding any inferences from such uncertain evidence, the outline of Young's character is too distinctly traceable in the well-attested facts of his life, and yet more in the
self-betrayal that runs through all his works, for us to fear
that our general estimate of him may be false. For, while

no poet seems less easy and spontaneous than Young, no poet discloses himself more completely. Men's minds have no hiding-place out of themselves; their affectations do but betray another phase of their nature. And if, in the present view of Young, we seem to be more intent on laying bare unfavorable facts than on shrouding them in "charitable speeches," it is not because we have any irreverential pleasure in turning men's characters "the seamy side without," but because we see no great advantage in considering a man as he was *not*. Young's biographers and critics have usually set out from the position that he was a great religious teacher, and that his poetry is morally sublime; and they have toned down his failings into harmony with their conception of the divine and the poet. For our own part, we set out from precisely the opposite conviction — namely, that the religious and moral spirit of Young's poetry is low and false; and we think it of some importance to show that the "Night Thoughts" are the reflex of a mind in which the higher human sympathies were inactive. This judgment is entirely opposed to our youthful predilections and enthusiasm. The sweet garden-breath of early enjoyment lingers about many a page of the "Night Thoughts," and even of the "Last Day," giving an extrinsic charm to passages of stilted rhetoric and false sentiment; but the sober and repeated reading of maturer years has convinced us that it would hardly be possible to find a more typical instance than Young's poetry, of the mistake which substitutes interested obedience for sympathetic emotion, and baptizes egoism as religion.

Pope said of Young, that he had "much of a sublime genius without common sense." The deficiency Pope meant to indicate was, we imagine, moral rather than intellectual; it was the want of that fine sense of what is fitting in speech and action, which is often eminently possessed by men and women whose intellect is of a very common order, but who have the sincerity and dignity which can never coexist with the selfish preoccupations of vanity or interest. This was the "common sense" in which Young was conspicuously deficient; and it was partly owing to this deficiency that his genius, waiting to be determined by the highest prize, fluttered uncertainly from effort to effort, until, when he was more than sixty, it suddenly spread its broad wing, and soared so as to arrest the gaze of other generations besides his own. For he had no versatility of faculty to mislead him. The "Night Thoughts" only differ from his previous works in the degree and not in the kind of power they manifest. Whether he writes prose or poetry, rhyme or blank verse, dramas, satires, odes, or meditations, we see everywhere the same Young, — the same narrow circle of thoughts, the same love of abstractions, the same telescopic view of human things, the same appetency towards antithetic apothegm and rhapsodic climax. The passages that arrest us in his tragedies are those in which he anticipates some fine passage in the "Night Thoughts," and where his characters are only transparent shadows, through which we see the bewigged *embonpoint* of the didactic poet, excogitating epigrams or ecstatic soliloquies by the light of a candle fixed in a skull. Thus in "The Revenge," Alonzo, in the conflict of jealousy and love that at once urges and forbids him to murder his wife, says, —

> "This vast and solid earth, that blazing sun,
> Those skies, through which it rolls, must all have end
> What then is man ? The smallest part of nothing.
> Day buries day ; month, month ; and year, the year !
> Our life is but a chain of many deaths.
> Can then Death's self be feared ? Our life much rather:
> *Life is the desert, life the solitude ;*
> Death joins us to the great majority :
> 'T is to be born to Plato and to Cæsar ;
> 'T is to be great forever ;
> 'T is pleasure, 't is ambition, then, to die."

His prose writings all read like the "Night Thoughts," either diluted into prose, or not yet crystallized into poetry. For example, in his "Thoughts for Age," he says, —

" Though we stand on its awful brink, such our leaden bias to the world, we turn our faces the wrong way; we are still looking on our old acquaintance, *Time,* though now so wasted and reduced, that we can see little more of him than his wings and his scythe : our age enlarges his wings to our imagination ; and our fear of death, his scythe ; as Time himself grows less.   His consumption is deep; his annihilation is at hand."

This is a dilution of the magnificent image : —

> " Time in advance behind him hides his wings,
> And seems to creep decrepit with his age.
> Behold him when past by !   What then is seen
> But his proud pinions, swifter than the winds ? "

Again : —

" A requesting Omnipotence ?   What can stun and confound thy reason more ?   What more can ravish and exalt thy heart ?   It cannot but ravish and exalt ; it cannot but gloriously disturb and perplex thee, to take in all *that* thought suggests.   Thou child of the dust !   Thou speck of misery and sin !   How abject thy weakness, how great is thy power !   Thou crawler on earth, and possible (I was about to say) controller of the skies !   Weigh, and weigh well, the wondrous truths I have in view: which cannot be weighed too much ; which the more they are weighed, amaze the more ; which to have supposed, before they were revealed, would have been as great madness, and to have presumed on as great sin, as it is now madness and sin not to believe."

Even in his Pindaric odes, in which he made the most violent efforts against nature, he is still neither more nor less than the Young of the " Last Day," emptied and swept of his genius, and possessed by seven demons of fustian and bad rhyme.   Even here, his " Ercles' Vein " alternates with his moral platitudes, and we have the perpetual text of the " Night Thoughts : " —

> " Gold, pleasure buys ;
> But pleasure dies,
> For soon the gross fruition cloys ;
> Though raptures court,
> The sense is short ;
> But virtue kindles living joys, —

> " Joys felt alone !
> Joys asked of none !
> Which Time's and Fortune's arrows miss :
> Joys that subsist,
> Though fates resist,
> An unprecarious, endless bliss !

> " Unhappy they !
> And falsely gay !
> Who bask forever in success ;
> A constant feast
> Quite palls the taste,
> *And long enjoyment is distress.*"

In the "Last Day," again, which is the earliest thing he wrote, we have an anticipation of all his greatest faults and merits.   Conspicuous among the faults is that attempt to exalt our conceptions of Deity by vulgar images and comparisons, which is so offensive in the later "Night Thoughts." In a burst of prayer and homage to God, called forth by the contemplation of Christ coming to Judgment, he asks, " Who brings the change of the seasons ? " and answers, —

> " Not the great Ottoman, or Greater Czar;
> Not Europe's arbitress of peace and war ! "

Conceive the soul in its most solemn moments, assuring God that it does n't place his power below that of Louis Napoleon or Queen Victoria !

But in the midst of uneasy rhymes, inappropriate imagery, vaulting sublimity that o'erleaps itself, and vulgar emotions, we have in this poem an occasional flash of genius, a touch of simple grandeur, which promises as much as Young ever achieved.   Describing the on-coming of the dissolution of all things, he says, —

> " No sun in radiant glory shines on high ;
> *No light but from the terrors of the sky.*"

And again, speaking of great armies, —

> " Whose rear lay wrapt in night, while breaking dawn
> Roused the broad front, and called the battle on."

And this wail of the lost souls is fine : —

> " And this for sin ?
> Could I offend if I had never been ?
> But still increased the senseless, happy mass,
> Flowed in the stream, *or shivered in the grass ?*
> Father of mercies ! Why from silent earth
> Didst thou awake and curse me into birth ?
> Tear me from quiet, ravish me from night,
> And make a thankless present of thy light ?
> Push into being a reverse of thee,
> And *animate a clod with misery ?* "

But it is seldom in Young's rhymed poems that the effect of a felicitous thought or image is not counteracted by our sense of the constraint he suffered from the necessities of rhyme, — that " Gothic demon," as he afterwards called it, " which modern poetry tasting, became mortal." In relation to his own power, no one will question the truth of his dictum, that " blank verse is verse unfallen, uncurst; verse reclaimed, reinthroned in the true language of the gods; who never thundered nor suffered their Homer to thunder in rhyme." His want of mastery in rhyme is especially a drawback on the effects of his Satires; for epigrams and witticisms are peculiarly susceptible to the intrusion of a superfluous word, or to an inversion which implies constraint. Here, even more than elsewhere, the art that conceals art is an absolute requisite, and to have a witticism presented to us in limping or cumbrous rhythm is as counteractive to any electrifying effect, as to see the tentative grimaces by which a comedian prepares a grotesque countenance. We discern the process, instead of being startled by the result.

This is one reason why the Satires, read *seriatim*, have a flatness to us, which, when we afterwards read picked passages, we are inclined to disbelieve in, and to attribute to some deficiency in our own mood. But there are deeper reasons for that dissatisfaction. Young is not a satirist of a high order. His satire has neither the terrible vigor, the lacerating energy, of genuine indignation, nor the humor

which owns loving fellowship with the poor human nature it
laughs at; nor yet the personal bitterness which, as in Pope's
characters of Sporus and Atticus, ensures those living touches
by virtue of which the individual and particular in Art becomes the universal and immortal.   Young could never
describe a real, complex human being ; but what he *could* do,
with eminent success, was to describe, with neat and finished
point, obvious *types* of manners rather than of character, —
to write cold and clever epigrams on personified vices and
absurdities.   There is no more emotion in his satire than if
he were turning witty verses on a waxen image of Cupid, or
a lady's glove.   He has none of those felicitous epithets, none
of those pregnant lines, by which Pope's Satires have enriched
the ordinary speech of educated men.   Young's wit will be
found in almost every instance to consist in that antithetic
combination of ideas which, of all the forms of wit, is most
within reach of clever effort.   In his gravest arguments, as
well as in his lightest satire, one might imagine that he had
set himself to work out the problem, how much antithesis
might be got out of a given subject.   And there he completely succeeds.   His neatest portraits are all wrought on
this plan.   Narcissus, for example, who

> "Omits no duty ; nor can Envy say
> He missed, these many years, the Church or Play :
> He makes no noise in Parliament, 't is true ;
> But pays his debts, and visit when 't is due ;
> His character and gloves are ever clean,
> And then he can out-bow the bowing Dean ;
> A smile eternal on his lip he wears,
> Which equally the wise and worthless shares.
> In gay fatigues, this most undaunted chief,
> Patient of idleness beyond belief,
> Most charitably lends the town his face
> For ornament in every public place ;
> As sure as cards he to th' assembly comes,
> And is the furniture of drawing-rooms :
> When Ombre calls, his hand and heart are free,
> And, joined to two, he fails not — to make three ;
> Narcissus is the glory of his race ;

> For who does nothing with a better grace ?
> To deck my list by nature were designed
> Such shining expletives of human kind,
> Who want, while through blank life they dream along,
> Sense to be right and passion to be wrong."

It is but seldom that we find a touch of that easy slyness which gives an additional zest to surprise; but here is an instance : —

> " See Tityrus, with merriment possest,
> Is burst with laughter ere he hears the jest;
> What need he stay, for when the joke is o'er,
> His *teeth* will be no whiter than before."

Like Pope, whom he imitated, he sets out with a psychological mistake as the basis of his satire, attributing all forms of folly to one passion, — the love of fame, or vanity, — a much grosser mistake, indeed, than Pope's exaggeration of the extent to which the "ruling passion" determines conduct in the individual. Not that Young is consistent in his mistake. He sometimes implies no more than what is the truth — that the love of fame is the cause, not of all follies, but of many.

Young's satires on women are superior to Pope's, which is only saying that they are superior to Pope's greatest failure. We can more frequently pick out a couplet as successful than an entire sketch. Of the too emphatic Syrena he says : —

> " Her judgment just, her sentence is too strong;
> Because she 's right, she 's ever in the wrong."

Of the diplomatic Julia : —

> " For her own breakfast she 'll project a scheme,
> Nor take her tea without a stratagem."

Of Lyce, the old painted coquette : —

> " In vain the cock has summoned sprites away ;
> She walks at noon and blasts the bloom of day."

Of the nymph who, " gratis, clears religious mysteries : "—

> " 'T is hard, too, she who makes no use but chat
> Of her religion, should be barred in that."

The description of the literary *belle*, Daphne, well pre-
faces that of Stella, admired by Johnson : —

> " With legs tossed high, on her sophee she sits,
>   Vouchsafing audience to contending wits :
>   Of each performance she 's the final test ;
>   One act read o'er, she prophesies the rest ;
>   And then, pronouncing with decisive air,
>   Fully convinces all the town — *she 's fair*.
>   Had lonely Daphne Hecatessa's face,
>   How would her elegance of taste decrease !
>   Some ladies' judgment in their features lies,
>   And all their genius sparkles in their eyes.
>   But hold, she cries, lampooner ! have a care !
>   Must I want common sense because I 'm fair ?
>   Oh no ; see Stella : her eyes shine as bright
>   As if her tongue was never in the right ;
>   And yet what real learning, judgment, fire !
>   She seems inspired, and can herself inspire.
>   How then (if malice ruled not all the fair)
>   *Could Daphne publish, and could she forbear ? " *

After all, when we have gone through Young's seven Satires, we seem to have made but an indifferent meal. They
are a sort of fricassee, with some little solid meat in them,
and yet the flavor is not always piquant. It is curious to
find him, when he pauses a moment from his satiric sketching, recurring to his old platitudes : —

> " Can gold calm passion, or make reason shine ?
>   Can we dig peace or wisdom from the mine ?
>   Wisdom to gold prefer : " —

platitudes which he seems inevitably to fall into, for the
same reason that some men are constantly asserting their
contempt for criticism — because he felt the opposite so
keenly.

The outburst of genius in the earlier books of the " Night
Thoughts " is the more remarkable, that, in the interval between them and the Satires, he had produced nothing but his

Pindaric odes, in which he fell far below the level of his previous works. Two sources of this sudden strength were the
freedom of blank verse and the presence of a genuine emotion. Most persons, in speaking of the "Night Thoughts,"
have in their minds only the two or three first Nights; the
majority of readers rarely getting beyond these, unless, as
Wilson says, they "have but few books, are poor, and live in
the country." And in these earlier Nights there is enough
genuine sublimity and genuine sadness to bribe us into too
favorable a judgment of them as a whole. Young had only
a very few things to say or sing, — such as that life is vain,
that death is imminent, that man is immortal, that virtue is
wisdom, that friendship is sweet, and that the source of virtue is the contemplation of death and immortality, — and
even in his two first Nights he had said almost all he had to
say in his finest manner. Through these first outpourings of
"complaint" we feel that the poet is really sad, that the
bird is singing over a rifled nest; and we bear with his
morbid picture of the world and of life, as the Job-like lament
of a man whom "the hand of God hath touched." Death
has carried away his best-beloved, and that "silent land,"
whither they are gone, has more reality for the desolate one
than this world, which is empty of their love : —

> " This is the desert, this the solitude ;
> How populous, how vital, is the grave ! "

Joy died with the loved one : —

> " The disenchanted earth
> Lost all her lustre.   Where her glittering towers ?
> Her golden mountains, where ?   All darkened down
> To naked waste ; a dreary vale of tears :
> *The great magician 's dead !* "

Under the pang of parting, it seems to the bereaved man
as if love were only a nerve to suffer with, and he sickens at
the thought of every joy of which he must one day say, " *It
was.*" In its unreasoning anguish, the soul rushes to the
idea of perpetuity as the one element of bliss : —

> " O ye blest scenes of permanent delight !
> Could ye, so rich in rapture, fear an end, —
> That ghastly thought would drink up all your joy,
> And quite unparadise the realms of light."

In a man under the immediate pressure of a great sorrow, we tolerate morbid exaggerations ; we are prepared to see him turn away a weary eye from sunlight and flowers and sweet human faces, as if this rich and glorious life had no significance but as a preliminary of death ; we do not criticise his views, we compassionate his feelings. And so it is with Young in these earlier Nights. There is already some artificiality even in his grief, and feeling often slides into rhetoric ; but through it all we are thrilled with the unmistakable cry of pain, which makes us tolerant of egoism and hyperbole : —

> " In every varied posture, place, and hour,
> How widowed every thought of every joy !
> Thought, busy thought ! too busy for my peace !
> Through the dark postern of time long elapsed
> Led softly, by the stillness of the night, —
> Led like a murderer (and such it proves !)
> Strays (wretched rover !) o'er the pleasing past, —
> In quest of wretchedness, perversely strays ;
> And finds all desert now ; and meets the ghosts
> Of my departed joys."

But when he becomes didactic, rather than complaining, — when he ceases to sing his sorrows, and begins to insist on his opinions, — when that distaste for life, which we pity as a transient feeling, is thrust upon us as a theory, we become perfectly cool and critical, and are not in the least inclined to be indulgent to false views and selfish sentiments.

Seeing that we are about to be severe on Young's failings and failures, we ought, if a reviewer's space were elastic, to dwell also on his merits, — on the startling vigor of his imagery, on the occasional grandeur of his thought, on the piquant force of that grave satire into which his meditations continually run. But, since our limits are rigorous, we must content ourselves with the less agreeable half of the critic's duty; and we may the rather do so, because it would be difficult to say anything new of Young in the way of admiration, while we think there are many salutary lessons remaining to be drawn from his faults.

One of the most striking characteristics of Young is his *radical insincerity as a poetic artist.* This, added to the thin and artificial texture of his wit, is the true explanation of the paradox — that a poet who is often inopportunely witty has the opposite vice of bombastic absurdity. The source of all grandiloquence is the want of taking for a criterion the true qualities of the object described, or the emotion expressed. The grandiloquent man is never bent on saying what he feels or what he sees, but on producing a certain effect on his audience; hence he may float away into utter inanity without meeting any criterion to arrest him. Here lies the distinction between grandiloquence and genuine fancy or bold imaginativeness. The fantastic or the boldly imaginative poet may be as sincere as the most realistic; he is true to his own sensibilities or inward vision, and in his wildest flights he never breaks loose from his criterion — the truth of his own mental state. Now, this disruption of language from genuine thought and feeling is what we are constantly detecting in Young; and his insincerity is the more likely to betray him into absurdity, because he habitually treats of abstractions, and not of concrete objects or specific emotions. He descants perpetually on virtue, religion, "the good man," life, death, immortality, eternity — subjects which are apt to give a factitious grandeur to empty wordiness. When a poet floats in the empyrean, and only takes a bird's-eye view of the earth, some people accept the mere fact of his soaring for sublimity, and mistake his dim vision of earth for proximity to heaven. Thus, —

> " His hand the good man fixes on the skies,
> And bids earth roll, nor feels her idle whirl,"

may, perhaps, pass for sublime with some readers. But pause a moment to realize the image, and the monstrous absurdity of a man's grasping the skies, and hanging habitually suspended there, while he contemptuously bids the earth roll, warns you that no genuine feeling could have suggested so unnatural a conception.

Again, —

> "See the man immortal: him, I mean,
> Who lives as such ; whose heart, full bent on Heaven,
> Leans all that way, his bias to the stars."

This is worse than the previous example : for you can at least form some imperfect conception of a man hanging from the skies, though the position strikes you as uncomfortable, and of no particular use ; but you are utterly unable to imagine how his heart can lean towards the stars. Examples of such vicious imagery, resulting from insincerity, may be found, perhaps, in almost every page of the "Night Thoughts." But simple assertions or aspirations, undisguised by imagery, are often equally false. No writer whose rhetoric was checked by the slightest truthful intentions, could have said, —

> "An eye of awe and wonder let me roll,
> And roll forever."

Abstracting the more poetical associations with the eye, this is hardly less absurd than if he had wished to stand forever with his mouth open.

Again, —

> "Far beneath
> A soul immortal is a mortal joy."

Happily for human nature, we are sure no man really believes that. Which of us has the impiety not to feel that our souls are only too narrow for the joy of looking into the trusting eyes of our children, of reposing on the love of a husband or a wife, — nay, of listening to the divine voice of music, or watching the calm brightness of autumnal afternoons ? But Young could utter this falsity without detecting it, because, when he spoke of "mortal joys," he rarely had in his mind any object to which he could attach sacredness. He was thinking of bishoprics and benefices, of smiling monarchs, patronizing prime-ministers, and a "much indebted muse." Of anything between these and eternal bliss, he was but rarely and moderately conscious. Often, indeed, he sinks very much below even the bishopric, and seems to have no notion of earthly pleasure, but such as breathes gaslight and the fumes of wine. His picture of life is precisely such as you would expect from a man who has risen from his bed at two o'clock in the afternoon with a headache, and a dim remembrance that he has added to his "debts of honor:" —

> "What wretched repetition cloys us here!
> What periodic potions for the sick,
> Distempered bodies, and distempered minds?"

And then he flies off to his usual antithesis : —

> "In an eternity what scenes shall strike!
> Adventures thicken, novelties surprise!"

"Earth" means lords and levees, duchesses and Delilahs, South-Sea dreams and illegal percentage; and the only things distinctly preferable to these, are eternity and the stars. Deprive Young of this antithesis, and more than half his eloquence would be shrivelled up. Place him on a breezy common, where the furze is in its golden bloom, where children are playing, and horses are standing in the sunshine with fondling necks, and he would have nothing to say. Here are neither depths of guilt nor heights of glory; and we doubt whether in such a scene he would be able to pay his usual compliment to the Creator : —

> "Where'er I turn, what claim on all applause!"

It is true that he sometimes — not often — speaks of virtue as capable of sweetening life, as well as of taking the sting from death and winning heaven; and, lest we should be guilty of any unfairness to him, we will quote the two passages which convey this sentiment the most explicitly. In the one, he gives Lorenzo this excellent recipe for obtaining cheerfulness : —

> " Go, fix some weighty truth ;
> Chain down some passion; do some generous good ;
> Teach Ignorance to see, or Grief to smile ;
> Correct thy friend; befriend thy greatest foe ;
> Or, with warm heart, and confidence divine,
> Spring up, and lay strong hold on Him who made thee."

The other passage is vague, but beautiful, and its music has murmured in our minds for many years : —

> " The cuckoo seasons sing
> The same dull note to such as nothing prize
> But what those seasons from the teeming earth
> To doting sense indulge.   But nobler minds,
> Which relish fruit unripened by the sun,
> Make their days various ; various as the dyes
> On the dove's neck, which wanton in his rays.
> On minds of dove-like innocence possessed,
> On lightened minds that bask in Virtue's beams,
> Nothing hangs tedious, nothing old revolves
> In that for which they long, for which they live.
> Their glorious efforts, winged with heavenly hopes,
> Each rising morning sees still higher rise ;
> Each bounteous dawn its novelty presents
> To worth maturing, new strength, lustre, fame ;
> While Nature's circle, like a chariot wheel,
> Rolling beneath their elevated aims,
> Makes their fair prospect fairer every hour ;
> Advancing virtue in a line to bliss."

Even here, where he is in his most amiable mood, you see at what a telescopic distance he stands from mother Earth and simple human joys, — " Nature's circle rolls beneath." Indeed, we remember no mind in poetic literature that seems to have absorbed less of the beauty and the healthy breath of the common landscape than Young's. His images, often grand and finely presented, witness that sublimely sudden leap of thought, —

> " Embryos we must be till we burst the shell,
>   *Yon ambient azure shell*, and spring to life," —

lie almost entirely within that circle of observation which would be familiar to a man who lived in town, hung about the theatres, read the newspaper, and went home often by moon and star light.

There is no natural object nearer than the moon that seems to have any strong attraction for him; and even to the moon he chiefly appeals for patronage, and "pays his court" to her. It is reckoned among the many deficiencies of Lorenzo, that he "never asked the moon one question" — an omission which Young thinks eminently unbecoming a rational being. He describes nothing so well as a comet, and is tempted to linger with fond detail over nothing more familiar than the Day of Judgment and an imaginary journey among the stars. Once on Saturn's ring, he feels at home, and his language becomes quite easy : —

> " What behold I now ?
> A wilderness of wonders burning round,
> Where larger suns inhabit higher spheres ;
> Perhaps *the villas of descending gods !* "

It is like a sudden relief from a strained posture when, in the "Night Thoughts," we come on any allusion that carries us to the lanes, woods, or fields. Such allusions are amazingly rare, and we could almost count them on a single hand. That we may do him no injustice, we will quote the three best : —

> " Like *blossomed trees o'erturned by vernal storm,*
> Lovely in death the beauteous ruin lay.
>
> .   .   .   .
>
> In the same brook none ever bathed him twice :
> To the same life none ever twice awoke.
> We call the brook the same — the same we think
> Our life, though still more rapid in its flow ;
> Nor mark the much irrevocably lapsed
> And mingled with the sea.
>
> .   .   .   .
>
> The crown of manhood is a winter joy ;
> An evergreen that stands the northern blast,
> And blossoms in the rigor of our fate."

The adherence to abstractions, or to the personification of abstractions, is closely allied in Young to the *want of genuine emotion.* He sees Virtue sitting on a mount serene, far above the mists and storms of earth ; he sees Religion coming down from the skies, with this world in her left hand and the other world in her right; but we never find him dwelling on virtue or religion as it really exists — in the emotions of a man dressed in an ordinary coat, and seated by his fireside of an evening, with his hand resting on the head of his little daughter, in courageous effort for unselfish ends, in the internal triumph of justice and pity over personal resentment, in all the sublime self-renunciation and sweet charities which are found in the details of ordinary life. Now emotion links itself with particulars, and only in a faint and secondary manner with abstractions. An orator may discourse very eloquently on injustice in general, and leave his audience cold; but let him state a special case of oppression, and every heart will throb. The most untheoretic persons are aware of this relation between true emotion and particular facts, as opposed to general terms, and implicitly recognize it in the repulsion they feel towards any one who professes strong feeling about abstractions, — in the interjectional "humbug !" which immediately rises to their lips. Wherever abstractions appear to excite strong emotion, this occurs in men of active intellect and imagination, in whom the abstract term rapidly and vividly calls up the particulars it represents, these particulars being the true source of the emotion; and such men, if they wished to express their feeling, would be infallibly prompted to the presentation of details. Strong emotion can no more be directed to generalities apart from particulars, than skill in figures can be directed to arithmetic apart from numbers. Generalities are the refuge at once of deficient intellectual activity and deficient feeling.

If we except the passages in "Philander," "Narcissa," and "Lucia," there is hardly a trace of human sympathy, of self-forgetfulness in the joy or sorrow of a fellow-being, throughout this long poem, which professes to treat the various phases of man's destiny. And even in the "Narcissa" Night,

Young repels us by the low moral tone of his exaggerated
lament. This married step-daughter died at Lyons, and,
being a Protestant, was denied burial, so that her friends had
to bury her in secret, — one of the many miserable results
of superstition, but not a fact to throw an educated, still less
a Christian man, into a fury of hatred and vengeance, in contemplating it after the lapse of five years. Young, however,
takes great pains to simulate a bad feeling : —

> " Of grief
> And indignation rival bursts I poured,
> Half execration mingled with my prayer;
> Kindled at man, while I his God adored ;
> Sore grudged the savage land her sacred dust;
> Stamped the cursed soil; *and with humanity*
> (*Denied Narcissa*) *wished them all a grave.*"

The odiously bad taste of this last clause makes us hope
that it is simply a platitude, and not intended as witticism,
until he removes the possibility of this favorable doubt by
immediately asking, " Flows my resentment into guilt ? "

When, by an afterthought, he attempts something like
sympathy, he only betrays more clearly his want of it. Thus,
in the first Night, when he turns from his private griefs to
depict earth as a hideous abode of misery for all mankind,
and asks, —

> " What then am I, who sorrow for myself ? "

he falls at once into calculating the benefit of sorrowing for
others : —

> " More generous sorrow, while it sinks, exalts ;
> *And conscious virtue mitigates the pang.*
> Nor virtue, more than prudence, bids me give
> Swollen thought a second channel."   •

This remarkable negation of sympathy is in perfect consistency with Young's theory of ethics : —

> " Virtue is a crime,
> A crime to reason, if it costs us pain
> Unpaid."

If there is no immortality for man, —

> "Sense! take the rein; blind Passion, drive us on;
> And Ignorance! befriend us on our way.
> Yes, give the Pulse full empire; live the Brute,
> Since as the brute we die.   The sum of man,
> Of godlike man, to revel and to rot.
>
> .   .   .   .
>
> If this life's gain invites him to the deed,
> Why not his country sold, his father slain?
>
> .   .   .   .
>
> Ambition, avarice, by the wise disdained,
> Is perfect wisdom, while mankind are fools,
> And think a turf or tombstone covers all.
>
> .   .   .   .
>
> Die for thy country, thou romantic fool!
> Seize, seize the plank thyself, and let her sink.
>
> .   .   .   .
>
> As in the dying parent dies the child,
> Virtue with Immortality expires.
> Who tells me he denies his soul immortal,
> *Whate'er his boast, has told me he's a knave.*
> *His duty 't is to love himself alone;*
> *Nor care though mankind perish, if he smiles.*"

We can imagine the man who "denies his soul immortal," replying: "It is quite possible that *you* would be a knave, and love yourself alone, if it were not for your belief in immortality; but you are not to force upon me what would result from your own utter want of moral emotion.   I am just and honest, not because I expect to live in another world, but because, having felt the pain of injustice and dishonesty towards myself, I have a fellow-feeling with other men, who would suffer the same pain if I were unjust or dishonest towards them.   Why should I give my neighbor short weight in this world, because there is not another world in which I should have nothing to weigh out to him?   I am honest, because I don't like to inflict evil on others in this life, not because I'm afraid of evil to myself in another.   The fact is, I do *not* love myself alone, whatever logical necessity there may be for that in your mind.   I have a tender love for my

wife and children and friends, and through that love I sympathize with like affections in other men. It is a pang to me to
witness the sufferings of a fellow-being, and I feel his suffering the more acutely because he is *mortal*, — because his life
is so short, and I would have it, if possible, filled with happiness and not misery. Through my union and fellowship
with the men and women I *have* seen, I feel a like, though a
fainter, sympathy with those I have *not* seen; and I am able
so to live in imagination with the generations to come, that
their good is not alien to me, and is a stimulus to me to labor
for ends which may not benefit myself, but will benefit them.
It is possible that you may prefer to live the brute, to sell
your country, or to slay your father, if you were not afraid of
some disagreeable consequences from the criminal laws of another world; but even if I could conceive no motive but my own
worldly interest, or the gratification of my animal desire, I
have not observed that beastliness, treachery, and parricide
are the direct way to happiness and comfort on earth. And I
should say that, if you feel no motive to common morality,
but your fear of a criminal bar in heaven, you are decidedly
a man for the police on earth to keep their eye upon, since it
is matter of world-old experience that fear of distant consequences is a very insufficient barrier against the rush of immediate desire. Fear of consequences is only one form of
egoism, which will hardly stand against half-a-dozen other
forms of egoism bearing down upon it. And in opposition to
your theory that a belief in immortality is the only source of
virtue, I maintain that, so far as moral action is dependent
on that belief, so far the emotion which prompts it is not
truly moral, — is still in the stage of egoism, and has not yet
attained the higher development of sympathy. In proportion
as a man would care less for the rights and welfare of his
fellow if he did not believe in a future life, in that proportion
is he wanting in the genuine feelings of justice and benevolence; as the musician who would care less to play a sonata
of Beethoven finely in solitude than in public, where he was
to be paid for it, is wanting in genuine enthusiasm for music."

Thus far might answer the man who "denies himself immortal;" and — allowing for that deficient recognition of the finer and more indirect influences exercised by the idea of immortality which might be expected from one who took up a dogmatic position on such a subject — we think he would have given a sufficient reply to Young, and other theological advocates who, like him, pique themselves on the loftiness of their doctrine when they maintain that "Virtue with Immortality expires." We may admit, indeed, that if the better part of virtue consists, as Young appears to think, in contempt for mortal joys, in "meditation of our own decease," and in "applause" of God in the style of a congratulatory address to her Majesty, — all which has small relation to the well-being of mankind on this earth, — the motive to it must be gathered from something that lies quite outside the sphere of human sympathy. But for certain other elements of virtue, which are of more obvious importance to untheological minds, — a delicate sense of our neighbor's rights, an active participation in the joys and sorrows of our fellow-men, a magnanimous acceptance of privation or suffering for ourselves when it is the condition of good to others, in a word, the extension and intensification of our sympathetic nature, — we think it of some importance to contend, that they have no more direct relation to the belief in a future state than the interchange of gases in the lungs has to the plurality of worlds. Nay, to us it is conceivable that in some minds the deep pathos lying in the thought of human mortality — that we are here for a little while and then vanish away, that this earthly life is all that is given to our loved ones and to our many suffering fellow-men — lies nearer the fountains of moral emotion than the conception of extended existence. And surely it ought to be a welcome fact, if the thought of *mortality*, as well as of immortality, be favorable to virtue. Do writers of sermons and religious novels prefer that men should be vicious in order that there may be a more evident political and social necessity for printed sermons and clerical fictions? Because learned gentlemen are theological, are we

to have no more simple honesty and good-will? We can
imagine that the proprietors of a patent water-supply have a
dread of common springs; but, for our own part, we think
there cannot be too great a security against a lack of fresh
water or of pure morality. To us it is a matter of unmixed
rejoicing that this latter necessary of healthful life is independent of theological ink, and that its evolution is ensured
in the interaction of human souls, as certainly as the evolution
of science or of art, with which, indeed, it is but a twin ray,
melting into them with undefinable limits.

To return to Young. We can often detect a man's deficiencies in what he admires, more clearly than in what he con-
temns, — in the sentiments he presents as laudable, rather
than in those he decries. And in Young's notion of what is
lofty he casts a shadow by which we can measure him without further trouble. For example, in arguing for human
immortality, he says: —

> " First, what is *true ambition?* The pursuit
> Of glory *nothing less than man can share.*
>
> .   .   .   .   .
>
> The Visible and Present are for brutes,
> A slender portion, and a narrow bound!
> These Reason, with an energy divine,
> O'erleaps, and claims the Future and Unseen, —
> The vast Unseen, the Future fathomless!
> When the great soul buoys up to this high point,
> Leaving gross Nature's sediments below,
> Then, and then only, Adam's offspring quits
> The sage and hero of the fields and woods,
> Asserts his rank, and rises into man."

So, then, if it were certified that, as some benevolent minds
have tried to infer, our dumb fellow-creatures would share a
future existence, in which it is to be hoped we should neither
beat, starve, nor maim them, our ambition for a future life
would cease to be "lofty!" This is a notion of loftiness
which may pair off with Dr. Whewell's celebrated observation,
that Bentham's moral theory is low, because it includes justice and mercy to brutes.

But, for a reflection of Young's moral personality on a colossal scale, we must turn to those passages where his rhetoric is at its utmost stretch of inflation — where he addresses the Deity, discourses of the divine operations, or describes the Last Judgment. As a compound of vulgar pomp, crawling adulation, and hard selfishness, presented under the guise of piety, there are few things in literature to surpass the Ninth Night, entitled "Consolation," especially in the pages where he describes the Last Judgment, — a subject to which, with naïve self-betrayal, he applies phraseology favored by the exuberant penny-a-liner. Thus, when God descends, and the groans of hell are opposed by "shouts of joy," — much as cheers and groans contend at a public meeting where the resolutions are *not* passed unanimously, — the poet completes his climax in this way : —

> "Hence, in one peal of loud, eternal praise,
> The *charmed spectators* thunder their applause."

In the same taste, he sings : —

> "Eternity, the various sentence past,
> Assigns the severed throng distinct abodes,
> *Sulphureous or ambrosial.*"

Exquisite delicacy of indication! He is too nice to be specific as to the interior of the "sulphureous" abode; but when once half the human race are shut up there, hear how he enjoys turning the key on them! —

> "What ensues?
> The deed predominant, the deed of deeds!
> Which makes a hell of hell, a *heaven of heaven!*
> The goddess, with determined aspect, turns
> Her adamantine key's enormous size
> Through destiny's inextricable wards,
> *Deep driving every bolt* on both their fates.
> Then, from the crystal battlements of heaven,
> Down, down she hurls it through the dark profound,
> Ten thousand, thousand fathom; there to rust
> And ne'er unlock her resolution more.
> The deep resounds; and hell, through all her glooms,
> Returns, in groans, the melancholy roar."

This is one of the blessings for which Dr. Young thanks God "most : " —

> "For all I bless thee, most, for the severe ;
> Her death — my own at hand — *the fiery gulf,*
> *That flaming bound of wrath omnipotent !*
> *It thunders ; but it thunders to preserve ;*
> . . . . . its wholesome dread
> Averts the dreaded pain ; *its hideous groans*
> *Join heaven's sweet Hallelujahs in thy praise,*
> Great Source of good alone !　How kind in all !
> In vengeance kind !　Pain, Death, Gehenna, *save* " . . .

i. e., save *me,* Dr. Young; who, in return for that favor, promise to give my divine patron the monopoly of that exuberance in laudatory epithet, of which specimens may be seen at any moment in a large number of dedications and odes to kings, queens, prime-ministers, and other persons of distinction. *That,* in Young's conception, is what God delights in.　His crowning aim in the drama of the ages is to vindicate his own renown.　The God of the "Night Thoughts" is simply Young himself, "writ large," — a didactic poet, who "lectures" mankind in the antithetic hyperbole of mortal and immortal joys, earth and the stars, hell and heaven, and expects the tribute of inexhaustible "applause."　Young has no conception of religion as anything else than egoism turned heavenward; and he does not merely imply this, he insists on it.　Religion, he tells us, in argumentative passages too long to quote, is "ambition, pleasure, and the love of gain," directed towards the joys of the future life instead of the present.　And his ethics correspond to his religion.　He vacillates, indeed, in his ethical theory, and shifts his position in order to suit his immediate purpose in argument; but he never changes his level so as to see beyond the horizon of mere selfishness.　Sometimes he insists, as we have seen, that the belief in a future life is the only basis of morality; but elsewhere he tells us —

> "In self-applause is virtue's golden prize."

Virtue, with Young, must always squint, — must never look straight towards the immediate object of its emotion and effort. Thus, if a man risks perishing in the snow himself, rather than forsake a weaker comrade, he must either do this because his hopes and fears are directed to another world, or because he desires to applaud himself afterwards! Young, if we may believe him, would despise the action as folly unless it had these motives. Let us hope he was not so bad as he pretended to be! The tides of the divine life in man move under the thickest ice of theory.

Another indication of Young's deficiency in moral — *i. e.*, in sympathetic — emotion, is his unintermitting habit of peda- gogic moralizing. On its theoretic and perceptive side, moral- ity touches science ; on its emotional side, art. Now, the products of art are great in proportion as they result from that immediate prompting of innate power which we call Genius, and not from labored obedience to a theory or rule ; and the presence of genius or innate prompting is directly op- posed to the perpetual consciousness of a rule. The action of faculty is imperious, and excludes the reflection *why* it should act. In the same way, in proportion as morality is emotional, *i. e.*, has affinity with art, it will exhibit itself in direct sympathetic feeling and action, and not as the recognition of a rule. Love does not say, "I ought to love," — it loves. Pity does not say, "It is right to be pitiful," — it pities. Justice does not say, "I am bound to be just," — it feels justly. It is only where moral emotion is comparatively weak that the contemplation of a rule or theory habitually mingles with its action ; and in accordance with this, we think experience, both in literature and life, has shown that the minds which are pre-eminently didactic — which in- sist on a lesson, and despise everything that will not convey a moral — are deficient in sympathetic emotion. A certain poet is recorded to have said, that he "wished everything of his burnt that did not impress some moral ; even in love- verses, it might be flung in by the way." What poet was it who took this medicinal view of poetry ? Dr. Watts, or

James Montgomery, or some other singer of spotless life and ardent piety? Not at all. It was Waller. A significant fact in relation to our position, that the predominant didactic tendency proceeds rather from the poet's perception that it is good for other men to be moral, than from any overflow of moral feeling in himself! A man who is perpetually thinking in apothegms, who has an unintermittent flux of admonition, can have little energy left for simple emotion. And this is the case with Young. In his highest flights of contemplation, and his most wailing soliloquies, he interrupts himself to fling an admonitory parenthesis at Lorenzo, or to hint that "folly's creed" is the reverse of his own. Before his thoughts can flow, he must fix his eye on an imaginary miscreant, who gives unlimited scope for lecturing, and recriminates just enough to keep the spring of admonition and argument going to the extent of nine Books. It is curious to see how this pedagogic habit of mind runs through Young's contemplation of Nature. As the tendency to see our own sadness reflected in the external world has been called by Mr. Ruskin the "pathetic fallacy," so we may call Young's disposition, to see a rebuke or a warning in every natural object, the "pedagogic fallacy." To his mind, the heavens are "for ever *scolding* as they shine;" and the great function of the stars is to be a "lecture to mankind." The conception of the Deity as a didactic author is not merely an implicit point of view with him; he works it out in elaborate imagery, and at length makes it the occasion of his most extraordinary achievement in the "art of sinking," by exclaiming, *apropos*, we need hardly say, of the nocturnal heavens : —

> "Divine Instructor! Thy first volume this
> For man's perusal! all in CAPITALS!"

It is this pedagogic tendency, this sermonizing attitude of Young's mind, which produces the wearisome monotony of his pauses. After the first two or three Nights, he is rarely singing, rarely pouring forth any continuous melody inspired by the spontaneous flow of thought or feeling. He is rather occupied with argumentative insistence, with hammering in the proofs of his propositions by disconnected verses, which he puts down at intervals. The perpetual recurrence of the pause at the end of the line throughout long passages, makes them as fatiguing to the ear as a monotonous chant, which consists of the endless repetition of one short musical phrase. For example : —

> " Past hours,
> If not by guilt, yet wound us by their flight,
> If folly bound our prospect by the grave,
> All feeling of futurity be numbed,
> All godlike passion for eternals quenched,
> All relish of realities expired ;
> Renounced all correspondence with the skies ;
> Our freedom chained ; quite wingless our desire ;
> In sense dark-prisoned all that ought to soar ;
> Prone to the centre ; crawling in the dust ;
> Dismounted every great and glorious aim ;
> Enthralled every faculty divine,
> Heart-buried in the rubbish of the world."

How different from the easy, graceful melody of Cowper's blank verse ! Indeed, it is hardly possible to criticise Young, without being reminded at every step of the contrast presented to him by Cowper. And this contrast urges itself upon us the more from the fact that there is, to a certain extent, a parallelism between the " Night Thoughts " and the " Task." In both poems the author achieves his greatest, in virtue of the new freedom conferred by blank verse ; both poems are professedly didactic, and mingle much satire with their graver meditations ; both poems are the productions of men whose estimate of this life was formed by the light of a belief in immortality, and who were intensely attached to Christianity. On some grounds we might have anticipated a more morbid view of things from Cowper than from Young. Cowper's religion was dogmatically the more gloomy, for he was a Calvinist ; while Young was a " low " Arminian, — believing that Christ died for all, and that the only obstacle to any man's salvation lay in his will, which he could change if

he chose. There was real and deep sadness involved in Cowper's personal lot; while Young, apart from his ambitious
and greedy discontent, seems to have had no great sorrow.

Yet, see how a lovely, sympathetic nature manifests itself
in spite of creed and circumstance ! Where is the poem that
surpasses the "Task," — in the genuine love it breathes, at
once towards inanimate and animate existence; in truthfulness of perception and sincerity of presentation; in the calm
gladness that springs from a delight in objects for their own
sake, without self-reference; in divine sympathy with the
lowliest pleasures, with the most short-lived capacity for
pain ? Here is no railing at the earth's "melancholy map,"
but the happiest lingering over her simplest scenes with all
the fond minuteness of attention that belongs to love ; no
pompous rhetoric about the inferiority of the brutes, but a
warm plea on their behalf against man's inconsiderateness
and cruelty, and a sense of enlarged happiness from their
companionship in enjoyment; no vague rant about human
misery and human virtue, but that close and vivid presentation of particular sorrows and privations, of particular deeds
and misdeeds, which is the direct road to the emotions. How
Cowper's exquisite mind falls with the mild warmth of morning sunlight on the commonest objects, at once disclosing
every detail, and investing every detail with beauty ! No object is too small to prompt his song, — not the sooty film on
the bars, or the spoutless teapot holding a bit of mignonette,
that serves to cheer the dingy town-lodging with a "hint that
Nature lives;" and yet his song is never trivial, for he is
alive to small objects, not because his mind is narrow, but because his glance is clear and his heart is large. Instead of
trying to edify us by supercilious allusions to the brutes
and the stalls, he interests us in that tragedy of the hen-
roost, when the thief has wrenched the door,

> " Where Chanticleer amidst his harem sleeps
> *in unsuspecting pomp;* "

in the patient cattle, that on the winter's morning

> " Mourn in corners where the fence
> Screens them, and seem half petrified to sleep
> *In unrecumbent sadness ;* "

in the little squirrel, that, surprised by him in his woodland
walk,

> " At once, swift as a bird,
> Ascends the neighboring beech ; there whisks his brush,
> And perks his ears, and stamps, and cries aloud,
> With all the prettiness of feigned alarm
> And anger insignificantly fierce."

And then he passes into reflection, not with curt apothegm
and snappish reproof, but with that melodious flow of utterance which belongs to thought when it is carried along in a
stream of feeling : —

> " The heart is hard in nature, and unfit
> For human fellowship, — as being void
> Of sympathy, and therefore dead alike
> To love and friendship both, — that is not pleased
> With sight of animals enjoying life,
> Nor feels their happiness augment his own."

His large and tender heart embraces the most every-day forms
of human life — the carter driving his team through the
wintry storm ; the cottager's wife who, painfully nursing the
embers on her hearth, while her infants " sit cowering o'er
the sparks,"

> " Retires, content to quake, so they be warmed ; "

or the villager, with her little ones, going out to pick

> " A cheap but wholesome salad from the brook ; "

and he compels our colder natures to follow his in its manifold sympathies, not by exhortations, not by telling us to
meditate at midnight, to indulge the thought of death, or
to ask ourselves how we shall " weather an eternal night,"
*but by presenting to us the object of his compassion truthfully
and lovingly.*   And when he handles greater themes, when he
takes a wider survey, and considers the men or the deeds

which have a direct influence on the welfare of communities
and nations, there is the same unselfish warmth of feeling,
the same scrupulous truthfulness. He is never vague in his
remonstrance or his satire; but puts his finger on some particular vice or folly, which excites his indignation or "dis-
solves his heart in pity," because of some specific injury it
does to his fellow-man or to a sacred cause. And when he is
asked why he interests himself about the sorrows and wrongs
of others, hear what is the reason he gives. Not, like Young,
that the movements of the planets show a mutual dependence,
and that, —

> " Thus man his sovereign duty learns in this
>   Material picture of benevolence ; "

or that, —

> " More generous sorrow while it sinks, exalts,
>   And conscious virtue mitigates the pang."

What is Cowper's answer, when he imagines some " sage
erudite, profound," asking him " What 's the world to
you ? " —

> " Much. *I was born of woman, and drew milk*
>   *As sweet as charity from human breasts.*
>   I think, articulate, I laugh and weep,
>   And exercise all functions of a man.
>   How then should I and any man that lives
>   Be strangers to each other ? "

Young is astonished that men can make war on each other
— that any one can " seize his brother's throat," while

> " The Planets cry, ' Forbear.' "

Cowper weeps because

> " There is no flesh in man's obdurate heart :
>   *It does not feel for man.*"

Young applauds God as a monarch with an empire, and a
court quite superior to the English, or as an author who produces "volumes for man's perusal." Cowper sees his Father's
love in all the gentle pleasures of the home fireside, in the
charms even of the wintry landscape, and thinks, —

> " Happy who walks with him! whom what he finds
> Of flavor or of scent in fruit or flower,
> Or what he views of beautiful or grand
> In nature, from the broad, majestic oak
> To the green blade that twinkles in the sun,
> *Prompts with remembrance of a present God.*"

To conclude, — for we must arrest ourselves in a contrast that would lead us beyond our bounds, — Young flies for his utmost consolation to the Day of Judgment, when

> " Final Ruin fiercely drives
> Her ploughshare o'er creation ; "

when earth, stars, and sun are swept aside, —

> " And now, all dross removed, heaven's own pure day,
> Full on the confines of our ether, flames :
> While (dreadful contrast !) far (how far !) beneath,
> Hell, bursting, belches forth her blazing seas,
> And storms sulphureous ; her voracious jaws
> Expanding wide, and roaring for her prey," —

Dr. Young, and similar " ornaments of religion and virtue," passing of course with grateful " applause " into the upper region. Cowper finds his highest inspiration in the Millennium — in the restoration of this, our beloved home of earth, to perfect holiness and bliss, when the Supreme

> " Shall visit earth in mercy ; shall descend
> Propitious in his chariot paved with love ;
> And what his storms have blasted and defaced
> For man's revolt, shall with a smile repair."

And into what delicious melody his song flows at the thought of that blessedness to be enjoyed by future generations on earth ! —

> " The dwellers in the vales and on the rocks
> Shout to each other, and the mountain-tops
> From distant mountains catch the flying joy ;
> Till, nation after nation taught the strain,
> Earth rolls the rapturous Hosanna round ! "

The sum of our comparison is this : In Young we have the type of that deficient human sympathy, that impiety towards

the present and the visible, which flies for its motives, its
sanctities, and its religion, to the remote, the vague, and the
unknown ; in Cowper we have the type of that genuine love
which cherishes things in proportion to their nearness, and
feels its reverence grow in proportion to the intimacy of its
knowledge.

GERMAN WIT: HEINRICH HEINE.

"NOTHING," says Goethe, "is more significant of men's character than what they find laughable." The truth of this observation would perhaps have been more apparent if he had said *culture* instead of character. The last thing in which the cultivated man can have community with the vulgar is their jocularity; and we can hardly exhibit more strikingly the wide gulf which separates him from them, than by comparing the object which shakes the diaphragm of a coal-heaver, with the highly complex pleasure derived from a real witticism. That any high order of wit is exceedingly complex, and demands a ripe and strong mental development, has one evidence in the fact that we do not find it in boys at all in proportion to their manifestation of other powers. Clever boys generally aspire to the heroic and poetic rather than the comic, and the crudest of all their efforts are their jokes. Many a witty man will remember how in his school-days a practical joke, more or less Rabelaisian, was for him the *ne plus ultra* of the ludicrous. It seems to have been the same with the boyhood of the human race. The history and literature of the ancient Hebrews give the idea of a people who went about their business and their pleasure as gravely as a society of beavers; the smile and the laugh are often mentioned metaphorically, but the smile is one of complacency, the laugh is one of scorn. Nor can we imagine that the facetious element was very strong in the Egyptians; no laughter lurks in the wondering eyes and the broad calm lips of their statues. Still less can the Assyrians have had any genius for the comic; the round eyes and simpering satisfaction of their ideal faces belong to a type which is not witty, but the cause of wit in others.   The fun of these early races was, we fancy, of the after-dinner kind — loud-throated laughter over the wine-cup, taken too little account of in sober moments to enter as an element into their Art, and differing as much from the laughter of a Chamfort or a Sheridan as the gastronomic enjoyment of an ancient Briton, whose dinner had no other removes than from acorns to beechmast and back again to acorns, differed from the subtle pleasures of the palate experienced by his turtle-eating descendant.   In fact they had to live seriously through the stages which to subsequent races were to become comedy, as those amiable-looking preadamite amphibia, which Professor Owen has restored for us in effigy at Sydenham, took perfectly *au sérieux* the grotesque physiognomies of their kindred.   Heavy experience in their case, as in every other, was the base from which the salt of future wit was to be made.

Humor is of earlier growth than wit, and it is in accordance with this earlier growth that it has more affinity with the poetic tendencies, while wit is more nearly allied to the ratiocinative intellect.   Humor draws its materials from situations and characteristics; wit seizes on unexpected and complex relations.   Humor is chiefly representative and descriptive; it is diffuse, and flows along without any other law than its own fantastic will; or it flits about like a will-of-the-wisp, amazing us by its whimsical transitions.   Wit is brief and sudden, and sharply defined as a crystal; it does not make pictures, it is not fantastic; but it detects an unsuspected analogy or suggests a startling or confounding inference.   Every one who has had the opportunity of making the comparison will remember that the effect produced on him by some witticisms is closely akin to the effect produced on him by subtle reasoning which lays open a fallacy or absurdity, and there are persons whose delight in such reasoning always manifests itself in laughter.   This affinity of wit with ratiocination is the more obvious in proportion as the species of wit is higher, and deals less with words and with

superficialities than with the essential qualities of things.
Some of Johnson's most admirable witticisms consist in the
suggestion of an analogy which immediately exposes the
absurdity of an action or proposition, and it is only their
ingenuity, condensation, and instantaneousness which lift
them from reasoning into wit; they are *reasoning raised to
a higher power*. On the other hand, humor, in its higher
forms, and in proportion as it associates itself with the sympathetic emotions, continually passes into poetry; nearly all
great modern humorists may be called prose poets.

Some confusion as to the nature of humor has been created by the fact, that those who have written most eloquently
on it have dwelt almost exclusively on its higher forms, and
have defined humor in general as the *sympathetic* presentation
of incongruous elements in human nature and life; a definition which only applies to its later development. A great
deal of humor may co-exist with a great deal of barbarism, as
we see in the Middle Ages; but the strongest flavor of the
humor in such cases will come, not from sympathy, but more
probably from triumphant egoism or intolerance; at best it
will be the love of the ludicrous exhibiting itself in illustrations of successful cunning and of the *lex talionis*, as in
" Reineke Fuchs," or shaking off in a holiday mood the yoke
of a too exacting faith, as in the old Mysteries. Again, it is
impossible to deny a high degree of humor to many practical
jokes, but no sympathetic nature can enjoy them. Strange
as the genealogy may seem, the original parentage of that
wonderful and delicious mixture of fun, fancy, philosophy,
and feeling, which constitutes modern humor, was probably
the cruel mockery of a savage at the writhings of a suffering
enemy, — such is the tendency of things towards the good
and beautiful on this earth! Probably the reason why high
culture demands more complete harmony with its moral
sympathies in humor than in wit, is that humor is in its
nature more prolix — that it has not the direct and irresistible force of wit. Wit is an electric shock, which takes us
by violence, quite independently of our predominant mental

disposition; but humor approaches us more deliberately and leaves us masters of ourselves. Hence it is, that while coarse and cruel humor has almost disappeared from contemporary literature, coarse and cruel wit abounds; even refined men cannot help laughing at a coarse *bon mot* or a lacerating per sonality, if the "shock" of the witticism is a powerful one; while mere fun will have no power over them if it jar on their moral taste. Hence, too, it is, that while wit is peren nial, humor is liable to become superannuated.

As is usual with definitions and classifications, however, this distinction between wit and humor does not exactly represent the actual fact. Like all other species, wit and humor overlap and blend with each other. There are *bon mots*, like many of Charles Lamb's, which are a sort of facetious hybrids; we hardly know whether to call them witty or humorous; there are rather lengthy descriptions or narratives, which, like Voltaire's "Micromégas," would be more humorous if they were not so sparkling and antithetic, so pregnant with suggestion and satire, that we are obliged to call them witty. We rarely find wit untempered by humor, or humor without a spice of wit; and sometimes we find them both united in the highest degree in the same mind, as in Shakspeare and Molière. A happy conjunction this, for wit is apt to be cold and thin-lipped and Mephistophelean in men who have no relish for humor, whose lungs do never crow like Chanticleer at fun and drollery; and broad-faced, rollicking humor needs the refining influence of wit. Indeed, it may be said that there is no really fine writing in which wit has not an implicit, if not an explicit, action. The wit may never rise to the surface, it may never flame out into a witticism; but it helps to give brightness and transparency, it warns off from flights and exaggerations which verge on the ridiculous; in every *genre* of writing it preserves a man from sinking into the *genre ennuyeux*. And it is eminently needed for this office in humorous writing; for as humor has no limits imposed on it by its material, no law but its own exuberance, it is apt to become preposterous and

wearisome unless checked by wit, which is the enemy of all
monotony, of all lengthiness, of all exaggeration.

Perhaps the nearest approach Nature has given us to a
complete analysis, in which wit is as thoroughly exhausted
of humor as possible, and humor as bare as possible of wit,
is in the typical Frenchman and the typical German. Voltaire, the intensest example of pure wit, fails in most of his
fictions from his lack of humor. "Micromégas" is a perfect
tale, because, as it deals chiefly with philosophic ideas
and does not touch the marrow of human feeling and life,
the writer's wit and wisdom were all-sufficient for his purpose. Not so with "Candide." Here Voltaire ·had to give
pictures of life as well as to convey philosophic truth and
satire, and here we feel the want of humor. The sense of
the ludicrous is continually defeated by disgust, and the
scenes, instead of presenting us with an amusing or agreeable
picture, are only the frame for a witticism. On the other
hand, German humor generally shows no sense of measure,
no instinctive tact; it is either floundering and clumsy as the
antics of a leviathan, or laborious and interminable as a Lap-
land day, in which one loses all hope that the stars and quiet
will ever come. For this reason, Jean Paul, the greatest of
German humorists, is unendurable to many readers, and frequently tiresome to all. Here, as elsewhere, the German
shows the absence of that delicate perception, that sensibility
to gradation, which is the essence of tact and taste, and the
necessary concomitant of wit. All his subtlety is reserved for
the region of metaphysics. For *Identität* in the abstract, no
one can have an acuter vision, but in the concrete he is satisfied with a very loose approximation. He has the finest nose
for *Empirismus* in philosophical doctrine, but the presence of
more or less tobacco-smoke in the air he breathes is imper-
ceptible to him. To the typical German — *Vetter Michel* —
it is indifferent whether his door-lock will catch; whether his
tea-cup be more or less than an inch thick; whether or not
his book have every other leaf unstitched; whether his
neighbor's conversation be more or less of a shout; whether

he pronounce *b* or *p, t* or *d ;* whether or not his adored one's
teeth be few and far between.   He has the same sort of in-
sensibility to gradations in time.   A German comedy is like
a German sentence ; you see no reason in its structure why
it should ever come to an end, and you accept the conclusion
as an arrangement of Providence rather than of the author.
We have heard Germans use the word *Langeweile,* the equivalent for ennui, and we have secretly wondered *what* it can
be that produces ennui in a German.   Not the longest of long
tragedies, for we have known him to pronounce that *höchst
fesselnd* (*so* enchaining !) ; not the heaviest of heavy books,
for he delights in that as *gründlich* (deep, sir, deep !) ; not
the slowest of journeys in a *Post-wagen,* for the slower the
horses, the more cigars he can smoke before he reaches his
journey's end.   German ennui must be something as superlative as Barclay's treble X, which, we suppose, implies an
extremely unknown quantity of stupefaction.

It is easy to see that this national deficiency in nicety of
perception must have its effect on the national appreciation
and exhibition of humor.   You find in Germany ardent
admirers of Shakspeare, who tell you that what they think
most admirable in him is his *Wortspiel,* his verbal quibbles ;
and one of these, a man of no slight culture and refinement,
once cited to a friend of ours Proteus's joke in " The Two
Gentlemen of Verona," " Nod, I ? why that 's Noddy," as
a transcendent specimen of Shakspearian wit.   German facetiousness is seldom comic to foreigners, and an Englishman
with a swelled cheek might take up " Kladderadatsch," the
German " Punch," without any danger of agitating his facial
muscles.   Indeed, it is a remarkable fact that, among the
five great races concerned in modern civilization, the German
race is the only one which, up to the present century, had
contributed nothing classic to the common stock of European
wit and humor; for " Reineke Fuchs " cannot be regarded as
a peculiarly Teutonic product.   Italy was the birthplace of
Pantomime and the immortal Pulcinello ; Spain had produced
Cervantes ; France had produced Rabelais and Molière, and

classic wits innumerable; England had yielded Shakspeare and a host of humorists. But Germany had borne no great comic dramatist, no great satirist, and she has not yet repaired the omission; she had not even produced any humorist of a high order. Among her great writers, Lessing is the one who is the most specifically witty. We feel the implicit influence of wit, the "flavor of mind," throughout his writings; and it is often concentrated into pungent satire, as every reader of the "Hamburgische Dramaturgie" remembers. Still, Lessing's name has not become European through his wit, and his charming comedy, "Minna von Barnhelm," has won no place on a foreign stage. Of course, we do not pretend to an exhaustive acquaintance with German literature; we not only admit, we are sure, that it includes much comic writing of which we know nothing. We simply state the fact, that no German production of that kind, before the present century, ranked as European; a fact which does not, indeed, determine the *amount* of the national facetiousness, but which is quite decisive as to its *quality*. Whatever may be the stock of fun which Germany yields for home-consumption, she has provided little for the palate of other lands. All honor to her for the still greater things she has done for us! She has fought the hardest fight for freedom of thought, has produced the grandest inventions, has made magnificent contributions to science, has given us some of the divinest poetry, and quite the divinest music, in the world. No one reveres and treasures the products of the German mind more than we do. To say that that mind is not fertile in wit, is only like saying that excellent wheat-land is not rich pasture; to say that we do not enjoy German facetiousness, is no more than to say that, though the horse is the finest of quadrupeds, we do not like him to lay his hoof playfully on our shoulder. Still, as we have noticed that the pointless puns and stupid jocularity of the boy may ultimately be developed into the epigrammatic brilliancy and polished playfulness of the man, as we believe that racy wit and chastened delicate humor are inevitably the results of invigorated and refined mental activity, we can also believe that Germany will, one day, yield a crop of wits and humorists.

Perhaps there is already an earnest of that future crop in the existence of Heinrich Heine, a German born with the present century, who, to Teutonic imagination, sensibility, and humor, adds an amount of *esprit* that would make him brilliant among the most brilliant of Frenchmen. True, this unique German wit is half a Hebrew; but he and his ancestors spent their youth in German air, and were reared on *Wurst* and *Sauerkraut,* so that he is as much a German as a pheasant is an English bird, or a potato an Irish vegetable. But whatever else he may be, Heine is one of the most remarkable men of this age: no echo, but a real voice, and therefore, like all genuine things in this world, worth studying; a surpassing lyric poet, who has uttered our feelings for us in delicious song; a humorist, who touches leaden folly with the magic wand of his fancy, and transmutes it into the fine gold of art — who sheds his sunny smile on human tears, and makes them a beauteous rainbow on the cloudy background of life; a wit, who holds in his mighty hand the most scorching lightnings of satire; an artist in prose literature, who has shown even more completely than Goethe the possibilities of German prose; and — in spite of all charges against him, true as well as false — a lover of freedom, who has spoken wise and brave words on behalf of his fellow-men. He is, moreover, a suffering man, who, with all the highly wrought sensibility of genius, has to endure terrible physical ills; and as such he calls forth more than an intellectual interest. It is true, alas! that there is a heavy weight in the other scale — that Heine's magnificent powers have often served only to give electric force to the expression of debased feeling, so that his works are no Phidian statue of gold and ivory and gems, but have not a little brass and iron and miry clay mingled with the precious metal. The audacity of his occasional coarseness and personality is unparalleled in contemporary literature, and has hardly been exceeded by the license of former days. Hence, before his volumes are put within the reach of immature minds, there is need of a friendly pen-knife to exercise a strict censorship. Yet, when all coarse-ness, all scurrility, all Mephistophelean contempt for the reverent feelings of other men, is removed, there will be a plenteous remainder of exquisite poetry, of wit, humor, and just thought. It is apparently too often a congenial task to write severe words about the transgressions committed by men of genius, especially when the censor has the advantage of being himself a man of *no* genius, so that those transgres-sions seem to him quite gratuitous; *he*, forsooth, never lac-erated any one by his wit, or gave irresistible piquancy to a coarse allusion, and his indignation is not mitigated by any knowledge of the temptation that lies in transcendent power. We are also apt to measure what a gifted man has done by our arbitrary conception of what he might have done, rather than by a comparison of his actual doings with our own or those of other ordinary men. We make ourselves over-zealous agents of heaven, and demand that our brother should bring usurious interest for his five Talents, forgetting that it is less easy to manage five Talents than two. Whatever ben-efit there may be in denouncing the evil, it is after all more edifying, and certainly more cheering, to appreciate the good. Hence, in endeavoring to give our readers some account of Heine and his works, we shall not dwell lengthily on his fail-ings; we shall not hold the candle up to dusty, vermin-haunted corners, but let the light fall as much as possible on the nobler and more attractive details. Our sketch of Heine's life, which has been drawn from various sources, will be free from everything like intrusive gossip, and will derive its coloring chiefly from the autobiographical hints and descrip-tions scattered through his own writings. Those of our read-ers who happen to know nothing of Heine, will in this way be making their acquaintance with the writer while they are learning the outline of his career.

We have said that Heine was born with the present century; but this statement is not precise, for we learn that, according to his certificate of baptism, he was born December

12, 1799.   However, as he himself says, the important
point is, that he was born, and born on the banks of the
Rhine at Düsseldorf, where his father was a merchant.   In
his "Reisebilder" he gives us some recollections, in his wild
poetic way, of the dear old town where he spent his childhood, and of his school boy troubles there.   We shall quote
from these in butterfly fashion, sipping a little nectar here
and there, without regard to any strict order : —

"I first saw the light on the banks of that lovely stream, where
folly grows on the green hills, and in autumn is plucked, pressed,
poured into casks, and sent into foreign lands.   Believe me, I yesterday heard some one utter folly which, in anno 1811, lay in a bunch of
grapes I then saw growing on the Johannisberg. . . . Mon Dieu! if
I had only such faith in me that I could remove mountains, the Johannisberg would be the very mountain I should send for wherever I
might be; but as my faith is not so strong, imagination must help me,
and it transports me at once to the lovely Rhine. . . . I am again
a child, and playing with other children on the Schlossplatz, at
Düsseldorf on the Rhine.   Yes, madam, there was I born ; and I note
this expressly, in case, after my death, seven cities — Schilda, Kräh-
winkel, Polkwitz, Bockum, Dülken, Göttingen, and Schöppenstädt —
should contend for the honor of being my birthplace.   Düsseldorf
is a town on the Rhine; sixteen thousand men live there, and many
hundred thousand men besides lie buried there. . . . Among them,
many of whom my mother says that it would be better if they were
still living, — for example, my grandfather and my uncle, the old Herr
von Geldern, and the young Herr von Geldern, both such celebrated doctors, who saved so many men from death, and yet must die themselves.
And the pious Ursula, who carried me in her arms when I was a child,
also lies buried there, and a rosebush grows on her grave; she loved
the scent of roses so well in life, and her heart was pure rose-incense
and goodness.   The knowing old Canon, too, lies buried there.
Heavens, what an object he looked when I last saw him !   *He was
made up of nothing but mind and plasters,* and nevertheless studied
day and night, as if he were alarmed lest the worms should find an
idea too little in his head.   And the little William lies there, and for
this I am to blame.   We were schoolfellows in the Franciscan mon-
astery, and were playing on that side of it where the Düssel flows between stone walls; and I said, 'William, fetch out the kitten that

has just fallen in;' and merrily he went down on to the plank which lay across the brook, snatched the kitten out of the water, but fell in himself, and was dragged out dripping and dead. *The kitten lived to o good old age.* . . . Princes in that day were not the tormented race as they are now; the crown grew firmly on their heads, and at night they drew a nightcap over it, and slept peacefully, and peacefully slept the people at their feet; and when the people waked in the morning, they said, ' Good-morning, father!' and the princes answered, ' Good-morning, dear children!' But it was suddenly quite otherwise; for when we awoke one morning at Düsseldorf, and were ready to say, ' Good-morning, father!'— lo! the father was gone away; and in the whole town there was nothing but dumb sorrow, everywhere a sort of funeral disposition; and people glided along silently to the market, and read the long placard placed on the door of the Town Hall. It was dismal weather; yet the lean tailor, Kilian, stood in his nankeen jacket, which he usually wore only in the house, and his blue worsted stockings hung down so that his naked legs peeped out mournfully, and his thin lips trembled while he muttered the announcement to himself. And an old soldier read rather louder, and at many a word a crystal tear trickled down to his brave old mustache. I stood near him and wept in company, and asked him *why we wept?* He answered, ' The Elector has abdicated.' And then he read again; and at the words, ' for the long-manifested fidelity of my subjects,' and ' hereby set you free from your allegiance,' he wept more than ever. It is strangely touching to see an old man like that, with faded uniform and scarred face, weep so bitterly all of a sudden. While we were reading, the Electoral arms were taken down from the Town Hall; everything had such a desolate air, that it was as if an eclipse of the sun were expected. . . . I went home and wept, and wailed out, 'The Elector has abdicated!' In vain my mother took a world of trouble to explain the thing to me. I knew what I knew; I was not to be persuaded, but went crying to bed, and in the night dreamed that the world was at an end."

The next morning, however, the sun rises as usual, and Joachim Murat is proclaimed Grand Duke, whereupon there is a holiday at the public school, and Heinrich (or Harry, for that was his baptismal name, which he afterwards had the good taste to change), perched on the bronze horse of the Electoral statue, sees quite a different scene from yesterday's : —

" The next day the world was again all in order, and we had school as before, and things were got by heart as before; the Roman emperors, chronology, the nouns in *im*, the *verba irregularia*, Greek, Hebrew, geography, mental arithmetic! — heavens! my head is still dizzy with it — all must be learned by heart! And a great deal of this came very conveniently for me in after life. For if I had not known the Roman kings by heart, it would subsequently have been quite indifferent to me whether Niebuhr had proved or had not proved that they never really existed. . . . But oh! the trouble I had at school with the endless dates. And with arithmetic it was still worse. What I understood best was subtraction, for that has a very practical rule : 'Four can't be taken from three, therefore I must borrow one.' But I advise every one in such a case to borrow a few extra pence, for no one can tell what may happen. . . . As for Latin, you have no idea, madam, what a complicated affair it is. The Romans would never have found time to conquer the world if they had first had to learn Latin. Luckily for them, they already knew in their cradles what nouns have their accusative in *im*. I, on the contrary, had to learn them by heart in the sweat of my brow; nevertheless, it is fortunate for me that I know them ; . . . and the fact that I have them at my finger-ends if I should ever happen to want them suddenly, affords me much inward repose and consolation in many troubled hours of life. . . . Of Greek I will not say a word, I should get too much irritated. The monks in the Middle Ages were not so far wrong when they maintained that Greek was an invention of the devil. God knows the suffering I endured over it. . . . With Hebrew it went somewhat better, for I had always a great liking for the Jews, though to this very hour they crucify my good name ; but I could never get on so far in Hebrew as my watch, which had much familiar intercourse with pawnbrokers, and in this way contracted many Jewish habits, — for example, it would n't go on Saturdays."

Heine's parents were apparently not wealthy, but his education was cared for by his uncle, Solomon Heine, a great banker in Hamburg, so that he had no early pecuniary disadvantages to struggle with. He seems to have been very happy in his mother, who was not of Hebrew, but of Teutonic blood; he often mentions her with reverence and affection, and in the " Buch der Lieder " there are two exquisite sonnets addressed to her, which tell how his proud spirit was always

subdued by the charm of her presence, and how her love was
the home of his heart after restless weary ramblings: —

> " Wie mächtig auch mein stolzer Muth sich blähe,
>   In deiner selig süssen, trauten Nähe
>   Ergreift mich oft ein demuthvolles Zagen.
>
>   .   .   .   .
>
>   Und immer irrte ich nach Liebe, immer
>   Nach Liebe, doch die Liebe fand ich nimmer,
>   Und kehrte um nach Hause, krank und trübe.
>   Doch da bist du entgegen mir gekommen,
>   Und ach ! was da in deinem Aug' geschwommen,
>   Das war die süsse, langgesuchte Liebe."

He was at first destined for a mercantile life, but nature
declared too strongly against this plan. " God knows," he has
lately said in conversation with his brother, " I would willingly have become a banker, but I could never bring myself
to that pass. I very early discerned that bankers would one
day be the rulers of the world." So commerce was at length
given up for law, the study of which he began in 1819 at the
University of Bonn. He had already published some poems
in the corner of a newspaper, and among them was one on
Napoleon, the object of his youthful enthusiasm. This poem,
he says in a letter to St. René Taillandier, was written when
he was only sixteen. It is still to be found in the " Buch der
Lieder" under the title " Die Grenadiere," and it proves that
even in its earliest efforts his genius showed a strongly
specific character.

It will be easily imagined that the germs of poetry sprouted
too vigorously in Heine's brain for jurisprudence to find
much room there. Lectures on history and literature, we are
told, were more diligently attended than lectures on law.
He had taken care, too, to furnish his trunk with abundant
editions of the poets, and the poet he especially studied at
that time was Byron. At a later period we find his taste
taking another direction, for he writes: " Of all authors,
Byron is precisely the one who excites in me the most intolerable emotion ; whereas Scott, in every one of his works,

gladdens my heart, soothes and invigorates me." Another
indication of his bent in these Bonn days was a newspaper
essay, in which he attacked the Romantic School; and here
also he went through that chicken-pox of authorship, the
production of a tragedy. Heine's tragedy, "Almansor," is,
as might be expected, better than the majority of these
youthful mistakes. The tragic collision lies in the conflict
between natural affection and the deadly hatred of religion
and of race, in the sacrifice of youthful lovers to the strife
between Moor and Spaniard, Moslem and Christian. Some
of the situations are striking, and there are passages of considerable poetic merit; but the characters are little more
than shadowy vehicles for the poetry, and there is a want
of clearness and probability in the structure. It was published two years later, in company with another tragedy in
one act, called " William Ratcliffe," in which there is rather
a feeble use of the Scotch second-sight after the manner of
the Fate in the Greek tragedy. We smile to find Heine saying of his tragedies, in a letter to a friend soon after their
publication : " I know they will be terribly cut up, but I will
confess to you in confidence that they are very good, better
than my collection of poems, which are not worth a shot."
Elsewhere he tells us, that when, after one of Paganini's concerts, he was passionately complimenting the great master on
his violin-playing, Paganini interrupted him thus : " But
how were you pleased with my *bows?* "

In 1820 Heine left Bonn for Göttingen. He there pursued
his omission of law studies ; and at the end of three months
he was rusticated for a breach of the laws against duelling.
Whilst there he had attempted a negotiation with Brockhaus
for the printing of a volume of poems, and had endured the
first ordeal of lovers and poets, a refusal. It was not until
a year after, that he found a Berlin publisher for his first
volume of poems, subsequently transformed, with additions,
into the " Buch der Lieder." He remained between two and
three years at Berlin, and the society he found there seems
to nave made these years an important epoch in his culture.

He was one of the youngest members of a circle which assembled at the house of the poetess Elise von Hohenhausen,
the translator of Byron, a circle which included Chamisso,
Varnhagen, and Rahel (Varnhagen's wife). For Rahel, Heine
had a profound admiration and regard; he afterwards dedicated to her the poems included under the title "Heimkehr;"
and he frequently refers to her or quotes her in a way that
indicates how he valued her influence. According to his
friend, F. von Hohenhausen, the opinions concerning Heine's
talent were very various among his Berlin friends, and it was
only a small minority that had any presentiment of his future
fame. In this minority was Elise von Hohenhausen, who
proclaimed Heine as the Byron of Germany; but her opinion
was met with much head-shaking and opposition. We can
imagine how precious was such a recognition as hers to the
young poet, then only two or three and twenty, and with by
no means an impressive personality for superficial eyes. Perhaps even the deep-sighted were far from detecting in that
small, blond, pale young man, with quiet, gentle manners, the
latent powers of ridicule and sarcasm — the terrible talons
that were one day to be thrust out from the velvet paw of
the young leopard.

It was apparently during this residence in Berlin that
Heine united himself with the Lutheran Church. He would
willingly, like many of his friends, he tells us, have remained
free from all ecclesiastical ties, if the authorities there had not
forbidden residence in Prussia, and especially in Berlin, to
every one who did not belong to one of the positive religions
recognized by the state.

"As Henry IV. once laughingly said, '*Paris vaut bien une messe,*'
so I might with reason say, *Berlin vaut bien une prêche;* and I could
afterwards, as before, accommodate myself to the very enlightened
Christianity, filtrated from all superstition, which could then be had
in the churches of Berlin, and which was even free from the divinity of
Christ, like turtle-soup without turtle."

At the same period, too, Heine became acquainted with
Hegel. In his lately published "Geständnisse" (Confes

sions), he throws on Hegel's influence over him the blue light of demoniacal wit, and confounds us by the most bewildering double-edged sarcasms; but that influence seems to have been at least more wholesome than the one which produced the mocking retractations of the "Geständnisse." Through all his self-satire, we discern that in those days he had some- thing like real earnestness and enthusiasm, which are cer- tainly not apparent in his present theistic confession of faith.

"On the whole, I never felt a strong enthusiasm for this philosophy, and conviction on the subject was out of question. I never was an abstract thinker, and I accepted the synthesis of the Hegelian doctrine without demanding any proof, since its consequences flattered my vanity. I was young and proud; and it pleased my vainglory when I learned from Hegel that the true God was not, as my grandmother believed, the God who lives in heaven, but myself here upon earth. This foolish pride had not in the least a pernicious influence on my feel- ings: on the contrary, it heightened these to the pitch of heroism. I was at that time so lavish in generosity and self-sacrifice, that I must assuredly have eclipsed the most brilliant deeds of those good *bourgeois* of virtue who acted merely from a sense of duty, and simply obeyed the laws of morality."

His sketch of Hegel is irresistibly amusing; but we must warn the reader that Heine's anecdotes are often mere devices of style by which he conveys his satire or opinions. The reader will see that he does not neglect an opportunity of giving a sarcastic lash or two, in passing, to Meyerbeer, for whose music he had a great contempt. The sarcasm conveyed in the substitution of *reputation* for *music*, and *journalists* for *musicians*, might perhaps escape any one unfamiliar with the sly and unexpected turns of Heine's ridicule.

"To speak frankly, I seldom understood him, and only arrived at the meaning of his words by subsequent reflection. I believe he wished not to be understood; and hence his practice of sprinkling his discourse with modifying parentheses; hence, perhaps, his preference for persons of whom he knew that they did not understand him, and to whom he all the more willingly granted the honor of his familiar acquaintance. Thus every one in Berlin wondered at the intimate com-panionship of the profound Hegel with the late Heinrich Beer, a brother of Giacomo Meyerbeer, who is universally known by his rep-utation, and who has been celebrated by the cleverest journalists. This Beer, namely Heinrich, was a thoroughly stupid fellow, and indeed was afterwards actually declared imbecile by his family, and placed under guardianship; because instead of making a name for himself in art or in science by means of his great fortune, he squandered his money on childish trifles, — and, for example, one day bought six thousand thalers' worth of walking-sticks. This poor man, who had no wish to pass either for a great tragic dramatist, or for a great star-gazer, or for a laurel-crowned musical genius, a rival of Mozart and Rossini, and preferred giving his money for walking-sticks — this degenerate Beer enjoyed Hegel's most confidential society; he was the philosopher's bosom-friend, his Pylades, and accompanied him every-where like his shadow. The equally witty and gifted Felix Mendels-sohn once sought to explain this phenomenon, by maintaining that Hegel did not understand Heinrich Beer. I now believe, however, that the real ground of that intimacy consisted in this : Hegel was con-vinced that no word of what he said was understood by Heinrich Beer; and he could therefore, in his presence, give himself up to all the in-tellectual outpourings of the moment. In general, Hegel's conversa-tion was a sort of monologue, sighed forth by starts in a noiseless voice; the odd roughness of his expressions often struck me, and many of them have remained in my memory. One beautiful starlight evening we stood together at the window, and I, a young man of one-and-twenty, having just had a good dinner and finished my coffee, spoke with en-thusiasm of the stars, and called them the habitations of the departed. But the master muttered to himself: ' The stars! hum! hum! The stars are only a brilliant leprosy on the face of the heavens.' ' For God's sake,' I cried, ' is there, then, no happy place above, where virtue is rewarded after death ? ' But he, staring at me with his pale eyes, said, cuttingly : ' So you want a bonus for having taken care of your sick mother, and refrained from poisoning your worthy brother ? ' At these words he looked anxiously round, but appeared immediately set at rest when he observed that it was only Heinrich Beer, who had approached to invite him to a game at whist."

In 1823 Heine returned to Göttingen to complete his career as a law-student, and this time he gave evidence of advanced mental maturity, not only by producing many of the charming poems subsequently included in the "Reisebilder," but also by prosecuting his professional studies diligently enough to leave Göttingen, in 1825, as *Doctor juris*. Hereupon he settled at Hamburg as an advocate, but his profession seems to have been the least pressing of his occupations. In those days a small blond young man, with the brim of his hat drawn over his nose, his coat flying open, and his hands stuck in his trouser-pockets, might have been seen stumbling along the streets of Hamburg, staring from side to side, and appearing to have small regard to the figure he made in the eyes of the good citizens. Occasionally an inhabitant, more literary than usual, would point out this young man to his companion as Heinrich Heine ; but in general the young poet had not to endure the inconveniences of being a lion. His poems were devoured, but he was not asked to devour flattery in return. Whether because the fair Hamburgers acted in the spirit of Johnson's advice to Hannah More, — to " consider what her flattery was worth before she choked him with it," — or for some other reason, Heine, according to the testimony of August Lewald, to whom we owe these particulars of his Hamburg life, was left free from the persecution of tea-parties. Not, however, from another persecution of genius, nervous headaches, — which some persons, we are told, regarded as an improbable fiction, intended as a pretext for raising a delicate white hand to his forehead. It is probable that the sceptical persons alluded to were themselves untroubled with nervous headache, and that their hands were *not* delicate. Slight details these, but worth telling about a man of genius, because they help us to keep in mind that he is, after all, our brother, having to endure the petty every-day ills of life as we have ; with this difference, that his heightened sensibility converts what are mere insect-stings for us into scorpion-stings for him.

It was, perhaps, in these Hamburg days that Heine paid the visit to Goethe, of which he gives us this charming little picture : —

"When I visited him in Weimar, and stood before him, I involuntarily glanced at his side, to see whether the eagle was not there with the lightning in his beak. I was nearly speaking Greek to him; but, as I observed that he understood German, I stated to him in German, that the plums on the road between Jena and Weimar were very good. I had for so many long winter-nights thought over what lofty and profound things I would say to Goethe, if ever I saw him! And when I saw him at last, I said to him, that the Saxon plums were very good! And Goethe smiled."

During the next few years Heine produced the most popular of all his works, those which have won him his place as the greatest of living German poets and humorists. Between 1826 and 1829 appeared the four volumes of the "Reisebilder" (Pictures of Travel), and the "Buch der Lieder" (Book of Songs) — a volume of lyrics, of which it is hard to say whether their greatest charm is the lightness and finish of their style, their vivid and original imaginativeness, or their simple, pure sensibility. In his "Reisebilder," Heine carries us with him to the Harz, to the isle of Norderney, to his native town, Düsseldorf, to Italy, and to England, sketching scenery and character, now with the wildest, most fantastic humor, now with the finest idyllic sensibility — letting his thoughts wander from poetry to politics, from criticism to dreamy reverie, and blending fun, imagination, reflection, and satire in a sort of exquisite, ever-varying shimmer, like the hues of the opal.

Heine's journey to England did not at all heighten his regard for the English. He calls our language the "hiss of egoism" (*Zischlaute des Egoismus*); and his ridicule of English awkwardness is as merciless as English ridicule of German awkwardness. His antipathy towards us seems to have grown in intensity, like many of his other antipathies; and in his "Vermischte Schriften" he is more bitter than ever. Let us quote one of his philippics, since bitters are understood to be wholesome.

"It is certainly a frightful injustice to pronounce sentence of condemnation on an entire people. But with regard to the English, momentary disgust might betray me into this injustice; and on looking at the mass, I easily forget the many brave and noble men who distinguished themselves by intellect and love of freedom. But these, especially the British poets, were always all the more glaringly in contrast with the rest of the nation; they were isolated martyrs to their national relations; and, besides, great geniuses do not belong to the particular land of their birth; they scarcely belong to this earth, the Golgotha of their sufferings. The mass — the English blockheads, God forgive me! — are hateful to me in my inmost soul; and I often regard them not at all as my fellow-men, but as miserable automata — machines, whose motive power is egoism. In these moods it seems to me as if I heard the whizzing wheelwork by which they think, feel, reckon, digest, and pray; their praying, their mechanical Anglican church-going, with the gilt prayer-book under their arms, their stupid, tiresome Sunday, their awkward piety, are most of all odious to me. I am firmly convinced that a blaspheming Frenchman is a more pleasing sight for the Divinity than a praying Englishman."

On his return from England, Heine was employed at Munich in editing the "Allgemeinen Politischen Annalen," but in 1830 he was again in the North, and the news of the July Revolution surprised him on the island of Heligoland. He has given us a graphic picture of his democratic enthusiasm in those days, in some letters, apparently written from Heligoland, which he had inserted in his book on Börne. We quote some passages, not only for their biographic interest as showing a phase of Heine's mental history, but because they are a specimen of his power in that kind of dithyrambic writing which, in less masterly hands, easily becomes ridiculous.

"The thick packet of newspapers arrived from the Continent with these warm, glowing-hot tidings. They were sunbeams wrapped up in packing-paper, and they inflamed my soul till it burst into the wildest conflagration.₄. . . . It is all like a dream to me; especially the name, Lafayette, sounds to me like a legend out of my earliest childhood. Does he really sit again on horseback, commanding the National Guard? I almost fear it may not be true, for it is in print. I will myself go to Paris, to be convinced of it with my bodily eyes. . . . It must be splendid, when he rides through the streets, the citizen of two worlds, the godlike old man, with his silver locks streaming down his sacred shoulder. . . . He greets, with his dear old eyes, the grandchildren of those who once fought with him for freedom and equality. . . . It is now sixty years since he returned from America with the Declaration of Human Rights, the Decalogue of the world's new creed, which was revealed to him amid the thunders and lightnings of cannon. . . . And the tri-colored flag waves again on the towers of Paris, and its streets resound with the Marseillaise! . . . It is all over with my yearning for repose. I now know again what I will do, what I ought to do, what I must do. . . . I am the son of the Revolution, and seize again the hallowed weapons on which my mother pronounced her magic benediction. . . . Flowers, flowers! I will crown my head for the death-fight. And the lyre, too; reach me the lyre, that I may sing a battle-song. . . . Words like flaming stars, that shoot down from the heavens, and burn up the palaces, and illuminate the huts. . . . Words like bright javelins, that whirr up to the seventh heaven and strike the pious hypocrites who have skulked into the Holy of Holies. . . . I am all joy and song, all sword and flame! Perhaps, too, all delirium. . . . One of those sunbeams wrapped in brown paper has flown to my brain, and set my thoughts aglow. In vain I dip my head into the sea. No water extinguishes this Greek fire. . . . Even the poor Heligolanders shout for joy, although they have only a sort of dim instinct of what has occurred. The fisherman who yesterday took me over to the little sand-island, which is the bathing-place here, said to me smilingly, ' The poor people have won!' Yes, instinctively the people comprehend such events, perhaps, better than we, with all our means of knowledge. Thus Frau von Varnhagen once told me that when the issue of the battle of Leipzig was not yet known, the maid-servant suddenly rushed into the room with the sorrowful cry, ' The nobles have won!' . . . This morning another packet of newspapers is come. I devour them like manna. Child that I am, affecting details touch me yet more than the momentous whole. Oh, if I could but see the dog Medor. . . . The dog Medor brought his master his gun and cartridge-box, and when his master fell, and was buried with his fellow-heroes in the Court of the Louvre, there stayed the poor dog like a monument of faithfulness, sitting motionless on the grave, day and night, eating but little of the food that was offered him, — burying the greater part of it in the earth, perhaps as nourishment for his buried master."

The enthusiasm which was kept thus at boiling heat by imagination, cooled down rapidly when brought into contact with reality. In the same book he indicates, in his caustic way, the commencement of that change in his political *temperature* — for it cannot be called a change in opinion — which has drawn down on him immense vituperation from some of the Patriotic party, but which seems to have resulted simply from the essential antagonism between keen wit and fanaticism.

"On the very first days of my arrival in Paris, I observed that things wore, in reality, quite different colors from those which had been shed on them, when in perspective, by the light of my enthusiasm. The silver locks which I saw fluttering so majestically on the shoulders of Lafayette, the hero of two worlds, were metamorphosed into a brown peruke, which made a pitiable covering for a narrow skull. And even the dog Medor, which I visited in the Court of the Louvre, and which, encamped under tri-colored flags and trophies, very quietly allowed himself to be fed, — he was not at all the right dog, but quite an ordinary brute, who assumed to himself merits not his own, as often happens with the French; and, like many others, he made a profit out of the glory of the Revolution. . . . He was pampered and patronized, perhaps promoted to the highest posts, while the true Medor, some days after the battle, modestly slunk out of sight, like the true people who created the Revolution."

That it was not merely interest in French politics which sent Heine to Paris in 1831, but also a perception that German air was not friendly to sympathizers in July Revolutions, is humorously intimated in the "Geständnisse."

"I had done much and suffered much, and when the sun of the July Revolution arose in France, I had become very weary and needed some recreation. Also my native air was every day more unhealthy for me, and it was time I should seriously think of a change of climate. I had visions; the clouds terrified me, and made all sorts of ugly faces at me. It often seemed to me as if the sun were a Prussian cockade; at night I dreamed of a hideous black eagle, which gnawed my liver; and I was very melancholy. Add to this, I had become acquainted with an old Berlin Justizrath, who had spent many years m the fortress of Spandau, and he related to me how unpleasant it is when one is obliged to wear irons in winter. For myself I thought it very unchristian that the irons were not warmed a trifle. If the irons were warmed a little for us, they would not make so unpleasant an impression, and even chilly natures might then bear them very well; it would be only proper consideration, too, if the fetters were perfumed with essence of roses and laurels, as is the case in this country [France]. I asked my Justizrath whether he often got oysters to eat at Spandau. He said, 'No, Spandau was too far from the sea.' Moreover, he said meat was very scarce there, and there was no kind of *volaille* except flies, which fell into one's soup. . . . Now, as I really needed some recreation, and, as Spandau is too far from the sea for oysters to be got there, and the Spandau fly-soup did not seem very appetizing to me; as, besides all this, the Prussian chains are very cold in winter, and could not be conducive to my health, I resolved to visit Paris."

Since this time Paris has been Heine's home, and his best prose works have been written either to inform the Germans on French affairs, or to inform the French on German philosophy and literature. He became a correspondent of the "Allgemeine Zeitung," and his correspondence, which extends, with an interruption of several years, from 1831 to 1844, forms the volume entitled " Französische Zustände " (French Affairs), and the second and third volume of his " Vermischte Schriften." It is a witty and often wise commentary on public men and public events. Louis Philippe, Casimir Périer, Thiers, Guizot, Rothschild, the Catholic party, the Socialist party, have their turn of satire and appreciation; for Heine deals out both with an impartiality which made his less favorable critics — Börne, for example — charge him with the rather incompatible sins of reckless caprice and venality. Literature and art alternate with politics: we have now a sketch of George Sand, or a description of one of Horace Vernet's pictures; now a criticism of Victor Hugo, or of Liszt; now an irresistible caricature of Spontini or Kalkbrenner; and occasionally the predominant satire is relieved by a fine saying, or a genial word of admiration. And all is done with that airy lightness, yet precision of touch, which distinguishes

Heine beyond any living writer. The charge of venality was loudly made against Heine in Germany: first, it was said that he was paid to write; then, that he was paid to abstain from writing; and the accusations were supposed to have an irrefragable basis in the fact that he accepted a stipend from the French government. He has never attempted to conceal the reception of that stipend, and we think his statement (in the "Vermischte Schriften") of the circumstances under which it was offered and received, is a sufficient vindication of himself and M. Guizot from any dishonor in the matter.

It may be readily imagined that Heine, with so large a share of the Gallic element as he has in his composition, was soon at his ease in Parisian society, and the years here were bright with intellectual activity and social enjoyment. "His wit," wrote August Lewald, "is a perpetual gushing fountain; he throws off the most delicious descriptions with amazing facility, and sketches the most comic characters in conversations." Such a man could not be neglected in Paris, and Heine was sought on all sides — as a guest in distinguished salons, as a possible proselyte in the circle of the Saint Simonians. His literary productiveness seems to have been furthered by this congenial life, which, however, was soon to some extent embittered by the sense of exile; for since 1835 both his works and his person have been the object of denunciation by the German governments. Between 1833 and 1845 appeared the four volumes of the "Salon," "Die Romantische Schule" (both written, in the first instance, in French); the book on Börne; "Atta Troll," a romantic poem; "Deutschland," an exquisitely humorous poem, describing his last visit to Germany, and containing some grand passages of serious writing; and the "Neue Gedichte," a collection of lyrical poems. Among the most interesting of his prose works are the second volume of the "Salon," which contains a survey of religion and philosophy in Germany, and the "Romantische Schule," a delightful introduction to that phase of German literature known as the Romantic School. The book on Börne, which appeared in

1840, two years after the death of that writer, excited great indignation in Germany, as a wreaking of vengeance on the dead, an insult to the memory of a man who had worked and suffered in the cause of freedom — a cause which was Heine's own. Börne — we may observe parenthetically, for the information of those who are not familiar with recent German literature — was a remarkable political writer of the ultra-liberal party in Germany, who resided in Paris at the same time with Heine, a man of stern, uncompromising partisanship and bitter humor. Without justifying Heine's production of this book, we see excuses for him which should temper the condemnation passed on it. There was a radical opposition of nature between him and Börne; to use his own distinction, Heine is a Hellene — sensuous, realistic, exquisitely alive to the beautiful, while Börne was a Nazarene — ascetic, spiritualistic, despising the pure artist as destitute of earnestness. Heine has too keen a perception of practical absurdities and damaging exaggerations ever to become a thoroughgoing partisan; and with a love of freedom, a faith in the ultimate triumph of democratic principles, of which we see no just reason to doubt the genuineness and consistency, he has been unable to satisfy more zealous and one-sided liberals by giving his adhesion to their views and measures, or by adopting a denunciatory tone against those in the opposite ranks. Börne could not forgive what he regarded as Heine's epicurean indifference and artistic dalliance, and he at length gave vent to his antipathy in savage attacks on him through the press, accusing him of utterly lacking character and principle, and even of writing under the influence of venal motives. To these attacks Heine remained absolutely mute — from contempt, according to his own account; but the retort, which he resolutely refrained from making during Börne's life, comes in this volume published after his death, with the concentrated force of long-gathering thunder. The utterly inexcusable part of the book is the caricature of Börne's friend, Madame Wohl, and the scurrilous insinuations concerning Börne's domestic life. It is said, we know not with how much truth,

that Heine had to answer for these in a duel with Madame
Wohl's husband, and that, after receiving a serious wound, he
promised to withdraw the offensive matter from a future
edition. That edition, however, has not been called for.
Whatever else we may think of the book, it is impossible to
deny its transcendent talent, the dramatic vigor with which
Börne is made present to us, the critical acumen with which
he is characterized, and the wonderful play of wit, pathos,
and thought which runs through the whole. But we will let
Heine speak for himself, and first we will give part of his
graphic description of the way in which Borne's mind and
manners grated on his taste : —

"To the disgust which, in intercourse with Börne, I was in danger
of feeling towards those who surrounded him, was added the annoyance I felt from his perpetual talk about politics. Nothing but political argument, and again political argument, even at table, where he
managed to hunt me out. At dinner, when I so gladly forget all the
vexations of the world, he spoiled the best dishes for me by his patriotic gall, which he poured as a bitter sauce over everything. Calf's
feet *à la maître d'hôtel,* then my innocent *bonne bouche,* he completely
spoiled for me by Job's tidings from Germany, which he scraped together out of the most unreliable newspapers. And then his accursed
remarks, which spoiled one's appetite ! . . . This was a sort of table-
talk which did not greatly exhilarate me, and I avenged myself by
affecting an excessive, almost impassioned indifference for the object of
Börne's enthusiasm. For example, Börne was indignant that immediately on my arrival in Paris, I had nothing better to do than to
write for German papers a long account of the Exhibition of Pictures.
I omit all discussion as to whether that interest in Art which induced
me to undertake this work was so utterly irreconcilable with the Revolutionary interests of the day; but Börne saw in it a proof of my
indifference towards the sacred cause of humanity, and I could in my
turn spoil the taste of his patriotic *sauerkraut* for him by talking all
dinner-time of nothing but pictures, of Robert's ' Reapers,' Horace
Vernet's ' Judith,' and Scheffer's ' Faust.' . . . That I never thought
it worth while to discuss my political principles with him it is needless
to say ; and once when he declared that he had found a contradiction
in my writings, I satisfied myself with the ironical answer, ' You are
mistaken, *mon cher;* such contradictions never occur in my works, for

always before I begin to write, I read over the statement of my political principles in my previous writings, that I may not contradict myself, and that no one may be able to reproach me with apostasy from my liberal principles.' "

And here is his own account of the spirit in which the book was written: —

" I was never Börne's friend, nor was I ever his enemy. The displeasure which he could often excite in me was never very important, and he atoned for it sufficiently by the cold silence which I opposed to all his accusations and raillery. While he lived I wrote not a line against him, I never thought about him, I ignored him completely; and that enraged him beyond measure. If I now speak of him, I do so neither out of enthusiasm nor out of uneasiness; I am conscious of the coolest impartiality. I write here neither an apology nor a critique; and, as in painting the man I go on my own observation, the image I present of him ought perhaps to be regarded as a real portrait. And such a monument is due to him — to the great wrestler who, in the arena of our political games, wrestled so courageously, and earned, if not the laurel, certainly the crown of oak-leaves. I give an image with his true features, without idealization — the more like him, the more honorable for his memory. He was neither a genius nor a hero; he was no Olympian god. He was a man, a denizen of this earth; he was a good writer and a great patriot. . . . Beautiful, delicious peace, which I feel at this moment in the depths of my soul! Thou rewardest me sufficiently for everything I have done and for everything I have despised. . . . I shall defend myself neither from the reproach of indifference nor from the suspicion of venality. I have for years, during the life of the insinuator, held such self-justification unworthy of me; now even decency demands silence. That would be a frightful spectacle, — polemics between Death and Exile! Dost thou stretch out to me a beseeching hand from the grave? Without rancor I reach mine towards thee. . . . See how noble it is, and pure! It was never soiled by pressing the hands of the mob, any more than by the impure gold of the people's enemy. In reality thou hast never injured me. . . . In all thy insinuations there is not a *louis d'or's* worth of truth."

In one of these years Heine was married, and, in deference to the sentiments of his wife, married according to the rites of the Catholic Church. On this fact busy rumor afterwards founded the story of his conversion to Catholicism, and could of course name the day and the spot on which he abjured Protestantism. In his "Geständnisse" Heine publishes a denial of this rumor; less, he says, for the sake of depriving the Catholics of the solace they may derive from their belief in a new convert, than in order to cut off from another party the more spiteful satisfaction of bewailing his instability : —

"That statement of time and place was entirely correct. I was actually on the specified day in the specified church, which was, moreover, a Jesuit church, namely St. Sulpice; and I then went through a religious act. But this act was no odious abjuration, but a very innocent conjugation; that is to say, my marriage, already performed according to the civil law, there received the ecclesiastical consecration, because my wife, whose family are stanch Catholics, would not have thought her marriage sacred enough without such a ceremony. And I would on no account cause this beloved being any uneasiness or disturbance in her religious views."

For sixteen years, from 1831 to 1847, Heine lived that rapid, concentrated life which is known only in Paris; but then, alas! stole on the "days of darkness," and they were to be many. In 1847 he felt the approach of the terrible spinal disease which has for seven years chained him to his bed in acute suffering. The last time he went out of doors, he tells us, was in May, 1848 : —

"With difficulty I dragged myself to the Louvre, and I almost sank down as I entered the magnificent hall where the ever-blessed goddess of beauty, our beloved Lady of Milo, stands on her pedestal. At her feet I lay long, and wept so bitterly that a stone must have pitied me. The goddess looked compassionately on me, but at the same time disconsolately, as if she would say : Dost thou not see, then, that I have no arms, and thus cannot help thee?"

Since 1848, then, this poet, whom the lovely objects of nature have always "haunted like a passion," has not descended from the second story of a Parisian house; this man of hungry intellect has been shut out from all direct observa-

tion of life, all contact with society, except such as is derived from visitors to his sick-room.   The terrible nervous
disease has affected his eyes; the sight of one is utterly gone,
and he can only raise the lid of the other by lifting it with
his finger.   Opium alone is the beneficent genius that stills
his pain.   We hardly know whether to call it an alleviation
or an intensification of the torture that Heine retains his
mental vigor, his poetic imagination, and his incisive wit;
for if this intellectual activity fills up a blank, it widens the
sphere of suffering.   His brother described him in 1851 as
still, in moments when the hand of pain was not too heavy
on him, the same Heinrich Heine, poet and satirist by turns.
In such moments, he would narrate the strangest things in
the gravest manner.   But when he came to an end, he would
roguishly lift up the lid of his right eye with his finger, to see
the impression he had produced; and if his audience had
been listening with a serious face, he would break into Homeric laughter.   We have other proof than personal testimony,
that Heine's disease allows his genius to retain much of its
energy, in the "Romanzero," a volume of poems published
in 1851, and written chiefly during the three first years of his
illness; and in the first volume of the "Vermischte Schriften," also the product of recent years.   Very plaintive is the
poet's own description of his condition, in the epilogue to the
"Romanzero:" —

"Do I really exist?   My body is so shrunken that I am hardly
anything but a voice; and my bed reminds me of the singing grave of
the magician Merlin, which lies in the forest of Brozeliand, in Brittany,
under tall oaks whose tops soar like green flames towards heaven.
Alas! I envy thee those trees and the fresh breeze that moves their
branches, brother Merlin, for no green leaf rustles about my mattress-
grave in Paris, where early and late I hear nothing but the rolling of
vehicles, hammering, quarrelling, and piano-strumming.   A grave
without repose, death without the privileges of the dead, who have no
debts to pay, and need write neither letters nor books — that is a piteous condition.   Long ago the measure has been taken for my coffin
and for my necrology, but I die so slowly, that the process is tedious

for me as well as my friends. But patience; everything has an end. You will one day find the booth closed where the puppet-show of my humor has so often delighted you."

As early as 1850 it was rumored, that since Heine's illness a change had taken place in his religious views ; and as rumor seldom stops short of extremes, it was soon said that he had become a thorough pietist, Catholics and Protestants by turns claiming him as a convert. Such a change in so uncompromising an iconoclast, in a man who had been so zealous in his negations as Heine, naturally excited considerable sensation in the camp he was supposed to have quitted, as well as in that he was supposed to have joined. In the second volume of the " Salon " and in the " Romantische Schule," written in 1834 and 1835, the doctrine of Pantheism is dwelt on with a fervor and unmixed seriousness which show that Pantheism was then an animating faith to Heine, and he attacks what he considers the false spiritualism and asceticism of Christianity as the enemy of true beauty in Art, and of social well-being. Now, however, it was said that Heine had recanted all his heresies ; but from the fact that visitors to his sick-room brought away very various impressions as to his actual religious views, it seemed probable that his love of mystification had found a tempting opportunity for exercise on this subject, and that, as one of his friends said, he was not inclined to pour out unmixed wine to those who asked for a sample out of mere curiosity. At length, in the epilogue to the " Romanzero," dated 1851, there appeared, amidst much mystifying banter, a declaration that he had embraced Theism and the belief in a future life, and what chiefly lent an air of seriousness and reliability to this affirmation, was the fact that he took care to accompany it with certain negations : —

" As concerns myself, I can boast of no particular progress in politics ; I adhered (after 1848) to the same democratic principles which had the homage of my youth, and for which I have ever since glowed with increasing fervor. In theology, on the contrary, I must accuse myself of retrogression, since, as I have already confessed, I returned to the old superstition — to a personal God. This fact is, once for all, not to be stifled, as many enlightened and well-meaning friends would fain have had it. But I must expressly contradict the report that my retrograde movement has carried me as far as to the threshold of a Church, and that I have even been received into her lap. No : my religious convictions and views have remained free from any tincture of ecclesiasticism ; no chiming of bells has allured me, no altar-candles have dazzled me. I have dallied with no dogmas, and have not utterly renounced my reason."

This sounds like a serious statement. But what shall we say to a convert who plays with his newly acquired belief in a future life, as Heine does in the very next page ? He says to his reader : —

" Console thyself; we shall meet again in a better world, where I also mean to write thee better books. I take for granted that my health will there be improved, and that Swedenborg has not deceived me. He relates, namely, with great confidence, that we shall peacefully carry on our old occupations in the other world, just as we have done in this; that we shall there preserve our individuality unaltered, and that death will produce no particular change in our organic development. Swedenborg is a thoroughly honorable fellow, and quite worthy of credit in what he tells us about the other world, where he saw with his own eyes the persons who had played a great part on our earth. Most of them, he says, remained unchanged, and busied themselves with the same things as formerly; they remained stationary, were old-fashioned, *rococo* — which now and then produced a ludicrous effect. For example, our dear Dr. Martin Luther kept fast by his doctrine of Grace, about which he had for three hundred years daily written down the same mouldy arguments; just in the same way as the late Baron Ekstein, who during twenty years printed in the " Allemeine Zeitung " one and the same article, perpetually chewing over again the old cud of Jesuitical doctrine. But, as we have said, all persons who once figured here below were not found by Swedenborg in such a state of fossil immutability; many had considerably developed their character, both for good and evil, in the other world, and this gave rise to some singular results. Some who had been heroes and saints on earth had *there* sunk into scamps and good-for-nothings; and there were examples, too, of a contrary transformation. For instance, the fumes of self-conceit mounted to Saint Anthony's head when he learned what immense veneration and adoration had been paid to him by all Christendom; and he who here below withstood the most terrible temptations, was now quite an impertinent rascal and dissolute gallows-bird, who vied with his pig in rolling himself in the mud. The chaste Susanna, from having been excessively vain of her virtue, which she thought indomitable, came to a shameful fall, and she who once so gloriously resisted the two old men, was a victim to the seductions of the young Absalom, the son of David. On the contrary, Lot's daughters had in the lapse of time become very virtuous, and passed in the other world for models of propriety; the old man, alas! had stuck to the wine-flask."

In his "Geständnisse" the retraction of former opinions and profession of Theism are renewed, but in a strain of irony that repels our sympathy and baffles our psychology. Yet what strange, deep pathos is mingled with the audacity of the following passage : —

"What avails it me, that enthusiastic youths and maidens crown my marble bust with laurel, when the withered hands of an aged nurse are pressing Spanish flies behind my ears? What avails it me, that all the roses of Shiraz glow and waft incense for me? Alas! Shiraz is two thousand miles from the Rue d'Amsterdam, where, in the wearisome loneliness of my sick-room, I get no scent, except it be, perhaps, the perfume of warmed towels. Alas! God's satire weighs heavily on me. The great Author of the universe, the Aristophanes of Heaven, was bent on demonstrating, with crushing force, to me, the little, earthly, German Aristophanes, how my wittiest sarcasms are only pitiful attempts at jesting in comparison with His, and how miserably I am beneath him in humor, in colossal mockery."

For our own part, we regard the paradoxical irreverence with which Heine professes his theoretical reverence as pathological, as the diseased exhibition of a predominant tendency, urged into anomalous action by the pressure of pain and mental privation, as the delirium of wit starved of its proper nourishment. It is not for us to condemn, who have never had the same burden laid on us; it is not for pygmies at their ease to criticise the writhings of the Titan chained to the rock.

On one other point we must touch before quitting Heine's personal history. There is a standing accusation against him, in some quarters, of wanting political principle, of wishing to denationalize himself, and of indulging in insults against his native country. Whatever ground may exist for these accusations, that ground is not, so far as we see, to be found in his writings. He may not have much faith in German revolutions and revolutionists; experience, in his case as in that of others, may have thrown his millennial anticipations into more distant perspective; but we see no evidence that he has ever swerved from his attachment to the principles of freedom, or written anything which to a philosophic mind is incompatible with true patriotism. He has expressly denied the report that he wished to become naturalized in France; and his yearning towards his native land and the accents of his native language is expressed with a pathos the more reliable from the fact that he is sparing in such effusions. We do not see why Heine's satire of the blunders and foibles of his fellow-countrymen should be denounced as the crime of *lèse-patrie*, any more than the political caricatures of any other satirist. The real offences of Heine are his occasional coarseness and his unscrupulous personalities, which are reprehensible, not because they are directed against his fellow-countrymen, but because they are personalities. That these offences have their precedents in men whose memory the world delights to honor does not remove their turpitude, but it is a fact which should modify our condemnation in a particular case; unless, indeed, we are to deliver our judgments on a principle of compensation, making up for our indulgence in one direction by our severity in another. On this ground of coarseness and personality, a true bill may be found against Heine; *not*, we think, on the ground that he has laughed at what is laughable in his compatriots. Here is a specimen of the satire under which we suppose German patriots wince : —

" Rhenish Bavaria was to be the starting-point of the German Revolution. Zweibrücken was the Bethlehem in which the infant Saviour
—Freedom — lay in the cradle, and gave whimpering promise of re-
deeming the world. Near his cradle bellowed many an ox, who afterwards, when his horns were reckoned on, showed himself a very
harmless brute. It was confidently believed that the German Revolution would begin in Zweibrücken, and everything was there ripe for an
outbreak. But, as has been hinted, the tender-heartedness of some
persons frustrated that illegal undertaking. For example, among the
Bipontine conspirators there was a tremendous braggart, who was
always loudest in his rage, who boiled over with the hatred of tyranny;
and this man was fixed on to strike the first blow, by cutting down a
sentinel who kept an important post. . . . 'What!' cried the man,
when this order was given him — 'What! — me! Can you expect so
horrible, so bloodthirsty an act of me? I — I, kill an innocent sentinel?
I, who am the father of a family! And this sentinel is perhaps also
father of a family. One father of a family kill another father of a
family? Yes! Kill — murder!'"

In political matters, Heine, like all men whose intellect
and taste predominate too far over their impulses to allow of
their becoming partisans, is offensive alike to the aristocrat
and the democrat. By the one he is denounced as a man
who holds incendiary principles; by the other as a half-
hearted "trimmer." He has no sympathy, as he says, with
" that vague, barren pathos, that useless effervescence of enthusiasm, which plunges, with the spirit of a martyr, into an
ocean of generalities, and which always reminds me of the
American sailor, who had so fervent an enthusiasm for
General Jackson, that he at last sprang from the top of a
mast into the sea, crying, ' I die for General Jackson ! ' ".

" But thou liest, Brutus, thou liest, Cassius, and thou, too, liest,
Asinius, in maintaining that my ridicule attacks those ideas which are
the precious acquisition of Humanity, and for which I myself have so
striven and suffered. No! for the very reason that those ideas constantly hover before the poet in glorious splendor and majesty, he is
the more irresistibly overcome by laughter when he sees how rudely,
awkwardly, and clumsily those ideas are seized and mirrored in the
contracted minds of contemporaries. . . . There are mirrors which

have so rough a surface that even an Apollo reflected in them becomes a caricature and excites our laughter. *But we laugh then only at the caricature, not at the god.*"

For the rest, why should we demand of Heine that he should be a hero, a patriot, a solemn prophet, any more than we should demand of a gazelle that it should draw well in harness? Nature has not made him of her sterner stuff — not of iron and adamant, but of pollen of flowers, the juice of the grape, and Puck's mischievous brain, plenteously mixing also the dews of kindly affection and the gold-dust of noble thoughts. It is, after all, a *tribute* which his enemies pay him when they utter their bitterest dictum, namely, that he is "*nur Dichter*" — only a poet. Let us accept this point of view for the present, and, leaving all consideration of him as a man, look at him simply as a poet and literary artist.

Heine is essentially a lyric poet. The finest products of his genius are

> "Short swallow-flights of song, that dip
> Their wings in tears, and skim away;"

and they are so emphatically songs that, in reading them, we feel as if each must have a twin melody born in the same moment and by the same inspiration. Heine is too impressible and mercurial for any sustained production; even in his short lyrics his tears sometimes pass into laughter, and his laughter into tears; and his longer poems, "Atta Troll" and "Deutschland," are full of Ariosto-like transitions. His song has a wide compass of notes; he can take us to the shores of the Northern Sea and thrill us by the sombre sublimity of his pictures and dreamy fancies; he can draw forth our tears by the voice he gives to our own sorrows, or to the sorrows of "Poor Peter;" he can throw a cold shudder over us by a mysterious legend, a ghost story, or a still more ghastly rendering of hard reality; he can charm us by a quiet idyl, shake us with laughter at his overflowing fun, or give us a piquant sensation of surprise by the ingenuity of his transitions from the lofty to the ludicrous. This last power is not, indeed, essentially poetical; but only a poet can use it with the same success as Heine, for only a poet can poise our emotion and expectation at such a height as to give effect to the sudden fall. Heine's greatest power as a poet lies in his simple pathos, in the ever-varied but always natural expression he has given to the tender emotions. We may perhaps indicate this phase of his genius by referring to Wordsworth's beautiful little poem, "She dwelt among the untrodden ways;" the conclusion —

> "She dwelt alone, and few could know
> When Lucy ceased to be;
> But she is in her grave, and, oh!
> The difference to me" —

is entirely in Heine's manner; and so is Tennyson's poem of a dozen lines, called "Circumstance." Both these poems have Heine's pregnant simplicity. But, lest this comparison should mislead, we must say that there is no general resemblance between either Wordsworth, or Tennyson, and Heine. Their greatest qualities lie quite away from the light, delicate lucidity, the easy, rippling music, of Heine's style. The distinctive charm of his lyrics may best be seen by comparing them with Goethe's. Both have the same masterly, finished simplicity and rhythmic grace; but there is more thought mingled with Goethe's feeling. His lyrical genius is a vessel that draws more water than Heine's, and, though it seems to glide along with equal ease, we have a sense of greater weight and force accompanying the grace of its movement.

But, for this very reason, Heine touches our hearts more strongly; his songs are all music and feeling; they are like birds, that not only enchant us with their delicious notes, but nestle against us with their soft breasts, and make us feel the agitated beating of their hearts. He indicates a whole sad history in a single quatrain; there is not an image in it, not a thought; but it is beautiful, simple, and perfect as a "big round tear;" it is pure feeling breathed in pure music: —

> " Anfangs wollt' ich fast verzagen
> Und ich glaubt' ich trug es nie,
> Und ich hab' es doch getragen, —
> Aber fragt mich nur nicht, wie." [1]

He excels equally in the more imaginative expression of feeling; he represents it by a brief image, like a finely cut cameo; he expands it into a mysterious dream, or dramatizes it in a little story, half-ballad, half-idyl; and in all these forms his art is so perfect that we never have a sense of artificiality or of unsuccessful effort, but all seems to have developed itself by the same beautiful necessity that brings forth vine-leaves and grapes and the natural curls of childhood.   Of Heine's humorous poetry, " Deutschland " is the most charming specimen — charming, especially, because its wit and humor grow out of a rich loam of thought.   " Atta Troll " is more original, more various, more fantastic; but it is too great a strain on the imagination to be a general favorite.   We have said that feeling is the element in which Heine's poetic genius habitually floats; but he can occasionally soar to a higher region, and impart deep significance to picturesque symbolism; he can flash a sublime thought over the past and into the future; he can pour forth a lofty strain of hope or indignation.   Few could forget, after once hearing them, the stanzas at the close of " Deutschland," in which he warns the King of Prussia not to incur the irredeemable hell which the injured poet can create for him, the *singing flames* of a Dante's *terza rima!*

> " Kennst du die Hölle des Dante nicht.
> Die schrecklichen Terzetten ?
> Wen da der Dichter hineingesperrt
> Den kann kein Gott mehr retten.

> " Kein Gott, kein Heiland, erlöst ihn je
> Aus diesen singenden flammen !
> Nimm dich in Acht, das wir dich nicht
> Zu solcher Hölle verdammen." [2]

[1] At first I was almost in despair, and I thought I could never bear it; and yet I have borne it, — only do not ask me *how?*

[2] It is not fair to the English reader to indulge in German quotations, but in our opinion poetical translations are usually worse than valueless.

As a prosaist, Heine is, in one point of view, even more distinguished than as a poet. The German language easily lends itself to all the purposes of poetry; like the ladies of the Middle Ages, it is gracious and compliant to the Troubadours. But as these same ladies were often crusty and repulsive to their unmusical mates, so the German language generally appears awkward and unmanageable in the hands of prose-writers. Indeed, the number of really fine German prosaists before Heine would hardly have exceeded the numerating powers of a New Hollander, who can count three and no more. Persons the most familiar with German prose testify that there is an extra fatigue in reading it, just as we feel an extra fatigue from our walk when it takes us over ploughed clay. But in Heine's hands German prose, usually so heavy, so clumsy, so dull, becomes like clay in the hands of the chemist, compact, metallic, brilliant; it is German in an allotropic condition. No dreary labyrinthine sentences in which you find " no end in wandering mazes lost; " no chains of adjectives in linked harshness long drawn out; no digressions thrown in as parentheses; but crystalline definiteness and clearness, fine and varied rhythm, and all that delicate precision, all those felicities of word and cadence, which belong to the highest order of prose. And Heine has proved — what Madame de Staël seems to have doubted — that it is possible to be witty in German; indeed, in reading him, you might imagine that German was pre-eminently the language of wit, so flexible, so subtle, so piquant does it become under his management. He is far more an artist in prose than Goethe. He has not the breadth and repose, and the calm development which belong to Goethe's style, for they are foreign to his mental character; but he excels Goethe in susceptibility to the manifold qualities of prose, and in mastery over its

For those who think differently, however, we may mention that Mr. Stores Smith has published a modest little book, containing " Selections from the Poetry of Heinrich Heine," and that a meritorious (American) translation of Heine's complete works by Charles Leland, is now appearing in shilling numbers.

effects. Heine is full of variety, of light and shadow; he alternates between epigrammatic pith, imaginative grace, sly allusion, and daring piquancy; and athwart all these there runs a vein of sadness, tenderness, and grandeur, which reveals the poet. He continually throws out those finely chiselled sayings which stamp themselves on the memory, and become familiar by quotation. For example: "The people have time enough, they are immortal; kings only are mortal." — "Wherever a great soul utters its thoughts, there is Golgotha." — "Nature wanted to see how she looked, and she created Goethe." — "Only the man who has known bodily suffering is truly a man; his limbs have their Passion history, they are spiritualized." He calls Rubens "this Flemish Titan, the wings of whose genius were so strong that he soared as high as the sun, in spite of the hundred-weight of Dutch cheeses that hung on his legs." Speaking of Börne's dislike to the calm creations of the true artist, he says: "He was like a child which, insensible to the glowing significance of a Greek statue, only touches the marble and complains of cold."

The most poetic and specifically humorous of Heine's prose writings are the "Reisebilder." The comparison with Sterne is inevitable here; but Heine does not suffer from it, for if he falls below Sterne in raciness of humor, he is far above him in poetic sensibility and in reach and variety of thought. Heine's humor is never persistent, it never flows on long in easy gayety and drollery; where it is not swelled by the tide of poetic feeling, it is continually dashing down the precipice of a witticism. It is not broad and unctuous; it is aerial and sprite-like, a momentary resting-place between his poetry and his wit. In the "Reisebilder" he runs through the whole gamut of his powers, and gives us every hue of thought, from the wildly droll and fantastic to the sombre and the terrible. Here is a passage almost Dantesque in conception : —

"Alas! one ought in truth to write against no one in this world. Each of us is sick enough in this great lazaretto, and many a polemi cal writing reminds me involuntarily of a revolting quarrel, in a little hospital at Cracow, of which I chanced to be a witness, and where it was horrible to hear how the patients mockingly reproached each other with their infirmities: how one who was wasted by consumption jeered at another who was bloated by dropsy; how one laughed at another's cancer in the nose, and this one again at his neighbor's locked jaw or squint; until at last the delirious fever-patient sprang out of bed and tore away the coverings from the wounded bodies of his companions, and nothing was to be seen but hideous misery and mutilation."

And how fine is the transition in the very next chapter, where, after quoting the Homeric description of the feasting gods, he says : —

"Then suddenly approached, panting, a pale Jew, with drops of blood on his brow, with a crown of thorns on his head, and a great cross laid on his shoulders; and he threw the cross on the high table of the gods, so that the golden cups tottered, and the gods became dumb and pale, and grew ever paler, till they at last melted away into vapor."

The richest specimens of Heine's wit are perhaps to be found in the works which have appeared since the "Reise-bilder." The years, if they have intensified his satirical bitterness, have also given his wit a finer edge and polish. His sarcasms are so subtly prepared and so slyly allusive, that they may often escape readers whose sense of wit is not very acute; but for those who delight in the subtle and delicate flavors of style, there can hardly be any wit more irresistible than Heine's. We may measure its force by the degree in which it has subdued the German language to its purposes, and made that language brilliant in spite of a long hereditary transmission of dulness. As one of the most harmless examples of his satire, take this on a man who has certainly had his share of adulation : —

"Assuredly it is far from my purpose to depreciate M. Victor Cousin. The titles of this celebrated philosopher even lay me under an obligation to praise him. He belongs to that living pantheon of France, which we call the peerage, and his intelligent legs rest on the velvet

benches of the Luxembourg. I must indeed sternly repress all private
feelings which might seduce me into an excessive enthusiasm. Otherwise I might be suspected of servility ; for M. Cousin is very influential in the state by means of his position and his tongue. This
consideration might even move me to speak of his faults as frankly as
of his virtues. Will he himself disapprove of this ? Assuredly not.
I know that we cannot do higher honor to great minds than when we
throw as strong a light on their demerits as on their merits. When
we sing the praises of a Hercules, we must also mention that he once
laid aside the lion's skin and sat down to the distaff: what then ? he
remains notwithstanding a Hercules ! So when we relate similar circumstances concerning M. Cousin, we must nevertheless add, with discriminating eulogy : *M. Cousin, if he has sometimes sat twaddling at the
distaff, has never laid aside the lion's skin.* . . . It is true that, having
been suspected of demagogy, he spent some time in a German prison,
just as Lafayette and Richard Cœur de Lion. But that M. Cousin
there in his leisure hours studied Kant's 'Critique of Pure Reason' is
to be doubted on three grounds. First, this book is written in German. Secondly, in order to read this book, a man must understand
German. Thirdly, M. Cousin does not understand German. . . . I
fear I am passing unawares from the sweet waters of praise into the
bitter ocean of blame. Yes, on one account I cannot refrain from bitterly blaming M. Cousin, — namely, that he who loves truth far more
than he loves Plato and Tenneman, is unjust to himself when he wants
to persuade us that he has borrowed something from the philosophy
of Schelling and Hegel. Against this self-accusation, I must take
M. Cousin under my protection. On my word and conscience, this
honorable man has not stolen a jot from Schelling and Hegel, and if he
brought home anything of theirs, it was merely their friendship. That
does honor to his heart. But there are many instances of such false
self-accusation in psychology. I knew a man who declared that he had
stolen silver spoons at the king's table; and yet we all knew that the
poor devil had never been presented at court, and accused himself of
stealing these spoons to make us believe that he had been a guest at
the palace. No ! In German philosophy M. Cousin has always kept the
sixth commandment; here he has never pocketed a single idea, not so
much as a salt-spoon of an idea. All witnesses agree in attesting that
in this respect M. Cousin is honor itself. . . . I prophesy to you that
the renown of M. Cousin, like the French Revolution, will go round
the world ! I hear some one wickedly add : Undeniably the renown of,

M. Cousin is going round the world, and *it has already taken its de-parture from France."*

The following "symbolical myth" about Louis Philippe is very characteristic of Heine's manner : —

"I remember very well that immediately on my arrival [in Paris] I hastened to the Palais Royal to see Louis Philippe. The friend who conducted me told me that the king now appeared on the terrace only at stated hours, but that formerly he was to be seen at any time for five francs. 'For five francs!' I cried with amazement; 'does he then show himself for money?' 'No; but he is shown for money, and it happens in this way : There is a society of *claqueurs, marchands de contremarques,* and such riff-raff, who offered every foreigner to show him the king for five francs; if he would give ten francs, he might see the king raise his eyes to heaven, and lay his hand protestingly on his heart; if he would give twenty francs, the king would sing the Marseillaise. If the foreigner gave five francs, they raised a loud cheering under the king's windows, and His Majesty appeared on the terrace, bowed, and retired. If ten francs, they shouted still louder, and gesticulated as if they had been possessed, when the king appeared, who then, as a sign of silent emotion, raised his eyes to heaven, and laid his hand on his heart. English visitors, however, would sometimes spend as much as twenty francs, and then the enthusiasm mounted to the highest pitch; no sooner did the king appear on the terrace, than the Marseillaise was struck up and roared out frightfully, until Louis Philippe, perhaps only for the sake of putting an end to the singing, bowed, laid his hand on his heart, and joined in the Marseillaise. Whether, as is asserted, he beat time with his foot, I cannot say.'"

One more quotation and it must be our last : —

"Oh the women! We must forgive them much, for they love much, and many. Their hate is properly only love turned inside out. Sometimes they attribute some delinquency to us, because they think they can in this way gratify another man. When they write, they have always one eye on the paper and the other on a man ; and this is true of all authoresses, except the Countess Hahn-Hahn, who has only one eye."

EVANGELICAL TEACHING: DR. CUMMING.

GIVEN, a man with moderate intellect, a moral standard not higher than the average, some rhetorical affluence and great glibness of speech, what is the career in which, without the aid of birth or money, he may most easily attain power and reputation in English society? Where is that Goshen of mediocrity in which a smattering of science and learning will pass for profound instruction, where platitudes will be accepted as wisdom, bigoted narrowness as holy zeal, unctuous egoism as God-given piety? Let such a man become an evangelical preacher; he will then find it possible to reconcile small ability with great ambition, superficial knowledge with the prestige of erudition, a middling morale with a high reputation for sanctity. Let him shun practical extremes and be ultra only in what is purely theoretic: let him be stringent on predestination, but latitudinarian on fasting; unflinching in insisting on the Eternity of punishment, but diffident of curtailing the substantial comforts of Time; ardent and imaginative on the pre-millennial advent of Christ, but cold and cautious towards every other infringement of the *status quo*. Let him fish for souls, not with the bait of inconvenient singularity, but with the drag-net of comfortable conformity. Let him be hard and literal in his interpretation only when he wants to hurl texts at the heads of unbelievers and adversaries; but when the letter of the Scriptures presses too closely on the genteel Christianity of the nineteenth century, let him use his spiritualizing alembic and disperse it into impalpable ether. Let him preach less of Christ than of Antichrist; let him be less definite in showing what sin is than in showing who is the Man of Sin, less expansive on the blessedness of faith than on the accursedness of infidelity. Above all, let him set up as an interpreter of prophecy, and rival Moore's Almanack in the prediction of political events, tickling the interest of hearers who are but moderately spiritual by showing how the Holy Spirit has dictated problems and charades for their benefit, and how, if they are ingenious enough to solve these, they may have their Christian graces nourished by learning precisely to whom they may point as the "horn that had eyes," "the lying prophet," and the "unclean spirits." In this way he will draw men to him by the strong cords of their passions, made reason-proof by being baptized with the name of piety. In this way he may gain a metropolitan pulpit; the avenues to his church will be as crowded as the passages to the opera; he has but to print his prophetic sermons and bind them in lilac and gold, and they will adorn the drawing-room table of all evangelical ladies, who will regard as a sort of pious "light reading" the demonstration that the prophecy of the locusts whose sting is in their tail is fulfilled in the fact of the Turkish commander's having taken a horse's tail for his standard, and that the French are the very frogs predicted in the Revelations.

Pleasant to the clerical flesh under such circumstances is the arrival of Sunday! Somewhat at a disadvantage during the week, in the presence of working-day interests and lay splendors, on Sunday the preacher becomes the cynosure of a thousand eyes, and predominates at once over the Amphitryon with whom he dines, and the most captious member of his church or vestry. He has an immense advantage over all other public speakers. The platform orator is subject to the criticism of hisses and groans. Counsel for the plaintiff expects the retort of counsel for the defendant. The honorable gentleman on one side of the House is liable to have his facts and figures shown up by his honorable friend on the opposite side. Even the scientific or literary lecturer, if he is dull or incompetent, may see the best part of his audience quietly slip out one by one. But the preacher is completely.

master of the situation: no one may hiss, no one may depart. Like the writer of imaginary conversations, he may put what imbecilities he pleases into the mouths of his antagonists, and swell with triumph when he has refuted them. He may riot in gratuitous assertions, confident that no man will contradict him; he may exercise perfect free-will in logic, and invent illustrative experience; he may give an evangelical edition of history with the inconvenient facts omitted; — all this he may do with impunity, certain that those of his hearers who are not sympathizing are not listening. For the Press has no band of critics who go the round of the churches and chapels, and are on the watch for a slip or defect in the preacher, to make a "feature" in their article; the clergy are, practically, the most irresponsible of all talkers. For this reason, at least, it is well that they do not always allow their discourses to be merely fugitive, but are often induced to fix them in that black and white in which they are open to the criticism of any man who has the courage and patience to treat them with thorough freedom of speech and pen.

It is because we think this criticism of clerical teaching desirable for the public good, that we devote some pages to Dr. Cumming. He is, as every one knows, a preacher of immense popularity; and of the numerous publications in which he perpetuates his pulpit labors, all circulate widely, and some, according to their titlepage, have reached the sixteenth thousand. Now, our opinion of these publications is the very opposite of that given by a newspaper eulogist: we do *not* "believe that the repeated issues of Dr. Cumming's thoughts are having a beneficial effect on society," but the reverse; and hence, little inclined as we are to dwell on his pages, we think it worth while to do so, for the sake of pointing out in them what we believe to be profoundly mistaken and pernicious. Of Dr. Cumming personally we know absolutely nothing; our acquaintance with him is confined to a perusal of his works, our judgment of him is founded solely on the manner in which he has written himself down on his pages. We know neither how he looks nor how he lives

We are ignorant whether, like St. Paul, he has a bodily presence that is weak and contemptible, or whether his person is
as florid and as prone to amplification as his style.   For
aught we know, he may not only have the gift of prophecy,
but may bestow the profits of all his works to feed the poor,
and be ready to give his own body to be burned with as much
alacrity as he infers the everlasting burning of Roman Catholics and Puseyites.   Out of the pulpit he may be a model of
justice, truthfulness, and the love that thinketh no evil; but
we are obliged to judge of his charity by the spirit we find
in his sermons, and shall only be glad to learn that his practice is, in many respects, an amiable *non sequitur* from his
teaching.

Dr. Cumming's mind is evidently not of the pietistic order.
There is not the slightest leaning towards mysticism in his
Christianity, — no indication of religious raptures, of delight
in God, of spiritual communion with the Father. He is most
at home in the forensic view of Justification, and dwells on
salvation as a scheme rather than as an experience. He
insists on good works as the sign of justifying faith, as labors
to be achieved to the glory of God; but he rarely represents
them as the spontaneous, necessary outflow of a soul filled
with Divine love.   He is at home in the external, the polem
ical, the historical, the circumstantial, and is only episodi-
cally devout and practical.   The great majority of his
published sermons are occupied with argument or philippic
against Romanists and unbelievers, with "vindications" of
the Bible, with the political interpretation of prophecy, or
the criticism of public events; and the devout aspiration,
or the spiritual and practical exhortation, is tacked to them as
a sort of fringe in a hurried sentence or two at the end. He
revels in the demonstration that the Pope is the Man of Sin;
he is copious on the downfall of the Ottoman Empire; he appears to glow with satisfaction in turning a story which tends
to show how he abashed an "infidel;" it is a favorite exercise with him to form conjectures of the process by which the

earth is to be burned up, and to picture Dr. Chalmers and
Mr. Wilberforce being caught up to meet Christ in the air,
while Romanists, Puseyites, and infidels are given over to
gnashing of teeth. But of really spiritual joys and sorrows,
of the life and death of Christ as a manifestation of love
that constrains the soul, of sympathy with that yearning over
the lost and erring which made Jesus weep over Jerusalem,
and prompted the sublime prayer, "Father, forgive them,"
of the gentler fruits of the Spirit, and the peace of God which
passeth understanding, — of all this, we find little trace in
Dr. Cumming's discourses.

His style is in perfect correspondence with this habit of
mind. Though diffuse, as that of all preachers must be, it
has rapidity of movement, perfect clearness, and some apt-
ness of illustration. He has much of that literary talent
which makes a good journalist, — the power of beating out
an idea over a large space, and of introducing far-fetched
àpropos. His writings have, indeed, no high merit: they
have no originality or force of thought, no striking felicity
of presentation, no depth of emotion. Throughout nine
volumes we have alighted on no passage which impressed us
as worth extracting, and placing among the "beauties" of
evangelical writers, such as Robert Hall, Foster the Essayist,
or Isaac Taylor. Everywhere there is commonplace cleverness, nowhere a spark of rare thought, of lofty sentiment, or
pathetic tenderness. We feel ourselves in company with a
voluble retail talker, whose language is exuberant but not
exact, and to whom we should never think of referring for
precise information or for well-digested thought and experience. His argument continually slides into wholesale assertion and vague declamation, and in his love of ornament he
frequently becomes tawdry. For example, he tells us [1] that
"Botany weaves around the cross her amaranthine garlands;
and Newton comes from his starry home, Linnæus from his
flowery resting-place, and Werner and Hutton from their sub-
terranean graves, at the voice of Chalmers, to acknowledge

[1] Apoc. Sketches, p. 265.

that all they learned and elicited in their respective provinces, has only served to show more clearly that Jesus of Nazareth is enthroned on the riches of the universe;" — and so prosaic an injunction to his hearers as that they should choose a residence within an easy distance of church, is magnificently draped by him as an exhortation to prefer a house "that basks in the sunshine of the countenance of God." Like all preachers of his class, he is more fertile in imaginative paraphrase than in close exposition, and in this way he gives us some remarkable fragments of what we may call the romance of Scripture, filling up the outline of the record with an elaborate coloring quite undreamed of by more literal minds. The serpent, he informs us, said to Eve, "Can it be so? Surely you are mistaken, that God hath said you shall die, a creature so fair, so lovely, so beautiful. It is impossible. *The laws of nature and physical science tell you that my interpretation is correct;* you shall not die. I can tell you by my own experience as an angel that you shall be as gods, knowing good and evil."[1] Again, according to Dr. Cumming, Abel had so clear an idea of the Incarnation and Atonement, that when he offered his sacrifice "he must have said, 'I feel myself a guilty sinner, and that in myself I cannot meet thee alive; I lay on thine altar this victim, and I shed its blood as my testimony that mine should be shed; and I look for forgiveness and undeserved mercy through Him who is to bruise the serpent's head, and whose atonement this typifies.'"[2] Indeed, his productions are essentially ephemeral; he is essentially a journalist, who writes sermons instead of leading articles, who, instead of venting diatribes against her Majesty's Ministers, directs his power of invective against Cardinal Wiseman and the Puseyites, — instead of declaiming on public spirit, perorates on the "glory of God." We fancy he is called, in the more refined evangelical circles, an "intellectual preacher;" by the plainer sort of Christians, a "flowery preacher;" and we are inclined to think that the more spiritually minded class of believers, who look with greater

[1] Apoc. Sketches, p. 294.   [2] Occas. Disc., vol. i. p. 23.

anxiety for the kingdom of God within them than for the visible advent of Christ in 1864, will be likely to find Dr. Cumming's declamatory flights and historico-prophetical exercitations as little better than "clouts o' cauld parritch."

Such is our general impression from his writings after an attentive perusal. There are some particular characteristics which we shall consider more closely, but in doing so we must be understood as altogether declining any doctrinal discussion. We have no intention to consider the grounds of Dr. Cumming's dogmatic system, to examine the principles of his prophetic exegesis, or to question his opinion concerning the little horn, the river Euphrates, or the seven vials. We identify ourselves with no one of the bodies whom he regards it as his special mission to attack; we give our adhesion neither to Romanism, Puseyism, nor to that anomalous combination of opinions which he introduces to us under the name of Infidelity. It is simply as spectators that we criticise Dr. Cumming's mode of warfare; and we concern ourselves less with what he holds to be Christian truth than with his manner of enforcing that truth, less with the doctrines he teaches than with the moral spirit and tendencies of his teaching.

One of the most striking characteristics of Dr. Cumming's writings is *unscrupulosity of statement.* His motto apparently is, *Christianitatem, quocunque modo Christianitatem;* and the only system he includes under the term Christianity is Calvinistic Protestantism. Experience has so long shown that the human brain is a congenial nidus for inconsistent beliefs that we do not pause to inquire how Dr. Cumming, who attributes the conversion of the unbelieving to the Divine Spirit, can think it necessary to co-operate with that Spirit by argumentative white lies. Nor do we for a moment impugn the genuineness of his zeal for Christianity, or the sincerity of his conviction that the doctrines he preaches are necessary to salvation; on the contrary, we regard the flagrant unveracity that we find on his pages as an indirect result of that conviction, — as a result, namely, of the intellectual and moral distortion of view which is inevitably produced by assigning to dogmas, based on a very complex structure of evidence, the place and authority of first truths. A distinct appreciation of the value of evidence — in other words, the intellectual perception of truth — is more closely allied to truthfulness of statement, or the moral quality of veracity, than is generally admitted. There is not a more pernicious fallacy afloat in common parlance than the wide distinction made between intellect and morality. Amiable impulses without intellect man may have in common with dogs and horses; but morality, which is specifically human, is dependent on the regulation of feeling by intellect. All human beings who can be said to be in any degree moral have their impulses guided, not indeed always by their own intellect, but by the intellect of human beings who have gone before them, and created traditions and associations which have taken the rank of laws. Now, that highest moral habit, the constant preference of truth both theoretically and practically, pre-eminently demands the co-operation of the intellect with the impulses; as is indicated by the fact that it is only found in anything like completeness in the highest class of minds. In accordance with this we think it is found that, in proportion as religious sects exalt feeling above intellect, and believe themselves to be guided by direct inspiration rather than by a spontaneous exertion of their faculties, — that is, in proportion as they are removed from rationalism, — their sense of truthfulness is misty and confused. No one can have talked to the more enthusiastic Methodists, and listened to their stories of miracles, without perceiving that they require no other passport to a statement than that it accords with their wishes and their general conception of God's dealings; nay, they regard as a symptom of sinful scepticism an inquiry into the evidence for a story which they think unquestionably tends to the glory of God, and in retailing such stories, new particulars, further tending to his glory, are "borne in" upon their minds. Now, Dr. Cumming, as we have said, is no enthusiastic pietist; within a certain circle, within the mill of evangelical orthodoxy, his intellect is perpetually at work; but that principle of sophistication which our friends the Methodists derive from the predominance of their pietistic feelings, is involved for him in the doctrine of verbal inspiration; what is for them a state of emotion submerging the intellect, is with him a formula imprisoning the intellect, depriving it of its proper function, — the free search for truth — and making it the mere servant-of-all-work to a foregone conclusion. Minds fettered by this doctrine no longer inquire concerning a proposition whether it is attested by sufficient evidence, but whether it accords with Scripture; they do not search for facts, as such, but for facts that will bear out their doctrine. They become accustomed to reject the more direct evidence in favor of the less direct, and where adverse evidence reaches demonstration they must resort to devices and expedients in order to explain away contradiction. It is easy to see that this mental habit blunts not only the perception of truth, but the sense of truthfulness, and that the man whose faith drives him into fallacies treads close upon the precipice of falsehood.

We have entered into this digression for the sake of mitigating the inference that is likely to be drawn from that characteristic of Dr. Cumming's works to which we have pointed. He is much in the same intellectual condition as that professor of Padua who, in order to disprove Galileo's discovery of Jupiter's satellites, urged that as there were only seven metals there could not be more than seven planets, — a mental condition scarcely compatible with candor. And we may well suppose that if the Professor had held the belief in seven planets, and no more, to be a necessary condition of salvation, his mental condition would have been so dazed that even if he had consented to look through Galileo's telescope, his eyes would have reported in accordance with his inward alarms rather than with the external fact. So long as a belief in propositions is regarded as indispensable to salvation, the pursuit of truth *as such* is not possible, any more than it is possible for a man who is swimming for his

life to make meteorological observations on the storm which
threatens to overwhelm him.   The sense of alarm and haste,
the anxiety for personal safety, which Dr. Cumming insists
upon as the proper religious attitude, unmans the nature, and
allows no thorough calm-thinking, no truly noble, disinterested feeling.   Hence we by no means suspect that the
unscrupulosity of statement with which we charge Dr. Cumming extends beyond the sphere of his theological prejudices;
we do not doubt that, religion apart, he appreciates and practises veracity.

A grave general accusation must be supported by details;
and in adducing those, we purposely select the most obvious
cases of misrepresentation, — such as require no argument to
expose them, but can be perceived at a glance.   Among Dr.
Cumming's numerous books, one of the most notable for unscrupulosity of statement is the " Manual of Christian Evidences," written, as he tells us in his preface, not to give the
deepest solutions of the difficulties in question, but to furnish Scripture-Readers, City Missionaries, and Sunday-school
Teachers with a " ready reply " to sceptical arguments.
This announcement that *readiness* was the chief quality
sought for in the solutions here given, modifies our inference
from the other qualities which those solutions present; and
it is but fair to presume that when the Christian disputant
is not in a hurry, Dr. Cumming would recommend replies less
ready and more veracious.   Here is an example of what in
another place [1] he tells his readers is " change in their pocket,
. . . a little ready argument which they can employ, and
therewith answer a fool according to his folly."   From the
nature of this argumentative small coin, we are inclined to
think Dr. Cumming understands answering a fool according
to his folly to mean, giving him a foolish answer.   We quote
from the " Manual of Christian Evidences," p. 62 : —

" Some of the gods which the heathen worshipped were among the
greatest monsters that ever walked the earth.   Mercury was a thief ;
and because he was an expert thief, he was enrolled among the gods.

[1] Lect. on Daniel, p. 6.

Bacchus was a mere sensualist and drunkard; and therefore he was
enrolled among the gods.   Venus was a dissipated and abandoned
courtesan; and therefore she was enrolled among the goddesses.
Mars was a savage, that gloried in battle and in blood; and therefore
he was deified and enrolled among the gods."

Does Dr. Cumming believe the purport of these sentences ?
If so, this passage is worth handing down as his theory of
the Greek myth, — as a specimen of the astounding ignorance
which was possible in a metropolitan preacher, A. D. 1854.
And if he does not believe them, — the inference must
then be, that he thinks delicate veracity about the ancient
Greeks is not a Christian virtue, but only a "splendid sin"
of the unregenerate.   This inference is rendered the more
probable by our finding, a little further on, that he is not
more scrupulous about the moderns, if they come under his
definition of "Infidels."   But the passage we are about to
quote in proof of this has a worse quality than its discrep-
ancy with fact.   Who that has a spark of generous feeling,
that rejoices in the presence of good in a fellow-being, has
not dwelt with pleasure on the thought that Lord Byron's
unhappy career was ennobled and purified towards its close
by a high and sympathetic purpose, by honest and energetic
efforts for his fellow-men ?   Who has not read with deep
emotion those last pathetic lines, beautiful as the after-glow
of sunset, in which love and resignation are mingled with
something of a melancholy heroism ?   Who has not lingered
with compassion over the dying scene at Missolonghi, — the
sufferer's inability to make his farewell messages of love intelligible, and the last long hours of silent pain ?   Yet for
the sake of furnishing his disciples with a "ready reply,"
Dr. Cumming can prevail on himself to inoculate them with
a bad-spirited falsity like the following : —

"We have one striking exhibition of *an infidel's brightest thoughts*
in some lines *written in his dying moments* by a man gifted with great
genius, capable of prodigious intellectual prowess, but of worthless
principle and yet more worthless practices, — I mean the celebrated
Lord Byron. He says : —

'Though gay companions o'er the bowl
    Dispel awhile the sense of ill,
Though pleasure fills the maddening soul,
    The heart — *the heart* is lonely still.

'Ay, but to die, and go, alas!
    Where all have gone and all must go;
To be the *Nothing* that I was,
    Ere born to life and living woe!

'Count o'er the joys thine hours have seen,
    Count o'er thy days from anguish free,
And know, whatever thou hast been,
    'T is *something better* not to be.

'Nay, for myself, so dark my fate
    Through every turn of life hath been,
Man and the *world* so much *I hate*,
    I care not when I quit the scene.'"

It is difficult to suppose that Dr. Cumming can have been so grossly imposed upon, — that he can be so ill-informed as really to believe that these lines were "written" by Lord Byron in his dying moments; but, allowing him the full benefit of that possibility, how shall we explain his introduction of this feebly rabid doggerel as "an infidel's brightest thoughts"?

In marshalling the evidences of Christianity, Dr. Cumming directs most of his arguments against opinions that are either totally imaginary or that belong to the past rather than to the present, while he entirely fails to meet the difficulties actually felt and urged by those who are unable to accept Revelation.   There can hardly be a stronger proof of misconception as to the character of free-thinking in the present day, than the recommendation of Leland's "Short and Easy Method with the Deists," — a method which is unquestionably short and easy for preachers disinclined to reconsider their stereotyped modes of thinking and arguing, but which has quite ceased to realize those epithets in the conversion of Deists.   Yet Dr. Cumming not only recommends this book, but takes the trouble himself to write a feebler version of its

arguments. For example, on the question of the genuineness and authenticity of the New Testament writings, he
says: "If, therefore, at a period long subsequent to the death
of Christ, a number of men had appeared in the world, drawn
up a book which they christened by the name of the Holy
Scripture, and recorded these things which appear in it as
facts when they were only the fancies of their own imagination, surely the *Jews* would have instantly reclaimed that no
such events transpired, that no such person as Jesus Christ
appeared in their capital, and that *their* crucifixion of Him,
and their alleged evil treatment of his apostles, were mere
fictions." [1] It is scarcely necessary to say that, in such argument as this, Dr. Cumming is beating the air. He is meeting
a hypothesis which no one holds, and totally missing the real
question. The only type of "infidel" whose existence Dr.
Cumming recognizes is that fossil personage who "calls the
Bible a lie and a forgery." He seems to be ignorant — or he
chooses to ignore the fact — that there is a large body of
eminently instructed and earnest men who regard the Hebrew
and Christian Scriptures as a series of historical documents,
to be dealt with according to the rules of historical criticism,
and that an equally large number of men, who are not historical critics, find the dogmatic scheme built on the letter of the
Scriptures opposed to their profoundest moral convictions.
Dr. Cumming's infidel is a man who, because his life is vicious,
tries to convince himself that there is no God, and that Christianity is an imposture, but who is all the while secretly conscious that he is opposing the truth, and cannot help "letting
out" admissions "that the Bible is the Book of God." We
are favored with the following "Creed of the Infidel:" —

"I believe that there is no God, but that matter is God, and God is
matter; and that it is no matter whether there is any God or not. I
believe also that the world was not made, but that the world made
itself, or that it had no beginning, and that it will last forever. I believe that man is a beast; that the soul is the body, and that the body
is the soul; and that after death there is neither body nor soul. I be-

[1] Man. of Evidences, p. 81.

lieve that there is no religion, that *natural religion is the only religion, and all religion unnatural.* I believe not in Moses; I believe in the first philosophers. I believe not in the evangelists ; I believe in Chubb, Collins, Toland, Tindal, and Hobbes. I believe in Lord Bolingbroke, and I believe not in St. Paul. I believe not in revelation; *I believe in tradition; I believe in the Talmud; I believe in the Korán;* I believe not in the Bible. I believe in Socrates; I believe in Confucius; I believe in Mahomet ; I believe not in Christ. And lastly, *I believe* in all unbelief."

The intellectual and moral monster whose creed is this complex web of contradictions is, moreover, according to Dr. Cumming, a being who unites much simplicity and imbecility with his Satanic hardihood, much tenderness of conscience with his obdurate vice. Hear the "proof:"—

"I once met with an acute and enlightened infidel, with whom I reasoned day after day, and for hours together; I submitted to him the internal, the external, and the experimental evidences, but made no impression on his scorn and unbelief. At length I entertained a suspicion that there was something morally, rather than intellectually wrong, and that the bias was not in the intellect, but in the heart; one day therefore I said to him, 'I must now state my conviction, and you may call me uncharitable, but duty compels me; you are living in some known and gross sin.' *The man's countenance became pale; he bowed and left me.*" [1]

Here we have the remarkable psychological phenomenon of an "acute and enlightened" man who, deliberately purposing to indulge in a favorite sin, and regarding the Gospel with scorn and unbelief, is, nevertheless, so much more scrupulous than the majority of Christians, that he cannot "embrace sin and the Gospel simultaneously;" who is so alarmed at the Gospel in which he does not believe, that he cannot be easy without trying to crush it; whose acuteness and enlightenment suggest to him, as a means of crushing the Gospel, to argue from day to day with Dr. Cumming; and who is withal so naïve that he is taken by surprise when Dr. Cumming, failing in argument, resorts to accusation, and so tender in

[1] Man. of Evidences, p. 254.

conscience that, at the mention of his sin, he turns pale and leaves the spot. If there be any human mind in existence capable of holding Dr. Cumming's "Creed of the Infidel," of at the same time believing in tradition and "believing in all unbelief," it must be the mind of the infidel just described, for whose existence we have Dr. Cumming's *ex officio* word as a theologian; and to theologians we may apply what Sancho Panza says of the bachelors of Salamanca, that they never tell lies — except when it suits their purpose.

The total absence from Dr. Cumming's theological mind of any demarcation between fact and rhetoric is exhibited in another passage, where he adopts the dramatic form : —

"Ask the peasant on the hill — *and I have asked amid the mountains of Braemar and Deeside,* — 'How do you know that this book is divine, and that the religion you profess is true? You never read Paley?' 'No, I never heard of him.' 'You have never read Butler?' 'No, I have never heard of him.' 'Nor Chalmers?' 'No, I do not know him.' 'You have never read any books on evidence?' 'No, I have read no such books.' 'Then how do you know this book is true?' 'Know it! Tell me that the Dee, the Clunie, and the Garrawalt, the streams at my feet, do not run; that the winds do not sigh amid the gorges of these blue hills; that the sun does not kindle the peaks of Loch-na-Gar; tell me my heart does not beat, and I will believe you; but do not tell me the Bible is not divine. I have found its truth illuminating my footsteps; its consolations sustaining my heart. May my tongue cleave to my mouth's roof, and my right hand forget its cunning, if I ever deny what is my deepest inner experience, that this blessed book is the book of God.'" [1]

Dr. Cumming is so slippery and lax in his mode of presentation, that we find it impossible to gather whether he means to assert, that this is what a peasant on the mountains of Braemar *did* say, or that it is what such a peasant *would* say: in the one case, the passage may be taken as a measure of his truthfulness; in the other, of his judgment.

His own faith, apparently, has not been altogether intuitive, like that of his rhetorical peasant, for he tells us [2]

---

[1] Church before the Flood, p. 35.   [2] Apoc. Sketches, p. 405.

that he has himself experienced what it is to have religious doubts. "I was tainted while at the University by this spirit of scepticism. I thought Christianity might not be true. The very possibility of its being true was the thought I felt I must meet and settle. Conscience could give me no peace till I had settled it. I read, and I have read from that day, for fourteen or fifteen years, till this, and now I am as convinced, upon the clearest evidence, that this book is the book of God as that I now address you." This experience, however, instead of impressing on him the fact that doubt may be the stamp of a truth-loving mind, — that *sunt quibus non credidisse honor est, et fidei futuræ pignus*, — seems to have produced precisely the contrary effect. It has not enabled him even to conceive the condition of a mind "perplext in faith but pure in deeds," craving light, yearning for a faith that will harmonize and cherish its highest powers and aspirations, but unable to find that faith in dogmatic Christianity. His own doubts apparently were of a different kind. Nowhere in his pages have we found a humble, candid, sympathetic attempt to meet the difficulties that may be felt by an ingenuous mind. Everywhere he supposes that the doubter is hardened, conceited, consciously shutting his eyes to the light, — a fool who is to be answered according to his folly, — that is, with ready replies made up of reckless assertions, of apocryphal anecdotes, and, where other resources fail, of vituperative imputation. As to the reading which he has prosecuted for fifteen years — *either* it has left him totally ignorant of the relation which his own religious creed bears to the criticism and philosophy of the nineteenth century, *or* he systematically blinks that criticism and that philosophy; and instead of honestly and seriously endeavoring to meet and solve what he knows to be the real difficulties, contents himself with setting up popinjays to shoot at, for the sake of confirming the ignorance and winning the cheap admiration of his evangelical hearers and readers. Like the Catholic preacher who, after throwing down his cap and apostrophizing it as Luther, turned to his audience and

said, "You see this heretical fellow has not a word to say
for himself," Dr. Cumming, having drawn his ugly portrait
of the infidel, and put arguments of a convenient quality into
his mouth, finds a "short and easy method" of confounding
this "croaking frog."

In his treatment of infidels, we imagine he is guided by a
mental process which may be expressed in the following syl-
logism: Whatever tends to the glory of God is true; it is for
the glory of God that infidels should be as bad as possible;
therefore, whatever tends to show that infidels are as bad as
possible is true. All infidels, he tells us, have been men of
"gross and licentious lives." Is there not some well-known
unbeliever — David Hume, for example — of whom even Dr.
Cumming's readers may have heard as an exception? No
matter. Some one suspected that he was *not* an exception;
and as that suspicion tends to the glory of God, it is one for
a Christian to entertain.[1] If we were unable to imagine this
kind of self-sophistication, we should be obliged to suppose
that, relying on the ignorance of his evangelical disciples, he
fed them with direct and conscious falsehoods. "Voltaire,"
he informs them, "declares there is no God;" he was "an
antitheist, that is, one who deliberately and avowedly opposed
and hated God, who swore in his blasphemy that he would
dethrone him," and "advocated the very depths of the lowest
sensuality." With regard to many statements of a similar
kind, equally at variance with truth, in Dr. Cumming's volumes, we presume that he has been misled by hearsay or by
the second-hand character of his acquaintance with free-
thinking literature. An evangelical preacher is not obliged
to be well-read. Here, however, is a case which the extrem-
est supposition of educated ignorance will not reach. Even
books of "evidences" quote from Voltaire the line, —

"Si Dieu n'existait pas, il faudrait l'inventer;"

even persons fed on the mere whey and buttermilk of literature must know that in philosophy Voltaire was nothing if

[1] See Man. of Evidences, p. 73.

not a theist, — must know that he wrote not against God, but against Jehovah, the God of the Jews, whom he believed to be a false God, — must know that to say Voltaire was an atheist on this ground is as absurd as to say that a Jacobite opposed hereditary monarchy because he declared the Brunswick family had no title to the throne. That Dr. Cumming should repeat the vulgar fables about Voltaire's death is' merely what we might expect from the specimens we have seen of his illustrative stories. A man whose accounts of his own experience are apocryphal, is not likely to put borrowed narratives to any severe test.

The alliance between intellectual and moral perversion is strikingly typified by the way in which he alternates from the unveracious to the absurd, from misrepresentation to contradiction. Side by side with the adduction of "facts" such as those we have quoted, we find him arguing on one page that the Trinity was too grand a doctrine to have been conceived by man, and was *therefore* Divine; and on another page, that the Incarnation *had* been preconceived by man, and is *therefore* to be accepted as Divine. But we are less concerned with the fallacy of his "ready replies" than with their falsity; and even of this we can only afford space for a very few specimens. Here is one: "There is a *thousand times* more proof that the gospel of John was written by him than there is that the Αναβασις was written by Xenophon, or the Ars Poetica by Horace." If Dr. Cumming had chosen Plato's Epistles or Anacreon's Poems, instead of the Anabasis or the Ars Poetica, he would have reduced the extent of the falsehood, and would have furnished a ready reply which would have been equally effective with his Sunday-school teachers and their disputants. Hence we conclude this prodigality of misstatement, this exuberance of mendacity, is an effervescence of zeal *in majorem gloriam Dei.* Elsewhere he tells us that "the idea of the author of the 'Vestiges' is, that man is the development of a monkey, that the monkey is the embryo man, so that *if you keep a baboon long enough, it will develop itself into a man.*" How well Dr. Cumming has qualified himself to judge of the ideas in "that very unphilosophical book," as he pronounces it, may be inferred from the fact that he implies the author of the "Vestiges" to have *originated* the nebular hypothesis.

In the volume from which the last extract is taken, even the hardihood of assertion is surpassed by the suicidal char-acter of the argument. It is called "The Church before the Flood," and is devoted chiefly to the adjustment of the ques-tion between the Bible and Geology. Keeping within the limits we have prescribed to ourselves, we do not enter into the matter of this discussion; we merely pause a little over the volume in order to point out Dr. Cumming's mode of treating the question. He first tells us that "the Bible has not a single scientific error in it;" that *its slightest intima-tions of scientific principles or natural phenomena have in every instance been demonstrated to be exactly and strictly true,*" and he asks : —

" How is it that Moses, with no greater education than the Hindoo or the ancient philosopher, has written his book, touching science at a thousand points, so accurately that scientific research has discov-ered no flaws in it; and yet in those investigations which have taken place in more recent centuries, it has not been shown that he has committed one single error, or made one solitary assertion which can be proved by the maturest science, or by the most eagle-eyed philoso-pher, to be incorrect, scientifically or historically?"

According to this, the relation of the Bible to Science should be one of the strong points of apologists for Revela-tion; the scientific accuracy of Moses should stand at the head of their evidences; and they might urge with some cogency, that since Aristotle, who devoted himself to science, and lived many ages after Moses, does little else than err in-geniously, this fact, that the Jewish Lawgiver, though touch-ing science at a thousand points, has written nothing that has not been "demonstrated to be exactly and strictly true," is an irrefragable proof of his having derived his knowledge from a supernatural source. How does it happen, then, that Dr. Cumming forsakes this strong position? How is it that we find him, some pages further on, engaged in reconciling Genesis with the discoveries of science, by means of imaginative hypotheses and feats of "interpretation"? Surely, that which has been demonstrated to be exactly and strictly true does not require hypothesis and critical argument, in order to show that it may *possibly* agree with those very discoveries by means of which its exact and strict truth has been demonstrated. And why should Dr. Cumming suppose, as we shall presently find him supposing, that men of science hesitate to accept the Bible, because it appears to contradict their discoveries? By his own statement, that appearance of contradiction does not exist; on the contrary, it has been demonstrated that the Bible precisely agrees with their discoveries. Perhaps, however, in saying of the Bible that its "slightest intimations of scientific principles or natural phenomena have in every instance been demonstrated to be exactly and strictly true," Dr. Cumming merely means to imply that theologians have found out a way of explaining the biblical text so that it no longer, in their opinion, appears to be in contradiction with the discoveries of science. One of two things, therefore: either he uses language without the slightest appreciation of its real meaning; or the assertions he makes on one page are directly contradicted by the arguments he urges on another.

Dr. Cumming's principles — or, we should rather say, confused notions — of biblical interpretation, as exhibited in this volume, are particularly significant of his mental calibre. He says:[1] "Men of science, who are full of scientific investigation and enamored of scientific discovery, will hesitate before they accept a book which, they think, contradicts the plainest and the most unequivocal disclosures they have made in the bowels of the earth or among the stars of the sky. To all these we answer, as we have already indicated, there is not the least dissonance between God's written book and the most mature discoveries of geological science. One thing, however, there may be; *there may be a contradiction*

[1] Church before the Flood, p. 93.

between the discoveries of geology and our preconceived inter-
pretations of the Bible.   But this is not because the Bible is
wrong, but because our interpretation is wrong." (The italics in all cases are our own.)

Elsewhere he says: "It seems to me plainly evident that
the record of Genesis, when read fairly and not in the light
of our prejudices, — *and, mind you, the essence of Popery is to*
read the Bible in the light of our opinions, instead of viewing
our opinions in the light of the Bible, in its plain and obvious
sense, — falls in perfectly with the assertion of geologists."

On comparing these two passages, we gather that when Dr.
Cumming, under stress of geological discovery, assigns to the
biblical text a meaning entirely different from that which, on
his own showing, was universally ascribed to it for more than
three thousand years, he regards himself as "viewing his
opinions in the light of the Bible in its plain and obvious
sense"! Now he is reduced to one of two alternatives:
either he must hold that the "plain and obvious meaning"
of the whole Bible differs from age to age, so that the criterion of its meaning lies in the sum of knowledge possessed
by each successive age, — the Bible being an elastic garment
for the growing thought of mankind; or he must hold that
some portions are amenable to this criterion, and others not
so. In the former case he accepts the principle of interpretation adopted by the early German rationalists; in the latter
case he has to show a further criterion by which we can
judge what parts of the Bible are elastic and what rigid. If
he says that the interpretation of the text is rigid wherever
it treats of doctrines necessary to salvation, we answer that
for doctrines to be necessary to salvation they must first be
true; and in order to be true, according to his own principle,
they must be founded on a correct interpretation of the biblical text. Thus he makes the necessity of doctrines to salvation the criterion of infallible interpretation, and infallible
interpretation the criterion of doctrines being necessary to
salvation. He is whirled round in a circle, having, by admitting the principle of novelty in interpretation, completely

deprived himself of a basis. That he should seize the very moment in which he is most palpably betraying that he has no test of biblical truth beyond his own opinion, as an appropriate occasion for flinging the rather novel reproach against Popery that its essence is to "read the Bible in the light of our opinions," would be an almost pathetic self-exposure, if it were not disgusting. Imbecility that is not even meek ceases to be pitiable and becomes simply odious.

Parenthetic lashes of this kind against Popery are very frequent with Dr. Cumming, and occur even in his more devout passages, where their introduction must surely disturb the spiritual exercises of his hearers. Indeed, Roman Catholics fare worse with him even than infidels. Infidels are the small vermin, — the mice to be bagged *en passant*. The main object of his chase — the rats which are to be nailed up as trophies — are the Roman Catholics. Romanism is the masterpiece of Satan; but reassure yourselves! Dr. Cumming has been created. Antichrist is enthroned in the Vatican; but he is stoutly withstood by the Boanerges of Crown Court. The personality of Satan, as might be expected, is a very prominent tenet in Dr. Cumming's discourses; those who doubt it are, he thinks, "generally specimens of the victims of Satan as a triumphant seducer;" and it is through the medium of this doctrine that he habitually contemplates Roman Catholics. They are the puppets of which the Devil holds the strings. It is only exceptionally that he speaks of them as fellow-men, acted on by the same desires, fears, and hopes as himself; his *rule* is to hold them up to his hearers as foredoomed instruments of Satan, and vessels of wrath. If he is obliged to admit that they are "no shams," that they are "thoroughly in earnest," — that is because they are inspired by hell, because they are under an "infra-natural" influence. If their missionaries are found wherever Protestant missionaries go, this zeal in propagating their faith is not in them a consistent virtue, as it is in Protestants, but a "melancholy fact," affording additional evidence that they are instigated and assisted by the Devil. And Dr. Cumming is inclined to think that they work miracles, because that is no more than might be expected from the known ability of Satan, who inspires them.[1]   He admits, indeed, that "there is a fragment of the Church of Christ in the very bosom of that awful apostasy,"[2] and that there are members of the Church of Rome in glory; but this admission is rare and episodical, — is a declaration, *pro formâ*, about as influential on the general disposition and habits as an aristocrat's profession of democracy.

This leads us to mention another conspicuous characteristic of Dr. Cumming's teaching, — the *absence of genuine charity*. It is true that he makes large profession of tolerance and liberality within a certain circle; he exhorts Christians to unity; he would have Churchmen fraternize with Dissenters, and exhorts these two branches of God's family to defer the settlement of their differences till the millennium.   But the love thus taught is the love of the *clan*, which is the correlative of antagonism to the rest of mankind.   It is not sympathy and helpfulness towards men as men, but towards men as Christians, and as Christians in the sense of a small minority.   Dr. Cumming's religion may demand a tribute of love, but it gives a charter to hatred; it may enjoin charity, but it fosters all uncharitableness.   If I believe that God tells me to love my enemies, but at the same time hates his own enemies and requires me to have one will with him, which has the larger scope, love or hatred?   And we refer to those pages of Dr. Cumming's in which he opposes Roman Catholics, Puseyites, and infidels, — pages which form the larger proportion of what he has published, — for proof that the idea of God which both the logic and spirit of his discourses keep present to his hearers, is that of a God who hates his enemies, a God who teaches love by fierce denunciations of wrath, a God who encourages obedience to his precepts by elaborately revealing to us that his own government is in precise opposition to those precepts.   We know the usual evasions on this subject.   We know Dr. Cumming

[1] Signs of the Times, p. 38.]   [2] Apoc. Sketches, p. 243.

would say that even Roman Catholics are to be loved and succored as men; that he would help even that "unclean spirit," Cardinal Wiseman, out of a ditch. But who that is in the slightest degree acquainted with the action of the human mind, will believe that any genuine and large charity can grow out of an exercise of love which is always to have an *arrière-pensée* of hatred? Of what quality would be the conjugal love of a husband who loved his spouse as a wife, but hated her as a woman? It is reserved for the regenerate mind, according to Dr. Cumming's conception of it, to be "wise, amazed, temperate and furious, loyal and neutral, in a moment." Precepts of charity uttered with faint breath at the end of a sermon are perfectly futile, when all the force of the lungs has been spent in keeping the hearer's mind fixed on the conception of his fellow-men, not as fellow-sinners and fellow-sufferers, but as agents of hell, as automata through whom Satan plays his game upon earth, — not on objects which call forth their reverence, their love, their hope of good even in the most strayed and perverted, but on a minute identification of human things with such symbols as the scarlet whore, the beast out of the abyss, scorpions whose sting is in their tails, men who have the mark of the beast, and unclean spirits like frogs. You might as well attempt to educate a child's sense of beauty by hanging its nursery with the horrible and grotesque pictures in which the early painters represented the Last Judgment, as expect Christian graces to flourish on that prophetic interpretation which Dr. Cumming offers as the principal nutriment of his flock. Quite apart from the critical basis of that interpretation, quite apart from the degree of truth there may be in Dr. Cumming's prognostications, — questions into which we do not choose to enter, — his use of prophecy must be *à priori* condemned in the judgment of right-minded persons, by its results as testified in the net moral effect of his sermons. The best minds that accept Christianity as a divinely inspired system believe that the great end of the Gospel is not merely the saving but the educating of men's souls, the creating within

them of holy dispositions, the subduing of egoistical pretensions, and the perpetual enhancing of the desire that the will
of God — a will synonymous with goodness and truth — may
be done on earth.   But what relation to all this has a system
of interpretation which keeps the mind of the Christian in
the position of a spectator at a gladiatorial show, of which
Satan is the wild beast in the shape of the great red dragon,
and two thirds of mankind the victims, — the whole provided
and got up by God for the edification of the saints ?   The
demonstration that the Second Advent is at hand, if true,
can have no really holy, spiritual effect; the highest state of
mind inculcated by the Gospel is resignation to the disposal
of God's providence, — "Whether we live, we live unto the
Lord; whether we die, we die unto the Lord," — not an eagerness to see a temporal manifestation which shall confound
the enemies of God and give exaltation to the saints; it is to
dwell in Christ by spiritual communion with his nature, not
to fix the date when he shall appear in the sky.   Dr. Cumming's delight in shadowing forth the downfall of the Man
of Sin, in prognosticating the battle of Gog and Magog, and
in advertising the premillennial Advent, is simply the trans-
portation of political passions on to a so-called religious platform; it is the anticipation of the triumph of "our party,"
accomplished by our principal men being "sent for" into the
clouds.   Let us be understood to speak in all seriousness.
If we were in search of amusement, we should not seek for it
by examining Dr. Cumming's works in order to ridicule them.
We are simply discharging a disagreeable duty in delivering
our opinion that, judged by the highest standard even of orthodox Christianity, they are little calculated to produce

> "A closer walk with God,
> A calm and heavenly frame;"

but are more likely to nourish egoistic complacency and pretension, a hard and condemnatory spirit towards one's fellow-
men, and a busy occupation with the minutiæ of events,
instead of a reverent contemplation of great facts and a wise

application of great principles. It would be idle to consider
Dr. Cumming's theory of prophecy in any other light; as a
philosophy of history or a specimen of biblical interpretation, it bears about the same relation to the extension of genuine knowledge as the astrological "house" in the heavens
bears to the true structure and relations of the universe.

The slight degree in which Dr. Cumming's faith is imbued
with truly human sympathies is exhibited in the way he
treats the doctrine of Eternal Punishment. *Here* a little of
that readiness to strain the letter of the Scriptures which he
so often manifests when his object is to prove a point against
Romanism would have been an amiable frailty if it had been
applied on the side of mercy. When he is bent on proving
that the prophecy concerning the Man of Sin, in the Second
Epistle to the Thessalonians, refers to the Pope, he can ex-
tort from the innocent word καθίσαι the meaning *cathedrize,*
though why we are to translate " He as God cathedrizes in
the temple of God," any more than we are to translate "Cathedrize here, while I go and pray yonder," it is for Dr. Cumming to show more clearly than he has yet done. But when
rigorous literality will favor the conclusion that the greater
proportion of the human race will be eternally miserable, —
then he is rigorously literal.

He says: "The Greek words, ἐς τοὺς αἰῶνας τῶν αἰώνων, here
translated 'everlasting,' signify literally 'unto the ages of
ages;' αἰεὶ ὤν, 'always being,' that is, everlasting, ceaseless
existence. Plato uses the word in this sense when he says,
'The Gods that live forever.' *But I must also admit,* that
this word is used several times in a limited extent, — as, for
instance, 'The everlasting hills.' Of course, this does not
mean that there never will be a time when the hills will
cease to stand; the expression here is evidently figurative,
but it implies eternity. The hills shall remain as long as
that earth lasts, and no hand has power to remove them but
that Eternal One which first called them into being; *so the
state of the soul* remains the same after death as long as the
soul exists, and no one has power to alter it. The same

word is often applied to denote the existence of God, — 'the Eternal God.' Can we limit the word when applied to him ? Because occasionally used in a limited sense, we must not infer it is always so. 'Everlasting' plainly means in Scripture 'without end;' it is only to be explained figuratively when it is evident it cannot be interpreted in any other way."

We do not discuss whether Dr. Cumming's interpretation accords with the meaning of the New Testament writers: we simply point to the fact that the text becomes elastic for him when he wants freer play for his prejudices, while he makes it an adamantine barrier against the admission that mercy will ultimately triumph, — that God, *i. e.*, Love, will be all in all. He assures us that he does not "delight to dwell on the misery of the lost; " and we believe him. That misery does not seem to be a question of feeling with him, either one way or the other. He does not merely resign himself to the awful mystery of eternal punishment; he contends for it. Do we object, he asks,[1] to everlasting happiness ? then why object to everlasting misery ? — reasoning which is perhaps felt to be cogent by theologians who anticipate the everlasting happiness for themselves and the everlasting misery for their neighbors.

The compassion of some Christians has been glad to take refuge in the opinion that the Bible allows the supposition of annihilation for the impenitent; but the rigid sequence of Dr. Cumming's reasoning will not admit of this idea. He sees that flax is made into linen, and linen into paper; that paper, when burnt, partly ascends as smoke and then again descends in rain or in dust and carbon. "Not one particle of the original flax is lost, although there may be not one particle that has not undergone an entire change : annihilation is not, but change of form is. *It will be thus with our bodies at the resurrection.* The death of the body means not annihilation. *Not one feature of the face* will be annihilated." Having established the perpetuity of the body by this close and clear analogy, namely, that *as* there is a total change in the parti-

[1] Man. of Christ. Evidences, p. 184.

cles of flax in consequence of which they no longer appear as flax, *so* there will *not* be a total change in the particles of the human body, but they will reappear as the human body, he does not seem to consider that the perpetuity of the body involves the perpetuity of the soul, but requires separate evidence for this, and finds such evidence by begging the very question at issue; namely, by asserting that the text of the Scriptures implies "the perpetuity of the punishment of the lost, and the consciousness of the punishment which they endure." Yet it is drivelling like this which is listened to and lauded as eloquence by hundreds, and which a Doctor of Divinity can believe that he has his "reward as a saint" for preaching and publishing!

One more characteristic of Dr. Cumming's writings, and we have done. This is the *perverted moral judgment* that everywhere reigns in them. Not that this perversion is peculiar to Dr. Cumming: it belongs to the dogmatic system which he shares with all evangelical believers. But the abstract tendencies of systems are represented in very different degrees according to the different characters of those who embrace them, just as the same food tells differently on different constitutions; and there are certain qualities in Dr. Cumming that cause the perversion of which we speak to exhibit itself with peculiar prominence in his teaching. A single extract will enable us to explain what we mean.

"The 'thoughts' are evil. If it were possible for human eye to discern and to detect the thoughts that flutter around the heart of an unregenerate man, to mark their hue and their multitude, it would be found that they are indeed 'evil.' We speak not of the thief, and the murderer, and the adulterer, and such like, whose crimes draw down the cognizance of earthly tribunals, and whose unenviable character it is to take the lead in the paths of sin; but we refer to the men who are marked out by their practice of many of the seemliest moralities of life, — by the exercise of the kindliest affections, and the interchange of the sweetest reciprocities, — and of these men, if unrenewed and unchanged, we pronounce that their thoughts are evil. To ascertain this, we must refer to the object around which our thoughts ought continually to circulate. The Scriptures assert that this object is *the glory of God;* that for this we ought to think, to act, and to speak; and that in thus thinking, acting, and speaking, there is involved the purest and most enduring bliss. Now it will be found true of the most amiable men, that with all their good society and kindliness of heart, and all their strict and unbending integrity, they never or rarely think of the glory of God. The question never occurs to them, Will this redound to the glory of God? Will this make his name more known, his being more loved, his praise more sung? And just inasmuch as their every thought comes short of this lofty aim, in so much does it come short of good, and entitle itself to the character of evil. If the glory of God is not the absorbing and the influential aim of their thoughts, then they are evil; but God's glory never enters into their minds. They are amiable, because it chances to be one of the constitutional tendencies of their individual character, left uneffaced by the Fall; and *they are just and upright, because they have perhaps no occasion to be otherwise, or find it subservient to their interests to maintain such a character.*" [1]

Again we read : [2] —

" There are traits in the Christian character which the mere worldly man cannot understand. He can understand the outward morality, but he cannot understand the inner spring of it ; he can understand Dorcas' liberality to the poor, but he cannot penetrate the ground of Dorcas' liberality. *Some men give to the poor because they are ostentatious, or because they think the poor will ultimately avenge their neglect; but the Christian gives to the poor, not only because he has sensibilities like other men,* but because, ' inasmuch as ye did it to the least of these my brethren, ye did it unto me.' "

Before entering on the more general question involved in these quotations, we must point to the clauses we have marked with italics, where Dr. Cumming appears to express sentiments which, we are happy to think, are not shared by the majority of his brethren in the faith. Dr. Cumming, it seems, is unable to conceive that the natural man can have any other motive for being just and upright than that it is useless to be otherwise, or that a character for honesty is

<hr/>

[1] Occ. Disc. vol. i. p. 8.   [2] Ibid. p. 236.

profitable; according to his experience, between the feelings of ostentation and selfish alarm and the feeling of love to Christ, there lie no sensibilities which can lead a man to relieve want. Granting, as we should prefer to think, that it is Dr. Cumming's exposition of his sentiments which is deficient rather than his sentiments themselves, still the fact that the deficiency lies precisely here, and that he can overlook it not only in the haste of oral delivery but in the examination of proof-sheets, is strongly significant of his mental bias, — of the faint degree in which he sympathizes with the disinterested elements of human feeling, and of the fact, which we are about to dwell upon, that those feelings are totally absent from his religious theory. Now, Dr. Cumming invariably assumes that, in fulminating against those who differ from him, he is standing on a moral elevation to which they are compelled reluctantly to look up; that his theory of motives and conduct is in its loftiness and purity a perpetual rebuke to their low and vicious desires and practice. It is time he should be told that the reverse is the fact; that there are men who do not merely cast a superficial glance at his doctrine, and fail to see its beauty or justice, but who, after a close consideration of that doctrine, pronounce it to be subversive of true moral development, and therefore positively noxious. Dr. Cumming is fond of showing up the teaching of Romanism, and accusing it of undermining true morality : it is time he should be told that there is a large body, both of thinkers and practical men, who hold precisely the same opinion of his own teaching, — with this difference, that they do not regard it as the inspiration of Satan, but as the natural crop of a human mind where the soil is chiefly made up of egoistic passions and dogmatic beliefs.

Dr. Cumming's theory, as we have seen, is that actions are good or evil according as they are prompted or not prompted by an exclusive reference to the "glory of God." God, then, in Dr. Cumming's conception, is a being who has no pleasure in the exercise of love and truthfulness and justice, considered as affecting the well-being of his creatures; he has satisfaction in us only in so far as we exhaust our motives and dispositions of all relation to our fellow-beings, and replace sympathy with men by anxiety for the "glory of God." The deed of Grace Darling, when she took a boat in the storm to rescue drowning men and women, was not good if it was only compassion that nerved her arm and impelled her to brave death for the chance of saving others; it was only good if she asked herself, Will this redound to the glory of God? The man who endures tortures rather than betray a trust, the man who spends years in toil in order to discharge an obligation from which the law declares him free, must be animated not by the spirit of fidelity to his fellow-man, but by a desire to make "the name of God more known." The sweet charities of domestic life — the ready hand and the soothing word in sickness, the forbearance towards frailties, the prompt helpfulness in all efforts and sympathy in all joys, are simply evil if they result from a "constitutional tendency," or from dispositions disciplined by the experience of suffering and the perception of moral loveliness. A wife is not to devote herself to her husband out of love to him and a sense of the duties implied by a close relation, — she is to be a faithful wife for the glory of God; if she feels her natural affections welling up too strongly, she is to repress them; it will not do to act from natural affection, — she must think of the glory of God. A man is to guide his affairs with energy and discretion, not from an honest desire to fulfil his responsibilities as a member of society and a father, but — that "God's praise may be sung." Dr. Cumming's Christian pays his debts for the glory of God; were it not for the coercion of that supreme motive, it would be evil to pay them. A man is not to be just from a feeling of justice; he is not to help his fellow-men out of good-will to his fellow-men; he is not to be a tender husband and father out of affection: all these natural muscles and fibres are to be torn away and replaced by a patent steel-spring, — anxiety for the "glory of God."

Happily, the constitution of human nature forbids the complete prevalence of such a theory. Fatally powerful as religious systems have been, human nature is stronger and wider than religious systems, and though dogmas may hamper, they cannot absolutely repress its growth: build walls round the living tree as you will, the bricks and mortar have by and by to give way before the slow and sure operation of the sap. But next to that hatred of the enemies of God which is the principle of persecution, there perhaps has been no perversion more obstructive of true moral development than this substitution of a reference to the glory of God for the direct promptings of the sympathetic feelings. Benevolence and justice are strong only in proportion as they are directly and inevitably called into activity by their proper objects: pity is strong only because we are strongly impressed by suffering; and only in proportion as it is compassion that speaks through the eyes when we soothe, and moves the arm when we succor, is a deed strictly benevolent. If the soothing or the succor be given because another being wishes or approves it, the deed ceases to be one of benevolence, and becomes one of deference, of obedience, of self-interest, or vanity. Accessory motives may aid in producing an *action*, but they presuppose the weakness of the direct motive; and conversely, when the direct motive is strong, the action of accessory motives will be excluded. If, then, as Dr. Cumming inculcates, the glory of God is to be "the absorbing and the influential aim" in our thoughts and actions, this must tend to neutralize the human sympathies; the stream of feeling will be diverted from its natural current in order to feed an artificial canal. The idea of God is really moral in its influence — it really cherishes all that is best and loveliest in man — only when God is contemplated as sympathizing with the pure elements of human feeling, as possessing infinitely all those attributes which we recognize to be moral in humanity. In this light, the idea of God and the sense of His presence intensify all noble feeling, and encourage all noble effort, on the same principle that human sympathy is

found a source of strength : the brave man feels braver when
he knows that another stout heart is beating time with his ;
the devoted woman who is wearing out her years in patient
effort to alleviate suffering or save vice from the last stages
of degradation, finds aid in the pressure of a friendly hand
which tells her that there is one who understands her deeds,
and in her place would do the like.   The idea of a God who
not only sympathizes with all we feel and endure for our
fellow-men, but who will pour new life into our too languid
love, and give firmness to our vacillating purpose, is an extension and multiplication of the effects produced by human
sympathy ; and it has been intensified for the better spirits
who have been under the influence of orthodox Christianity
by the contemplation of Jesus as " God manifest in the flesh."
But Dr. Cumming's God is the very opposite of all this.   He
is a God who, instead of sharing and aiding our human sympathies, is directly in collision with them ; who, instead of
strengthening the bond between man and man, by encouraging the sense that they are both alike the objects of His love
and care, thrusts Himself between them and forbids them to
feel for each other except as they have relation to Him.   He
is a God who, instead of adding His solar force to swell the
tide of those impulses that tend to give humanity a common
life in which the good of one is the good of all, commands us
to check those impulses, lest they should prevent us from
thinking of His glory.   It is in vain for Dr. Cumming to say
that we are to love man for God's sake : with the conception
of God which his teaching presents, the love of man for God's
sake involves, as his writings abundantly show, a strong
principle of hatred.   We can only love one being for the
sake of another when there is an habitual delight in associat-
ing the idea of those two beings, — that is, when the object
of our indirect love is a source of joy and honor to the object
of our direct love ; but, according to Dr. Cumming's theory,
the majority of mankind — the majority of his neighbors —
are in precisely the opposite relation to God.   His soul has
no pleasure in them, they belong more to Satan than to Him,

and if they contribute to His glory, it is against their will. Dr. Cumming then can only love *some* men for God's sake; the rest he must in consistency *hate* for God's sake.

There must be many, even in the circle of Dr. Cumming's admirers, who would be revolted by the doctrine we have just exposed, if their natural good sense and healthy feeling were not early stifled by dogmatic beliefs, and their reverence misled by pious phrases. But as it is, many a rational question, many a generous instinct, is repelled as the suggestion of a supernatural enemy, or as the ebullition of human pride and corruption. This state of inward contradiction can be put an end to only by the conviction that the free and diligent exertion of the intellect, instead of being a sin, is part of their responsibility, — that Right and Reason are synonymous. The fundamental faith for man is, faith in the result of a brave, honest, and steady use of all his faculties : —

> " Let knowledge grow from more to more,
>   But more of reverence in us dwell;
>   That mind and soul according well
> May make one music as before,
>   But vaster."

Before taking leave of Dr. Cumming, let us express a hope that we have in no case exaggerated the unfavorable character of the inferences to be drawn from his pages. His creed often obliges him to hope the worst of men, and exert himself in proving that the worst is true; but thus far we are happier than he. We have no theory which requires us to attribute unworthy motives to Dr. Cumming, no opinions, religious or irreligious, which can make it a gratification to us to detect him in delinquencies. On the contrary, the better we are able to think of him as a man, while we are obliged to disapprove him as a theologian, the stronger will be the evidence for our conviction that the tendency towards good in human nature has a force which no creed can utterly counteract, and which ensures the ultimate triumph of that tendency over all dogmatic perversions.

THE INFLUENCE OF RATIONALISM.

THERE is a valuable class of books on great subjects which have something of the character and functions of good popular lecturing. They are not original, not subtle, not of close logical texture, not exquisite either in thought or style; but by virtue of these negatives they are all the more fit to act on the average intelligence. They have enough of organizing purpose in them to make their facts illustrative, and to leave a distinct result in the mind even when most of the facts are forgotten; and they have enough of vagueness and vacillation in their theory to win them ready acceptance from a mixed audience. The vagueness and vacillation are not devices of timidity; they are the honest result of the writer's own mental character, which adapts him to be the instructor and the favorite of the "general reader." For the most part, the general reader of the present day does not exactly know what distance he goes; he only knows that he does not go "too far." Of any remarkable thinker, whose writings have excited controversy, he likes to have it said that "his errors are to be deplored," leaving it not too certain what those errors are; he is fond of what may be called disembodied opinions, that float in vapory phrases above all systems of thought or action; he likes an undefined Christianity which opposes itself to nothing in particular, an undefined education of the people, an undefined amelioration of all things : in fact, he likes sound views, — nothing extreme, but something between the excesses of the past and the excesses of the present. This modern type of the general reader may be known in conversation by the cordiality with which he assents to indistinct, blurred statements: say that black is black, he will shake his head and hardly think it; say that black is not so very black, he will reply, "Exactly." He has no hesitation, if you wish it, even to get up a public meeting and express his conviction that at times, and within certain limits, the radii of a circle have a tendency to be equal; but, on the other hand, he would urge that the spirit of geometry may be carried a little too far. His only bigotry is a bigotry against any clearly defined scepticism, but belonging to a lack of coherent thought, — a spongy texture of mind, that gravitates strongly to nothing. The one thing he is stanch for, is the utmost liberty of private haziness.

But precisely these characteristics of the general reader, rendering him incapable of assimilating ideas unless they are administered in a highly diluted form, make it a matter of rejoicing that there are clever, fair-minded men, who will write books for him, — men very much above him in knowledge and ability, but not too remote from him in their habits of thinking, and who can thus prepare for him infusions of history and science, that will leave some solidifying deposit, and save him from a fatal softening of the intellectual skeleton. Among such serviceable writers, Mr. Lecky's "History of the Rise and Influence of the Spirit of Rationalism in Europe" entitles him to a high place. He has prepared himself for its production by an unusual amount of well-directed reading; he has chosen his facts and quotations with much judgment; and he gives proofs of those important moral qualifications, impartiality, seriousness, and modesty. This praise is chiefly applicable to the long chapter on the History of Magic and Witchcraft, which opens the work, and to the two chapters on the Antecedents and History of Persecution, which occur, the one at the end of the first volume, the other at the beginning of the second. In these chapters Mr. Lecky has a narrower and better traced path before him than in other portions of his work; he is more occupied with presenting a particular class of facts in their historical sequence, and in their relation to certain grand tide-marks of opinion, than with disquisition; and his writing is freer than elsewhere from an apparent confusedness of thought, and an exuberance of approximative phrases, which can be serviceable in no other way than as diluents needful for the sort of reader we have just described.

The history of magic and witchcraft has been judiciously chosen by Mr. Lecky, as the subject of his first section on the declining sense of the miraculous, because it is strikingly illustrative of a position, with the truth of which he is strongly impressed, though he does not always treat of it with desirable clearness and precision; namely, that certain beliefs become obsolete, not in consequence of direct arguments against them, but because of their incongruity with prevalent habits of thought. Here is his statement of the two classes of influences by which the mass of men, in what is called civilized society, get their beliefs gradually modified : —

"If we ask why it is that the world has rejected what was once so universally and so intensely believed, why a narrative of an old woman who had been seen riding on a broomstick, or who was proved to have transformed herself into a wolf, and to have devoured the flocks of her neighbors, is deemed so entirely incredible, most persons would probably be unable to give a very definite answer to the question. It is not because we have examined the evidence and found it insufficient, for the disbelief always precedes, when it does not prevent, examination. It is rather because the idea of absurdity is so strongly attached to such narratives, that it is difficult even to consider them with gravity. Yet at one time no such improbability was felt, and hundreds of persons have been burnt simply on the two grounds I have mentioned.

"When so complete a change takes place in public opinion, it may be ascribed to one or other of two causes. It may be the result of a controversy which has conclusively settled the question, establishing to the satisfaction of all parties a clear preponderance of argument or fact in favor of one opinion, and making that opinion a truism which is accepted by all enlightened men, even though they have not themselves examined the evidence on which it rests. Thus, if any one in a company of ordinarily educated persons were to deny the motion of the earth or the circulation of the blood, his statement would be received with derision, though it is probable that some of his audience would be unable to demonstrate the first truth, and that very few of them could give sufficient reasons for the second. They may not themselves be able to defend their position; but they are aware that, at certain known periods of history, controversies on those subjects took place, and that known writers then brought forward some definite arguments or experiments, which were ultimately accepted by the whole learned world as rigid and conclusive demonstrations. It is possible, also, for as complete a change to be effected by what is called the spirit of the age. The general intellectual tendencies pervading the literature of a century profoundly modify the character of the public mind. They form a new tone and habit of thought. They alter the measure of probability. They create new attractions and new antipathies, and they eventually cause as absolute a rejection of certain old opinions as could be produced by the most cogent and definite arguments."

Mr. Lecky proceeds to some questionable views concerning the evidences of witchcraft, which seem to be irreconcilable even with his own remarks later on; but they lead him to the statement, thoroughly made out by his historical survey that "the movement was mainly silent, unargumentative, and insensible; that men came gradually to disbelieve in witchcraft, because they came gradually to look upon it as absurd; and that this new tone of thought appeared, first of all, in those who were least subject to theological influences, and soon spread through the educated laity, and, last of all, took possession of the clergy."

We have rather painful proof that this "second class of influences" with a vast number go hardly deeper than fashion, and that witchcraft to many of us is absurd only on the same ground that our grandfather's gigs are absurd. It is felt preposterous to think of spiritual agencies in connection with ragged beldames soaring on broomsticks, in an age when it is known that mediums of communication with the invisible world are usually unctuous personages dressed in excellent broadcloth, who soar above the curtain-poles without any broomstick, and who are not given to unprofitable intrigues. The enlightened imagination rejects the figure of a witch with her profile in dark relief against the moon, and her broomstick cutting a constellation. No undiscovered natural laws, no names of "respectable" witnesses, are invoked to make us feel our presumption in questioning the diabolic intimacies of that obsolete old woman, for it is known now that the undiscovered laws, and the witnesses qualified by the payment of income tax, are all in favor of a different conception, — the image of a heavy gentleman in boots and black coat-tails foreshortened against the cornice.   Yet no less a person than Sir Thomas Browne once wrote that those who denied there were witches, inasmuch as they thereby denied spirits also, were "obliquely and upon consequence a sort, not of infidels, but of atheists."   At present, doubtless, in certain circles unbelievers in heavy gentlemen who float in the air by means of undiscovered laws are also taxed with atheism; illiberal as it is not to admit that mere weakness of understanding may prevent one from seeing how that phenomenon is necessarily involved in the divine origin of things.   With still more remarkable parallelism, Sir Thomas Browne goes on: "Those that, to refute their incredulity, desire to see apparitions, shall questionless never behold any, nor have the power to be so much as witches.   The Devil hath made them already in a heresy as capital as witchcraft, *and to appear to them were but to convert them.*"   It would be difficult to see what has been changed here but the mere drapery of circumstance, if it were not for this prominent difference between our days and the days of witchcraft, that instead of torturing, drowning, or burning the innocent, we give hospitality and large pay to the highly distinguished medium.   At least we are safely rid of certain horrors; but if the multitude — that "farraginous concurrence of all conditions, tempers, sexes, and ages" — do not roll back even to a superstition that carries cruelty in its train, it is not because they possess a cultivated reason, but because they are pressed upon and held up by what we may call an external reason, — the sum of conditions resulting from the laws of material growth, from changes produced by great historical collisions shattering the structures of ages and making new highways for events and ideas, and from the activities of higher minds no longer existing merely as opinions and teachings, but as institutions and organizations with which the interests, the affections, and the habits of the multitude are inextricably interwoven. No undiscovered laws accounting for small phenomena going forward under drawing-room tables are likely to affect the tremendous facts of the increase of population, the rejection of convicts by our colonies, the exhaustion of the soil by cotton plantations, which urge even upon the foolish certain questions, certain claims, certain views concerning the scheme of the world, that can never again be silenced.

If right reason is a right representation of the co-existences and sequences of things, here are co-existences and sequences that do not wait to be discovered, but press themselves upon us like bars of iron. No seances at a guinea a head for the sake of being pinched by "Mary Jane" can annihilate railways, steamships, and electric telegraphs, which are demonstrating the interdependence of all human interests, and making self-interest a duct for sympathy. These things are part of the external reason to which internal silliness has inevitably to accommodate itself.

Three points in the history of magic and witchcraft are well brought out by Mr. Lecky : First, that the cruelties connected with it did not begin until men's minds had ceased to repose implicitly in a sacramental system which made them feel well armed against evil spirits ; that is, until the eleventh century, when there came a sort of morning dream of doubt and heresy, bringing on the one side the terror of timid consciences, and on the other the terrorism of authority or zeal bent on checking the rising struggle. In that time of comparative mental repose, says Mr. Lecky, —

"all those conceptions of diabolical presence, all that predisposition towards the miraculous, which acted so fearfully upon the imaginations of the fifteenth and sixteenth centuries, existed ; but the implicit faith, the boundless and triumphant credulity, with which the virtue of ecclesiastical rites was accepted, rendered them comparatively innocuous. If men had been a little less superstitious, the effects of their superstition would have been much more terrible. It was firmly believed that any one who deviated from the strict line of orthodoxy must soon succumb beneath the power of Satan; but as there was no spirit of rebellion or doubt, this persuasion did not produce any extraordinary terrorism."

The Church was disposed to confound heretical opinion with sorcery; false doctrine was especially the devil's work, and it was a ready conclusion that a denier or innovator had held consultation with the father of lies. It is a saying of a zealous Catholic in the sixteenth century, quoted by Maury in his excellent work, " De la Magie," — " *Crescit cum magia hæresis, cum hæresi magia.*" Even those who doubted were terrified at their doubts, for trust is more easily undermined than terror; fear is easier born than hope, lays a stronger grasp on man's system than any other passion, and remains master of a larger group of involuntary actions. A chief aspect of man's moral development is the slow subduing of fear by the gradual growth of intelligence, and its suppression as a motive by the presence of impulses less animally selfish; so that in relation to invisible power fear at last ceases to exist, save in that interfusion with higher faculties which we call awe.

Secondly, Mr. Lecky shows clearly that dogmatic Protestantism, holding the vivid belief in Satanic agency to be an essential of piety, would have felt it shame to be a whit behind Catholicism in severity against the Devil's servants. Luther's sentiments were, that he would not suffer a witch to live (he was not much more merciful to Jews); and, in spite of his fondness for children, believing a certain child to have been begotten by the Devil, he recommended the parents to throw it into the river. The torch must be turned on the worst errors of heroic minds, not in irreverent ingratitude, but for the sake of measuring our vast and various debt to all the influences which have concurred in the intervening ages to make us recognize as detestable errors the honest convictions of men who in mere individual capacity and moral force were very much above us. Again, the Scotch Puritans, during the comparatively short period of their ascendency, surpassed all Christians before them in the elaborate ingenuity of the tortures they applied for the discovery of witchcraft and sorcery, and did their utmost to prove that if Scotch Calvinism was the true religion, the chief "note" of the true religion was cruelty. It is hardly an endurable task to read the story of their doings; thoroughly to imagine them as a past reality is already a sort of torture. One detail is enough, and it is a comparatively mild one. It was the regular profession of men, called "prickers," to thrust long pins into the body of a suspected witch in order to detect the insensible spot which was the infallible sign of her guilt. On a superficial view one would be in danger of saying that the main difference between the teachers who sanctioned these things, and the much-despised ancestors who offered human victims inside a huge wicker idol, was that they arrived at a more elaborate barbarity by a longer series of dependent propositions. We do not share Mr. Buckle's opinion that a Scotch minister's groans were a part of his deliberate plan for keeping the people in a state of terrified subjection; the ministers themselves held the belief they taught, and well might groan over it. What a blessing has a little false logic been to the world! Seeing that men are so slow to question their premises, they must have made each other much more miserable, if pity had not sometimes drawn tender conclusions not warranted by major and minor; if there had not been people with an amiable imbecility of reasoning which enabled them at once to cling to hideous beliefs, and to be conscientiously inconsistent with them in their conduct. There is nothing like acute deductive reasoning for keeping a man in the dark; it might be called the technique of the intellect, and the concentration of the mind upon it corresponds to that predominance of technical skill in art which ends in degradation of the artist's function, unless new inspiration and invention come to guide it.

And of this there is some good illustration furnished by that third node in the history of witchcraft, the beginning of its end, which is treated in an interesting manner by Mr. Lecky. It is worth noticing that the most important defences of the belief in witchcraft, against the growing scepticism in the latter part of the sixteenth century and in the seventeenth, were the productions of men who in some departments were among the foremost thinkers of their time. One of them was Jean Bodin, the famous writer on government and jurisprudence, whose "Republic," Hallam thinks, had an important influence in England, and furnished "a store of arguments and examples that were not lost on the thoughtful minds of our countrymen." In some of his views he was original and bold; for example, he anticipated Montesquieu in attempting to appreciate the relations of government and climate. Hallam inclines to the opinion that he was a Jew, and attached Divine authority only to the Old Testament. But this was enough to furnish him with his chief data for the existence of witches and for their capital punishment; and in the account of his "Republic," given by Hallam, there is enough evidence that the sagacity which often enabled him to make fine use of his learning was also often entangled in it, to temper our surprise at finding a writer on political science of whom it could be said that, along with Montesquieu, he was "the most philosophical of those who had read so deeply, the most learned of those who had thought so much," in the van of the forlorn hope to maintain the reality of witchcraft. It should be said that he was equally confident of the unreality of the Copernican hypothesis, on the ground that it was contrary to the tenets of the theologians and philosophers and to common-sense, and therefore subversive of the foundations of every science. Of his work on witchcraft, Mr. Lecky says : —

"The 'Demonomanie des Sorciers' is chiefly an appeal to authority, which the author deemed on this subject so unanimous and so conclusive that it was scarcely possible for any sane man to resist it. He appealed to the popular belief in all countries, in all ages, and in all religions. He cited the opinions of an immense multitude of the greatest writers of pagan antiquity, and of the most illustrious of the fathers. He showed how the laws of all nations recognized the existence of witchcraft; and he collected hundreds of cases which had been investigated before the tribunals of his own or of other countries. He relates with the most minute and circumstantial detail, and with the most unfaltering confidence, all the proceedings at the witches' Sabbath, the methods which the witches employed in transporting themselves through the air, their transformations, their carnal intercourse with the Devil, their various means of injuring their enemies, the signs that led to their detection, their confessions when condemned, and their demeanor at the stake."

Something must be allowed for a lawyer's affection towards a belief which had furnished so many "cases." Bodin's work had been prompted by the treatise, "De Prestigiis Dæmonum," written by John Wier, a German physician, — a treatise which is worth notice as an example of a transitional form of opinion for which many analogies may be found in the history of both religion and science. Wier believed in demons, and in possession by demons; but his practice as a physician had convinced him that the so-called witches were patients and victims, that the Devil took advantage of their diseased condition to delude them, and that there was no consent of an evil will on the part of the women. He argued that the word in Leviticus translated "witch" meant "poisoner," and besought the princes of Europe to hinder the further spilling of innocent blood. These heresies of Wier threw Bodin into such a state of amazed indignation that if he had been an ancient Jew, instead of a modern economical one, he would have rent his garments. "No one had ever heard of pardon being accorded to sorcerers;" and probably the reason why Charles IX. died young was because he had pardoned the sorcerer, Trois Echelles! We must remember that this was in 1581, when the great scientific movement of the Renaissance had hardly begun, when Galileo was a youth of seventeen, and Kepler a boy of ten.

But directly afterwards, on the other side, came Montaigne, whose sceptical acuteness could arrive at negatives without any apparatus of method. A certain keen narrowness of nature will secure a man from many absurd beliefs which the larger soul, vibrating to more manifold influences, would have a long struggle to part with.   And so we find the charming, chatty Montaigne, in one of the brightest of his essays, "Des Boiteux," where he declares that, from his own observation of witches and sorcerers, he should have recommended them to be treated with curative hellebore, stating in his own way a pregnant doctrine, since taught more gravely.   It seems to him much less of a prodigy that men should lie, or that their imaginations should deceive them, than that a human body should be carried through the air on a broomstick or up a chimney by some unknown spirit.   He thinks it a sad business to persuade one's self that the test of truth lies in the multitude of believers : " En une presse ou les fols surpassent de tant les sages en nombre."   Ordinarily he has observed, when men have something stated to them as a fact, they are more ready to explain it than to inquire whether it is real : " Ils passent par-dessus les propositions, mais ils examinent les consequences ; *ils laissent les choses, et courent aux causes.*" There is a sort of strong and generous ignorance which is as honorable and courageous as science : " Ignorance pour laquelle concevoir il n'y a pas moins de science qu'a concevoir la science."   And apropos of the immense traditional evidence which weighed with such men as Bodin, he says : " As for the proofs and arguments founded on experience and facts, I do not pretend to unravel these.   What end of a thread is there to lay hold of ?   I often cut them, as Alexander did his knot.   *Après tout, c'est mettre ses conjectures a bien haut prix, que d'en faire cuire un homme tout vif.*"

Writing like this, when it finds eager readers, is a sign that the weather is changing ; yet much later, namely, after 1665, when the Royal Society had been founded, our own Glanvil, the author of the " Scepsis Scientifica," — a work that was a remarkable advance towards a true definition of the limits of inquiry, and that won him his election as fellow of the Society, — published an energetic vindication of the belief in witchcraft, of which Mr. Lecky gives the following sketch : —

"The 'Sadducismus Triumphatus,' which is probably the ablest book ever published in defence of the superstition, opens with a striking picture of the rapid progress of the scepticism in England. Everywhere a disbelief in witchcraft was becoming fashionable in the upper classes; but it was a disbelief that arose entirely from a strong sense of its antecedent improbability. All who were opposed to the Orthodox faith united in discrediting witchcraft. They laughed at it, as palpably absurd, as involving the most grotesque and ludicrous conceptions, as so essentially incredible that it would be a waste of time to examine it. This spirit had arisen since the restoration, although the laws were still in force, and although little or no direct reasoning had been brought to bear upon the subject. In order to combat it, Glanvil proceeded to examine the general question of the credibility of the miraculous. He saw that the reason why witchcraft was ridiculed was because it was a phase of the miraculous, and the work of the Devil; that the scepticism was chiefly due to those who disbelieved in miracles and the Devil; and that the instances of witchcraft or possession in the Bible were invariably placed on a level with those that were tried in the courts of England. That the evidence of the belief was overwhelming, he firmly believed; and this, indeed, was scarcely disputed; but, until the sense of *a priori* improbability was removed, no possible accumulation of facts would cause men to believe it. To that task he accordingly addressed himself. Anticipating the idea and almost the words of modern controversialists, he urged that there was such a thing as a credulity of unbelief; and that those who believed so strange a concurrence of delusions as was necessary on the supposition of the unreality of witchcraft, were far more credulous than those who accepted the belief. He made his very scepticism his principal weapon; and, analyzing with much acuteness the *a priori* objections, he showed that they rested upon an unwarrantable confidence in our knowledge of the laws of the spirit world, that they implied the existence of some strict analogy between the faculties of men and of spirits, and that, as such analogy most probably did not exist, no reasoning based on the supposition could dispense men from examining the evidence. He concluded with a large collection of cases, the evidence of which was, as he thought, incontestable."

We have quoted this sketch because Glanvil's argument against the *a priori* objection of absurdity is fatiguingly urged in relation to other alleged marvels which to busy people, seriously occupied with the difficulties of affairs, of science, or of art, seem as little worthy of examination as aeronautic broomsticks; and also because we here see Glanvil, in combating an incredulity that does not happen to be his own, wielding that very argument of traditional evidence which he had made the subject of vigorous attack in his "Scepsis Scientifica." But perhaps large minds have been peculiarly liable to this fluctuation concerning the sphere of tradition, because, while they have attacked its misapplications, they have been the more solicited by the vague sense that tradition is really the basis of our best life. Our sentiments may be called organized traditions; and a large part of our actions gather all their justification, all their attraction and aroma, from the memory of the life lived, of the actions done, before we were born. In the absence of any profound research into psychological functions or into the mysteries of inheritance, in the absence of any profound comprehensive view of man's historical development and the dependence of one age on another, a mind at all rich in sensibilities must always have had an indefinite uneasiness in an undistinguishing attack on the coercive influence of tradition. And this may be the apology for the apparent inconsistency of Glanvil's acute criticism on the one side, and his indignation at the "looser gentry," who laughed at the evidences for witchcraft on the other. We have already taken up too much space with this subject of witchcraft, else we should be tempted to dwell on Sir Thomas Browne, who far surpassed Glanvil in magnificent incongruity of opinion, and whose works are the most remarkable combination existing, of witty sarcasm against ancient nonsense and modern obsequiousness, with indications of a capacious credulity. After all, we may be sharing what seems to us the hardness of these men, who sat in their studies and argued at their ease about a belief that would be reckoned to have caused more misery and bloodshed than any other superstition, if there had been no such thing as persecution on the ground of religious opinion.

On this subject of persecution, Mr. Lecky writes his best;

with clearness of conception, with calm justice, bent on appreciating the necessary tendency of ideas, and with an appropriateness of illustration that could be supplied only by extensive and intelligent reading. Persecution, he shows, is not in any sense peculiar to the Catholic church; it is a direct sequence of the doctrines that salvation is to be had only within the Church, and that erroneous belief is damnatory, — doctrines held as fully by Protestant sects as by the Catholics; and in proportion to its power, Protestantism has been as persecuting as Catholicism. He maintains, in opposition to the favorite modern notion of persecution defeating its own object, that the Church, holding the dogma of exclusive salvation, was perfectly consequent, and really achieved its end of spreading one belief and quenching another, by calling in the aid of the civil arm. Who will say that governments, by their power over institutions and patronage, as well as over punishment, have not power over the interests and inclinations of men, and over most of those external conditions into which subjects are born, and which make them adopt the prevalent belief as a second nature? Hence, to a sincere believer in the doctrine of exclusive salvation, governments had it in their power to save men from perdition; and wherever the clergy were at the elbow of the civil arm, no matter whether they were Catholic or Protestant, persecution was the result. "Compel them to come in," was a rule that seemed sanctioned by mercy; and the horrible sufferings it led men to inflict seemed small to minds accustomed to contemplate, as a perpetual source of motive, the eternal, unmitigated miseries of a hell that was the inevitable destination of a majority amongst mankind.

It is a significant fact, noted by Mr. Lecky, that the only two leaders of the Reformation who advocated tolerance were Zuinglius and Socinus, both of them disbelievers in exclusive salvation. And in corroboration of other evidence that the chief triumphs of the Reformation were due to coercion, he commends to the special attention of his readers the following quotation from a work attributed without question to the famous Protestant theologian, Jurieu, who had himself been hindered, as a Protestant, from exercising his professional functions in France, and was settled as pastor at Rotterdam. It should be remembered that Jurieu's labors fell in the latter part of the seventeenth century and in the beginning of the eighteenth, and that he was the contemporary of Bayle, with whom he was in bitter controversial hostility. He wrote, then, at a time when there was warm debate on the question of toleration; and it was his great object to vindicate himself and his French fellow-Protestants from all laxity on this point : —

"Peut on nier que le paganisme est tombé dans le monde par l'autorité des empereurs romains ? On peut assurer sans témérité que le paganisme seroit encore debout, et que les trois quarts de l'Europe seroient encore payens si Constantin et ses successeurs n'avaient employé leur autorité pour l'abolir. Mais, je vous prie, de quelles voies Dieu s'est il servi dans ces derniers siècles pour rétablir la véritable religion dans l'occident ? *Les rois de Suède, ceux de Danemarck, ceux d'Angleterre, les magistrats souverains de Suisse, des Pais Bas, des villes libres d'Allemagne, les princes électeurs, et autres princes souverains de l'empire, n'ont ils pas emploie leur autorité pour abbattre le papisme ?* "

Indeed, wherever the tremendous alternative of everlasting torments is believed in, — believed in so that it becomes a motive determining the life, — not only persecution, but every other form of severity and gloom, is the legitimate consequence. There is much ready declamation in these days against the spirit of asceticism and against zeal for doctrinal conversion; but surely the macerated form of a St. Francis, the fierce denunciations of a St. Dominic, the groans and prayerful wrestlings of the Puritan who seasoned his bread with tears, and made all pleasurable sensation sin, are more in keeping with the contemplation of unmending anguish as the destiny of a vast multitude whose nature we share, than the rubicund cheerfulness of some modern divines, who profess to unite a smiling liberalism with a well-bred and tacit but unshaken confidence in the reality of the bottomless pit.

But, in fact, as Mr. Lecky maintains, that awful image, with its group of associated dogmas concerning the inherited curse, and the damnation of unbaptized infants, of heathens, and of heretics, has passed away from what he is fond of calling "the realizations" of Christendom. These things are no longer the objects of practical belief. They may be mourned for in encyclical letters; bishops may regret them; doctors of divinity may sign testimonials to the excellent character of these decayed beliefs; but for the mass of Christians they are no more influential than unrepealed but forgotten statutes. And with these dogmas has melted away the strong basis for the defence of persecution. No man now writes eager vindications of himself and his colleagues from the suspicion of adhering to the principle of toleration. And this momentous change, it is Mr. Lecky's object to show, is due to that concurrence of conditions which he has chosen to call "the advance of the spirit of rationalism."

In other parts of his work, where he attempts to trace the action of the same conditions on the acceptance of miracles and on other chief phases of our historical development, Mr. Lecky has laid himself open to considerable criticism. The chapters on the miracles of the Church, the æsthetic, scientific, and moral development of rationalism, the secularization of politics, and the industrial history of rationalism, embrace a wide range of diligently gathered facts; but they are nowhere illuminated by a sufficiently clear conception and statement of the agencies at work, or the mode of their action, in the gradual modification of opinion and of life. The writer frequently impresses us as being in a state of hesitation concerning his own standing-point, which may form a desirable stage in private meditation but not in published exposition. Certain epochs in theoretic conception, certain considerations, which should be fundamental to his survey, are introduced quite incidentally in a sentence or two, or in a note which seems to be an afterthought. Great writers and their ideas are touched upon too slightly and with too little discrimination, and important theories are sometimes characterized with a rashness which conscientious revision will correct. There is a fatiguing use of vague or shifting phrases, such as "Modern Civilization," "Spirit of the Age," "Tone of Thought," "Intellectual Type of the Age," "Bias of the Imagination," "Habits of Religious Thought," unbalanced by any precise definition; and the spirit of rationalism is sometimes treated of as if it lay outside the specific mental activities of which it is a generalized expression. Mr. Curdle's famous definition of the dramatic unities as "a sort of a general oneness," is not totally false; but such luminousness as it has could only be perceived by those who already knew what the unities were. Mr. Lecky has the advantage of being strongly impressed with the great part played by the emotions in the formation of opinion, and with the high complexity of the causes at work in social evolution; but he frequently writes as if he had never yet distinguished between the complexity of the conditions that produce prevalent states of mind, and the inability of particular minds to give distinct reasons for the preferences or persuasions produced by those states. In brief, he does not discriminate, or does not help his reader to discriminate, between objective complexity and subjective confusion. But the most muddle-headed gentleman who represents the spirit of the age by observing, as he settles his collar, that the development theory is quite "the thing," is a result of definite processes, if we could only trace them. "Mental attitudes" and "predispositions," however vague in consciousness, have not vague causes, any more than the "blind motions of the spring" in plants and animals.

The word "rationalism" has the misfortune, shared by most words in this gray world, of being somewhat equivocal. This evil may be nearly overcome by careful preliminary definition; but Mr. Lecky does not supply this, and the original specific application of the word to a particular phase of Biblical interpretation seems to have clung about his use of it with a misleading effect. Through some parts of his book he appears to regard the grand characteristics of modern thought and civilization, compared with ancient, as a radiation in the first instance from a change in religious conceptions. The supremely important fact that the gradual reduction of all phenomena within the sphere of established law, which carries as a consequence the rejection of the miraculous, has its determining current in the development of physical science, seems to have engaged comparatively little of his attention; at least, he gives it no prominence. The great conception of universal regular sequence, without partiality and without caprice, — the conception which is the most potent force at work in the modification of our faith, and of the practical form given to our sentiments, — could only grow out of that patient watching of external fact and that silencing of preconceived notions which are urged upon the mind by the problems of physical science.

There is not room here to explain and justify the impressions of dissatisfaction which have been briefly indicated; but a serious writer, like Mr. Lecky, will not find such suggestions altogether useless. The objections, even the misunderstandings, of a reader who is not careless or ill-disposed, may serve to stimulate an author's vigilance over his thoughts as well as his style. It would be gratifying to see some future proof that Mr. Lecky has acquired juster views than are implied in the assertion that philosophers of the sensational school "can never rise to the conception of the disinterested;" and that he has freed himself from all temptation to that mingled laxity of statement and ill-pitched elevation of tone which are painfully present in the closing pages of his second volume.

THE NATURAL HISTORY OF GERMAN LIFE.

IT is an interesting branch of psychological observation to note the images that are habitually associated with abstract or collective terms, — what may be called the picture-writing of the mind, which it carries on concurrently with the more subtle symbolism of language. Perhaps the fixity or variety of these associated images would furnish a tolerably fair test of the amount of concrete knowledge and experience which a given word represents in the minds of two persons who use it with equal familiarity. The word *railways*, for example, will probably call up, in the mind of a man who is not highly locomotive, the image either of a Bradshaw, or of the station with which he is most familiar, or of an indefinite length of tram-road; he will alternate between these three images, which represent his stock of concrete acquaintance with railways. But suppose a man to have had successively the experience of a navvy, an engineer, a traveller, a railway director and shareholder, and a landed proprietor in treaty with a railway company, and it is probable that the range of images which would by turns present themselves to his mind at the mention of the *word* railways, would include all the essential facts in the existence and relations of the *thing*. Now it is possible for the first-mentioned personage to entertain very expanded views as to the multiplication of railways in the abstract, and their ultimate function in civilization. He may talk of a vast network of railways stretching over the globe, of future lines in Madagascar, and elegant refreshment-rooms in the Sandwich Islands, with none the less glibness because his distinct

conceptions on the subject do not extend beyond his one station and his indefinite length of tram-road. But it is evident that if we want a railway to be made, or its affairs to
be managed, this man of wide views and narrow observation
will not serve our purpose.

Probably, if we could ascertain the images called up by the
terms "the people," "the masses," "the proletariat," "the
peasantry," by many who theorize on those bodies with eloquence, or who legislate without eloquence, we should find
that they indicate almost as small an amount of concrete
knowledge, that they are as far from completely representing
the complex facts summed up in the collective term, as the
railway images of our non-locomotive gentleman. How little
the real characteristics of the working-classes are known to
those who are outside them, how little their natural history
has been studied, is sufficiently disclosed by our art as well as
by our political and social theories. Where, in our picture-
exhibitions, shall we find a group of true peasantry ? What
English artist even attempts to rival in truthfulness such
studies of popular life as the pictures of Teniers or the ragged
boys of Murillo ? Even one of the greatest painters of the
pre-eminently realistic school, while, in his picture of "The
Hireling Shepherd," he gave us a landscape of marvellous
truthfulness, placed a pair of peasants in the foreground
who were not much more real than the idyllic swains and
damsels of our chimney-ornaments. Only a total absence
of acquaintance and sympathy with our peasantry could
give a moment's popularity to such a picture as "Cross-
Purposes," where we have a peasant-girl who looks as if she
knew L. E. L.'s poems by heart, and English rustics, whose
costume seems to indicate that they are meant for ploughmen, with exotic features that remind us of a handsome
primo tenore. Rather than such cockney sentimentality as
this, as an education for the taste and sympathies, we prefer
the most crapulous group of boors that Teniers ever painted.
But even those among our painters, who aim at giving the
rustic type of features, who are far above the effeminate

feebleness of the "Keepsake" style, treat their subjects under the influence of traditions and prepossessions rather than of direct observation. The notion that peasants are joyous, that the typical moment to represent a man in a smock-frock is when he is cracking a joke and showing a row of sound teeth, that cottage matrons are usually buxom and village children necessarily rosy and merry, are prejudices difficult to dislodge from the artistic mind, which looks for its subjects into literature instead of life. The painter is still under the influence of idyllic literature, which has always expressed the imagination of the cultivated and town-bred, rather than the truth of rustic life. Idyllic ploughmen are jocund when they drive their team afield; idyllic shepherds make bashful love under hawthorn bushes; idyllic villagers dance in the checkered shade, and refresh themselves, not immoderately, with spicy nut-brown ale. But no one who has seen much of actual ploughmen thinks them jocund; no one who is well acquainted with the English peasantry can pronounce them merry. The slow gaze, in which no sense of beauty beams, no humor twinkles, the slow utterance, and the heavy slouching walk, remind one rather of that melancholy animal the camel, than of the sturdy countryman, with striped stockings, red waistcoat, and hat aside, who represents the traditional English peasant. Observe a company of haymakers. When you see them at a distance, tossing up the forkfuls of hay in the golden light, while the wagon creeps slowly with its increasing burden over the meadow, and the bright-green space, which tells of work done, gets larger and larger, you pronounce the scene "smiling," and you think these companions in labor must be as bright and cheerful as the picture to which they give animation. Approach nearer, and you will certainly find that haymaking time is a time for joking, especially if there are women among the laborers; but the coarse laugh that bursts out every now and then, and expresses the triumphant taunt, is as far as possible from your conception of idyllic merriment. That delicious effervescence of the mind which we call fun, has no equivalent for the northern peasant, except tipsy revelry; the only realm of fancy and imagination for the English clown exists at the bottom of the third quart-pot.

The conventional countryman of the stage, who picks up pocket-books and never looks into them, and who is too simple even to know that honesty has its opposite, represents the still lingering mistake, that an unintelligible dialect is a guarantee for ingenuousness, and that slouching shoulders indicate an upright disposition. It is quite true that a thresher is likely to be innocent of any adroit arithmetical cheating, but he is not the less likely to carry home his master's corn in his shoes and pocket; a reaper is not given to writing begging-letters, but he is quite capable of cajoling the dairymaid into filling his small-beer bottle with ale. The selfish instincts are not subdued by the sight of buttercups, nor is integrity in the least established by that classic rural occupation, sheep-washing. To make men moral, something more is requisite than to turn them out to grass.

Opera peasants, whose unreality excites Mr. Ruskin's indignation, are surely too frank an idealization to be misleading; and since popular chorus is one of the most effective elements of the opera, we can hardly object to lyric rustics in elegant lace bodices and picturesque motley, unless we are prepared to advocate a chorus of colliers in their pit costume, or a ballet of char-women and stocking-weavers. But our social novels profess to represent the people as they are, and the unreality of their representations is a grave evil. The greatest benefit we owe to the artist, whether painter, poet, or novelist, is the extension of our sympathies. Appeals founded on generalizations and statistics require a sympathy ready-made, a moral sentiment already in activity; but a picture of human life such as a great artist can give, surprises even the trivial and the selfish into that attention to what is apart from themselves, which may be called the raw material of moral sentiment. When Scott takes us into Luckie Mucklebackit's cottage, or tells the story of "The Two Drovers;" when Wordsworth sings to us the reverie of "Poor Susan;" when Kingsley shows us Alton Locke gazing yearningly over the gate which leads from the highway into the first wood he ever saw; when Hornung paints a group of chimney-sweepers,—more is done towards linking the higher classes with the lower, towards obliterating the vulgarity of exclusiveness, than by hundreds of sermons and philosophical dissertations. Art is the nearest thing to life; it is a mode of amplifying experience and extending our contact with our fellow-men beyond the bounds of our personal lot. All the more sacred is the task of the artist when he undertakes to paint the life of the people. Falsification here is far more pernicious than in the more artificial aspects of life. It is not so very serious that we should have false ideas about evanescent fashions, about the manners and conversation of beaux and duchesses; but it *is* serious that our sympathy with the perennial joys and struggles, the toil, the tragedy, and the humor in the life of our more heavily-laden fellow-men, should be perverted, and turned towards a false object instead of the true one.

This perversion is not the less fatal because the misrepresentation which gives rise to it has what the artist considers a moral end. The thing for mankind to know is, not what are the motives and influences which the moralist thinks *ought* to act on the laborer or the artisan, but what are the motives and influences which *do* act on him. We want to be taught to feel, not for the heroic artisan or the sentimental peasant, but for the peasant in all his coarse apathy, and the artisan in all his suspicious selfishness.

We have one great novelist who is gifted with the utmost power of rendering the external traits of our town population; and if he could give us their psychological character — their conception of life, and their emotions — with the same truth as their idiom and manners, his books would be the greatest contribution Art has ever made to the awakening of social sympathies. But while he can copy Mrs. Plornish's colloquial style with the delicate accuracy of a sun-picture, while there is the same startling inspiration in his description of the gestures and phrases of Boots, as in the

speeches of Shakspeare's mobs or numskulls, he scarcely
ever passes from the humorous and external to the emotional
and tragic, without becoming as transcendent in his unreality
as he was a moment before in his artistic truthfulness.   But
for the precious salt of his humor, which compels him to reproduce external traits that serve in some degree as a corrective to his frequently false psychology, his preternaturally
virtuous poor children and artisans, his melodramatic boatmen
and courtesans, would be as obnoxious as Eugène Sue's ideal-
ized proletaires, in encouraging the miserable fallacy, that
high morality and refined sentiment can grow out of harsh
social relations, ignorance, and want; or that the working-
classes are in a condition to enter at once into a millennial
state of *altruism*, wherein every one is caring for every one
else, and no one for himself.

If we need a true conception of the popular character to
guide our sympathies rightly, we need it equally to check
our theories, and direct us in their application.   The tendency created by the splendid conquests of modern generalization, to believe that all social questions are merged in
economical science, and that the relations of men to their
neighbors may be settled by algebraic equations; the dream
that the uncultured classes are prepared for a condition
which appeals principally to their moral sensibilities; the
aristocratic dilettanteism which attempts to restore the "good
old times" by a sort of idyllic masquerading, and to grow
feudal fidelity and veneration as we grow prize turnips, by
an artificial system of culture, — none of these diverging
mistakes can co-exist with a real knowledge of the people,
with a thorough study of their habits, their ideas, their motives.   The landholder, the clergyman, the mill-owner, the
mining-agent, have each an opportunity for making precious
observations on different sections of the working-classes, but
unfortunately their experience is too often not registered at
all, or its results are too scattered to be available as a source
of information and stimulus to the public mind generally.
If any man of sufficient moral and intellectual breadth,

whose observations would not be vitiated by a foregone conclusion or by a professional point of view, would devote
himself to studying the natural history of our social classes,
especially of the small shopkeepers, artisans, and peasantry, —
the degree in which they are influenced by local conditions,
their maxims and habits, the points of view from which they
regard their religious teachers, and the degree in which they
are influenced by religious doctrines, the interaction of the
various classes on each other, and what are the tendencies in
their position towards disintegration or towards development,
— and if, after all this study, he would give us the result of
his observations in a book well nourished with specific facts,
his work would be a valuable aid to the social and political
reformer.

What we are desiring for ourselves has been in some degree done for the Germans by Riehl; and we wish to make
his books known to our readers, not only for the sake of
the interesting matter they contain, and the important reflections they suggest, but also as a model for some future or
actual student of our own people. By way of introducing
Riehl to those who are unacquainted with his writings, we
will give a rapid sketch from his picture of the German peasantry; and perhaps this indication of the mode in which he
treats a particular branch of his subject, may prepare them to
follow us with more interest when we enter on the general
purpose and contents of his works.

In England, at present, when we speak of the peasantry,
we mean scarcely more than the class of farm-servants and
farm-laborers; and it is only in the most primitive districts,
as in Wales, for example, that farmers are included under
the term. In order to appreciate what Riehl says of the
German peasantry, we must remember what the tenant-
farmers and small proprietors were in England half a century ago, when the master helped to milk his own cows,
and the daughters got up at one o'clock in the morning to
brew, — when the family dined in the kitchen with the servants, and sat with them round the kitchen-fire in the even-

ing. In those days the quarried parlor was innocent of a carpet, and its only specimens of art were a framed sampler and the best tea-board; the daughters, even of substantial farmers, had often no greater accomplishment in writing and spelling than they could procure at a dame-school; and, instead of carrying on sentimental correspondence, they were spinning their future table-linen, and looking after every saving in butter and eggs that might enable them to add to the little stock of plate and china which they were laying in against their marriage. In our own day, setting aside the superior order of farmers, whose style of living and mental culture are often equal to that of the professional class in provincial towns, we can hardly enter the least imposing farmhouse without finding a bad piano in the "drawing-room," and some old annuals, disposed with a symmetrical imitation of negligence, on the table; though the daughters may still drop their *h*'s, their vowels are studiously narrow; and it is only in very primitive regions that they will consent to sit in a covered vehicle without springs, which was once thought an advance in luxury on the pillion.

The condition of the tenant-farmers and small proprietors in Germany is, we imagine, about on a par, not, certainly, in material prosperity, but in mental culture and habits, with that of the English farmers who were beginning to be thought old-fashioned nearly fifty years ago; and if we add to these the farm servants and laborers, we shall have a class approximating in its characteristics to the *Bauernthum*, or peasantry, described by Riehl.

In Germany, perhaps more than in any other country, it is among the peasantry that we must look for the historical type of the national *physique*. In the towns this type has become so modified to express the personality of the individual, that even family likeness is often but faintly marked. But the peasants may still be distinguished into groups, by their physical peculiarities. In one part of the country we find a longer-legged, in another a broader-shouldered race, which has inherited these peculiarities for centuries. For example, in certain districts of Hesse are seen long faces, with high foreheads, long, straight noses, and small eyes, with arched eyebrows and large eyelids. On comparing these physiognomies with the sculptures in the church of St. Elizabeth, at Marburg, executed in the thirteenth century, it will be found that the same old Hessian type of face has subsisted unchanged; with this distinction only, that the sculptures represent princes and nobles, whose features then bore the stamp of their race, while that stamp is now to be found only among the peasants. A painter who wants to draw mediæval characters with historic truth, must seek his models among the peasantry. This explains why the old German painters gave the heads of their subjects a greater uniformity of type than the painters of our day; the race had not attained to a high degree of individualization in features and expression. It indicates, too, that the cultured man acts more as an individual, the peasant more as one of a group. Hans drives the plough, lives, and thinks just as Kunz does; and it is this fact, that many thousands of men are as like each other in thoughts and habits as so many sheep or oysters, which constitutes the weight of the peasantry in the social and political scale.

In the cultivated world each individual has his style of speaking and writing; but among the peasantry it is the race, the district, the province, that has its style, — namely, its dialect, its phraseology, its proverbs, and its songs, which belong alike to the entire body of the people. This provincial style of the peasant is again, like his *physique*, a remnant of history, to which he clings with the utmost tenacity. In certain parts of Hungary there are still descendants of German colonists of the twelfth and thirteenth centuries, who go about the country as reapers, retaining their old Saxon songs and manners, while the more cultivated German emigrants in a very short time forget their own language, and speak Hungarian. Another remarkable case of the same kind is that of the Wends, a Sclavonic race settled in Lusatia, whose numbers amount to two hundred thousand, living either scattered among the German population, or in separate parishes.   They have their own schools and churches, and are taught in the Sclavonic tongue.   The Catholics among them are rigid adherents of the Pope ; the Protestants, not less rigid adherents of Luther, or *Doctor* Luther, as they are particular in calling him — a custom which, a hundred years ago, was universal in Protestant Germany.   The Wend clings tenaciously to the usages of his Church, and perhaps this may contribute not a little to the purity in which he maintains the specific characteristics of his race.   German education, German law and government, service in the standing army, and many other agencies, are in antagonism to his national exclusiveness ; but the wives and mothers here, as elsewhere, are a conservative influence, and the habits temporarily laid aside in the outer world are recovered by the fireside.   The Wends form several stout regiments in the Saxon army ; they are sought far and wide, as diligent and honest servants ; and many a weakly Dresden or Leipzig child becomes thriving under the care of a Wendish nurse.   In their villages they have the air and habits of genuine, sturdy peasants, and all their customs indicate that they have been, from the first, an agricultural people.   For example, they have traditional modes of treating their domestic animals.   Each cow has its own name, generally chosen carefully, so as to express the special qualities of the animal ; and all important family events are narrated to the *bees*, a custom which is found also in Westphalia.   Whether by the help of the bees or not, the Wend farming is especially prosperous ; and when a poor Bohemian peasant has a son born to him, he binds him to the end of a long pole and turns his face towards Lusatia, that he may be as lucky as the Wends, who live there.

. The peculiarity of the peasant's language consists chiefly in his retention of historical peculiarities, which gradually disappear under the friction of cultivated circles.   He prefers any proper name that may be given to a day in the calendar. rather than the abstract date, by which he very rarely reckons.   In the baptismal names of his children he is guided by

the old custom of the country, not at all by whim and fancy.
Many old baptismal names, formerly common in Germany,
would have become extinct but for their preservation among
the peasantry, especially in North Germany; and so firmly
have they adhered to local tradition in this matter, that it
would be possible to give a sort of topographical statistics of
proper names, and distinguish a district by its rustic names,
as we do by its Flora and Fauna. The continuous inheritance of certain favorite proper names in a family, in some
districts, forces the peasant to adopt the princely custom of
attaching a numeral to the name, and saying, when three
generations are living at once, Hans I., II., and III.; or — in
the more antique fashion — Hans the elder, the middle, and
the younger. In some of our English counties there is a
similar adherence to a narrow range of proper names; and, as
a mode of distinguishing collateral branches in the same
family, you will hear of Jonathan's Bess, Thomas's Bess, and
Samuel's Bess — the three Bessies being cousins.

The peasant's adherence to the traditional has much greater
inconvenience than that entailed by a paucity of proper
names. In the Black Forest and in Hüttenberg you will see
him in the dog-days wearing a thick fur cap — because it is
an historical fur cap, a cap worn by his grandfather. In the
Wetterau, that peasant-girl is considered the handsomest who
wears the most petticoats. To go to field-labor in seven
petticoats can be anything but convenient or agreeable, but
it is the traditionally correct thing; and a German peasant-
girl would think herself as unfavorably conspicuous in an
untraditional costume, as an English servant-girl would now
think herself in a linsey-woolsey apron or a thick muslin cap.
In many districts no medical advice would induce the rustic
to renounce the tight leather belt with which he injures his
digestive functions; you could more easily persuade him to
smile on a new communal system than on the unhistorical
invention of braces. In the eighteenth century, in spite of
the philanthropic preachers of potatoes, the peasant for
years threw his potatoes to the pigs and the dogs, before he

could be persuaded to put them on his own table. However, the unwillingness of the peasant to adopt innovations has a not unreasonable foundation in the fact, that for him experiments are practical, not theoretical, and must be made with expense of money instead of brains ; a fact that is not, perhaps, sufficiently taken into account by agricultural theorists, who complain of the farmer's obstinacy. The peasant has the smallest possible faith in theoretic knowledge ; he thinks it rather dangerous than otherwise, as is well indicated by a Lower Rhenish proverb : " One is never too old to learn, said an old woman ; so she learned to be a witch."

Between many villages an historical feud, once perhaps the occasion of much bloodshed, is still kept up under the milder form of an occasional round of cudgelling, and the launching of traditional nicknames. An historical feud of this kind still exists, for example, among many villages on the Rhine and more inland places in the neighborhood. *Rheinschnacke* (of which the equivalent is perhaps " water-snake ") is the standing term of ignominy for the inhabitant of the Rhine village, who repays it in kind by the epithet *karst* (mattock) or *kukuk* (cuckoo), according as the object of his hereditary hatred belongs to the field or the forest. If any Romeo among the " mattocks " were to marry a Juliet among the " water-snakes," there would be no lack of Tybalts and Mercutios to carry the conflict from words to blows, though neither side knows a reason for the enmity.

A droll instance of peasant conservatism is told of a village on the Taunus, whose inhabitants, from time immemorial, had been famous for impromptu cudgelling. For this historical offence the magistrates of the district had always inflicted the equally historical punishment of shutting up the most incorrigible offenders, not in prison, but in their own pigsty. In recent times, however, the government, wishing to correct the rudeness of these peasants, appointed an " enlightened " man as a magistrate, who at once abolished the original penalty above mentioned. But this relaxation of punishment was so far from being welcome to the villagers, that they presented a petition praying that a more energetic man might be given them as a magistrate, who would have the courage to punish according to law and justice, "as had been beforetime." And the magistrate who abolished incarceration in the pigsty could never obtain the respect of the neighborhood. This happened no longer ago than the beginning of the present century.

But it must not be supposed that the historical piety of the German peasant extends to anything not immediately connected with himself. He has the warmest piety towards the old tumble-down house which his grandfather built, and which nothing will induce him to improve; but towards the venerable ruins of the old castle that overlooks his village, he has no piety at all, and carries off its stones to make a fence for his garden, or tears down the gothic carving of the old monastic church, which is "nothing to him," to mark off a foot-path through his field. It is the same with historical traditions. The peasant has them fresh in his memory, so far as they relate to himself. In districts where the peasantry are unadulterated, you discern the remnants of the feudal relations in innumerable customs and phrases, but you will ask in vain for historical traditions concerning the empire, or even concerning the particular princely house to which the peasant is subject. He can tell you what "half people and whole people" mean; in Hesse you will still hear of "four horses making a whole peasant," or of "four-day and three-day peasants;" but you will ask in vain about Charlemagne and Frederic Barbarossa.

Riehl well observes that the feudal system, which made the peasant the bondman of his lord, was an immense benefit in a country, — the greater part of which had still to be colonized, — rescued the peasant from vagabondage, and laid the foundation of persistency and endurance in future generations. If a free German peasantry belongs only to modern times, it is to his ancestor who was a serf, — and even, in the earliest times, a slave, — that the peasant owes the foundation of his independence, namely, his capability of a settled existence, — nay, his unreasoning persistency, which has its important function in the development of the race.

Perhaps the very worst result of that unreasoning persistency is the peasant's inveterate habit of litigation. Every one remembers the immortal description of Dandie Dinmont's importunate application to Lawyer Pleydell to manage his "bit lawsuit," till at length Pleydell consents to help him to ruin himself, on the ground that Dandie may fall into worse hands. It seems this is a scene which has many parallels in Germany. The farmer's lawsuit is his point of honor; and he will carry it through, though he knows from the very first day that he shall get nothing by it. The litigious peasant piques himself, like Mr. Saddletree, on his knowledge of the law, and this vanity is the chief impulse to many a lawsuit. To the mind of the peasant, law presents itself as the "custom of the country," and it is his pride to be versed in all customs. *Custom with him holds the place of sentiment, of theory, and, in many cases, of affection.* Riehl justly urges the importance of simplifying law proceedings, so as to cut off this vanity at its source, and also of encouraging, by every possible means, the practice of arbitration.

The peasant never begins his lawsuit in summer, for the same reason that he does not make love and marry in summer, — because he has no time for that sort of thing. Anything is easier to him than to move out of his habitual course, and he is attached even to his privations. Some years ago a peasant youth, out of the poorest and remotest region of the Westerwald, was enlisted as a recruit, at Weilburg in Nassau. The lad, having never in his life slept in a bed, when he had got into one for the first time began to cry like a child; and he deserted twice because he could not reconcile himself to sleeping in a bed, and to the "fine" life of the barracks; he was homesick at the thought of his accustomed poverty and his thatched hut. A strong contrast, this, with the feeling of the poor in towns, who would be far enough from deserting because their condition was too much improved! The genuine peasant is never ashamed of his rank and calling; he is rather inclined to look down on every one who does not wear a smock frock, and thinks a man who has the manners of the gentry is likely to be rather windy and unsubstantial. In some places, even in French districts, this feeling is strongly symbolized by the practice of the peasantry, on certain festival days, to dress the images of the saints in peasant's clothing. History tells us of all kinds of peasant insurrections, the object of which was to obtain relief for the peasants from some of their many oppressions; but of an effort on their part to step out of their hereditary rank and calling, to become gentry, to leave the plough and carry on the easier business of capitalists or government-functionaries, there is no example.

The German novelists who undertake to give pictures of peasant-life, fall into the same mistake as our English novelists; they transfer their own feelings to ploughmen and woodcutters, and give them both joys and sorrows of which they know nothing. The peasant never questions the obligation of family ties, — he questions *no custom*, — but tender affection, as it exists amongst the refined part of mankind, is almost as foreign to him as white hands and filbert-shaped nails. That the aged father who has given up his property to his children on condition of their maintaining him for the remainder of his life, is very far from meeting with delicate attentions, is indicated by the proverb current among the peasantry, "Don't take your clothes off before you go to bed." Among rustic moral tales and parables, not one is more universal than the story of the ungrateful children, who made their gray-headed father, dependent on them for a maintenance, eat at a wooden trough, because he shook the food out of his trembling hands. Then these same ungrateful children observed one day that their own little boy was making a tiny wooden trough; and when they asked him what it was for, he answered, that his father and mother might eat out of it, when he was a man and had to keep them.

Marriage is a very prudential affair, especially among the peasants who have the largest share of property. Politic

marriages are as common among them as among princes; and
when a peasant-heiress in Westphalia marries, her husband
adopts her name, and places his own after it with the prefix
geborner (*née*). The girls marry young, and the rapidity with
which they get old and ugly is one among the many proofs
that the early years of marriage are fuller of hardships than
of conjugal tenderness. " When our writers of village stories," says Riehl, " transferred their own emotional life to
the peasant, they obliterated what is precisely his most predominant characteristic, namely, that with him general custom holds the place of individual feeling."

We pay for greater emotional susceptibility too often by
nervous diseases of which the peasant knows nothing. To
him headache is the least of physical evils, because he thinks
headwork the easiest and least indispensable of all labor.
Happily, many of the younger sons in peasant families, by
going to seek their living in the towns, carry their hardy
nervous system to amalgamate with the overwrought nerves
of our town population, and refresh them with a little rude
vigor. And a return to the habits of peasant life is the best
remedy for many moral as well as physical diseases induced
by perverted civilization. Riehl points to colonization as
presenting the true field for this regenerative process. On
the other side of the ocean, a man will have the courage to
begin life again as a peasant, while at home, perhaps, opportunity as well as courage will fail him. *Apropos* of this
subject of emigration, he remarks the striking fact, that the
native shrewdness and mother-wit of the German peasant
seem to forsake him entirely when he has to apply them
under new circumstances, and on relations foreign to his
experience. Hence it is that the German peasant who
emigrates, so constantly falls a victim to unprincipled ad-
venturers in the preliminaries to emigration; but if once he
gets his foot on the American soil, he exhibits all the first-
rate qualities of an agricultural colonist; and among all German emigrants, the peasant class are the most successful.

But many disintegrating forces have been at work on the

peasant character, and degeneration is unhappily going on at a greater pace than development. In the wine districts especially, the inability of the small proprietors to bear up under the vicissitudes of the market, or to insure a high quality of wine by running the risks of a late vintage, and the competition of beer and cider with the inferior wines, have tended to produce that uncertainty of gain which, with the peasant, is the inevitable cause of demoralization. The small peasant proprietors are not a new class in Germany, but many of the evils of their position are new. They are more dependent on ready money than formerly : thus, where a peasant used to get his wood for building and firing from the common forest, he has now to pay for it with hard cash; he used to thatch his own house, with the help perhaps of a neighbor, but now he pays a man to do it for him; he used to pay taxes in kind, he now pays them in money. The chances of the market have to be discounted, and the peasant falls into the hands of money-lenders. Here is one of the cases in which social policy clashes with a purely economical policy.

Political vicissitudes have added their influence to that of economical changes in disturbing that dim instinct, that reverence for traditional custom, which is the peasant's principle of action. He is in the midst of novelties for which he knows no reason — changes in political geography, changes of the government to which he owes fealty, changes in bureaucratic management and police regulations. He finds himself in a new element, before an apparatus for breathing in it is developed in him. His only knowledge of modern history is in some of its results — for instance, that he has to pay heavier taxes from year to year. His chief idea of a government is of a power that raises his taxes, opposes his harmless customs, and torments him with new formalities. The source of all this is the false system of "enlightening" the peasant which has been adopted by the bureaucratic governments. A system which disregards the traditions and hereditary attachments of the peasant, and appeals only to a logical under-

standing which is not yet developed in him, is simply disintegrating and ruinous to the peasant character. The inter-
ference with the communal regulations has been of this fatal
character. Instead of endeavoring to promote to the utmost
the healthy life of the Commune, as an organism the conditions of which are bound up with the historical characteristics of the peasant, the bureaucratic plan of government is
bent on improvement by its patent machinery of state-
appointed functionaries and off-hand regulations in accordance
with modern enlightenment. The spirit of communal exclusiveness, the resistance to the indiscriminate establishment of strangers, is an intense traditional feeling in the
peasant. "This gallows is for us and our children," is the
typical motto of this spirit. But such exclusiveness is
highly irrational, and repugnant to modern liberalism; therefore a bureaucratic government at once opposes it, and
encourages to the utmost the introduction of new inhabitants
in the provincial communes. Instead of allowing the peasants to manage their own affairs, and, if they happen to
believe that five and four make eleven, to unlearn the
prejudice by their own experience in calculation, so that they
may gradually understand processes, and not merely see
results, bureaucracy comes with its "Ready Reckoner" and
works all the peasant's sums for him — the surest way of
maintaining him in his stupidity, however it may shake his
prejudice.

Another questionable plan for elevating the peasant is the
supposed elevation of the clerical character, by preventing
the clergyman from cultivating more than a trifling part of
the land attached to his benefice, that he may be as much as
possible of a scientific theologian, and as little as possible of
a peasant. In this, Riehl observes, lies one great source of
weakness to the Protestant Church as compared with the
Catholic, which finds the great majority of its priests among
the lower orders; and we have had the opportunity of making
an analogous comparison in England, where many of us can
remember country districts in which the great mass of the

people were Christianized by illiterate Methodist and Independent ministers, while the influence of the parish clergyman among the poor did not extend much beyond a few old women in scarlet cloaks, and a few exceptional church-going laborers.

Bearing in mind the general characteristics of the German peasant, it is easy to understand his relation to the revolutionary ideas and revolutionary movements of modern times. The peasant, in Germany as elsewhere, is a born grumbler. He has always plenty of grievances in his pocket, but he does not generalize those grievances; he does not complain of government or society, probably because he has good reason to complain of the burgomaster. When a few sparks from the first French Revolution fell among the German peasantry, and in certain villages of Saxony the country-people assembled together to write down their demands, there was no glimpse in their petition of the universal rights of man, but simply of their own particular affairs as Saxon peasants. Again, after the July Revolution of 1830, there were many insignificant peasant insurrections; but the object of almost all was the removal of local grievances. Toll-houses were pulled down; stamped paper was destroyed; in some places there was a persecution of wild boars; in others, of that plentiful tame animal, the German *Rath*, or councillor who is never called into council. But in 1848 it seemed as if the movements of the peasants had taken a new character; in the small western states of Germany it seemed as if the whole class of peasantry was in insurrection. But, in fact, the peasant did not know the meaning of the part he was playing. He had heard that everything was being set right in the towns, and that wonderful things were happening there; so he tied up his bundle and set off. Without any distinct object or resolution, the country-people presented themselves on the scene of commotion, and were warmly received by the party leaders. But, seen from the windows of ducal palaces and ministerial hotels, these swarms of peasants had quite another aspect, and it was imagined that they had a common plan of co-operation. This, however, the peasants have never had. Systematic co-operation implies general conceptions, and a provisional subordination of egoism, to which even the artisans of towns have rarely shown themselves equal, and which are as foreign to the mind of the peasant as logarithms or the doctrine of chemical proportions. And the revolutionary fervor of the peasant was soon cooled. The old mistrust of the towns was reawakened on the spot. The Tyrolese peasants saw no great good in the freedom of the press, and the constitution, because these changes "seemed to please the gentry so much." Peasants who had given their voices stormily for a German parliament, asked afterwards, with a doubtful look, whether it were to consist of infantry or cavalry. When royal domains were declared the property of the state, the peasants in some small principalities rejoiced over this, because they interpreted it to mean that every one would have his share in them, after the manner of the old common and forest rights.

The very practical views of the peasants, with regard to the demands of the people, were in amusing contrast with the abstract theorizing of the educated townsmen. The peasant continually withheld all state payments until he saw how matters would turn out, and was disposed to reckon up the solid benefit, in the form of land or money, that might come to him from the changes obtained. While the townsman was heating his brains about representation on the broadest basis, the peasant asked if the relation between tenant and landlord would continue as before, and whether the removal of the feudal obligations meant that the farmer should become owner of the land.

It is in the same naïve way that Communism is interpreted by the German peasantry. The wide spread among them of communistic doctrines, the eagerness with which they listened to a plan for the partition of property, seemed to countenance the notion that it was a delusion to suppose the peasant would be secured from this intoxication by his love of secure possession and peaceful earnings. But, in fact, the

peasant contemplated partition by the light of an historical reminiscence rather than of novel theory. The golden
age, in the imagination of the peasant, was the time when
every member of the commune had a right to as much wood
from the forest as would enable him to sell some, after using
what he wanted in firing, — in which the communal possessions were so profitable that, instead of his having to pay
rates at the end of the year, each member of the commune
was something in pocket. Hence the peasants in general
understood by " partition " that the state lands, especially the
forests, would be divided among the communes, and that, by
some political legerdemain or other, everybody would have
free firewood, free grazing for his cattle, and over and above
that, a piece of gold without working for it. That he should
give up a single clod of his own to further the general partition had never entered the mind of the peasant commun-
ist; and the perception that this was an essential preliminary
to partition, was often a sufficient cure for his Communism.

In villages lying in the neighborhood of large towns,
however, where the circumstances of the peasantry are very
different, quite another interpretation of Communism is prevalent. Here the peasant is generally sunk to the position
of the proletaire, living from hand to mouth ; he has nothing
to lose, but everything to gain by partition. The coarse
nature of the peasant has here been corrupted into bestiality
by the disturbance of his instincts, while he is as yet incapable of principles ; and in this type of the degenerate peasant is seen the worst example of ignorance intoxicated by
theory.

A significant hint as to the interpretation the peasants put
on revolutionary theories may be drawn from the way they
employed the few weeks in which their movements were unchecked. They felled the forest trees and shot the game ;
they withheld taxes; they shook off the imaginary or real
burdens imposed on them by their mediatized princes, by
presenting their demands in a very rough way before the
ducal or princely Schloss; they set their faces against the

bureaucratic management of the communes, deposed the government functionaries who had been placed over them as burgomasters and magistrates, and abolished the whole bureaucratic system of procedure, simply by taking no notice of its regulations, and recurring to some tradition, some old order or disorder of things. In all this it is clear that they were animated not in the least by the spirit of modern revolution, but by a purely narrow and personal impulse towards reaction.

The idea of constitutional government lies quite beyond the range of the German peasant's conceptions. His only notion of representation is that of a representation of ranks, of classes; his only notion of a deputy is of one who takes care, not of the national welfare, but of the interests of his own order. Herein lay the great mistake of the democratic party, in common with the bureaucratic governments, that they entirely omitted the peculiar character of the peasant from their political calculations. They talked of the people, and forgot that the peasants were included in the term. Only a baseless misconception of the peasant's character could induce the supposition that he would feel the slightest enthusiasm about the principles involved in the reconstitution of the Empire, or even about the reconstitution itself. He has no zeal for a written law, as such, but only so far as it takes the form of a living law, a tradition. It was the external authority which the revolutionary party had won in Baden that attracted the peasants into a participation of the struggle.

Such, Riehl tells us, are the general characteristics of the German peasantry, characteristics which subsist amidst a wide variety of circumstances. In Mecklenburg, Pomerania, and Brandenburg, the peasant lives on extensive estates; in Westphalia he lives in large isolated homesteads; in the Westerwald and in Sauerland, in little groups of villages and hamlets; on the Rhine, land is for the most part parcelled out among small proprietors, who live together in large villages. Then, of course, the diversified physical geography of

Germany gives rise to equally diversified methods of land-culture ; and out of these various circumstances grow numerous specific differences in manner and character. But the generic character of the German peasant is everywhere the same, —in the clean mountain-hamlet and in the dirty fishing-village on the coast, in the plains of North Germany and in the backwoods of America. "Everywhere he has the same historical character, everywhere custom is his supreme law. Where religion and patriotism are still a naïve instinct, are still a sacred *custom*, there begins the class of the German Peasantry."

Our readers will perhaps already have gathered from the foregoing portrait of the German peasant, that Riehl is not a man who looks at objects through the spectacles either of the doctrinaire or the dreamer ; and they will be ready to believe what he tells us in his Preface, namely, that years ago he began his wanderings over the hills and plains of Germany for the sake of obtaining, in immediate intercourse with the people, that completion of his historical, political, and economical studies which he was unable to find in books. He began his investigations with no party prepossessions, and his present views were evolved entirely from his own gradually amassed observations. He was, first of all, a pedestrian, and only in the second place a political author. The views at which he has arrived by this inductive process he sums up in the term, *social-political-conservatism ;* but his conservatism is, we conceive, of a thoroughly philosophical kind. He sees in European society *incarnate history*, and any attempt to disengage it from its historical elements must, he believes, be simply destructive of social vitality.[1] What has grown up historically can only die out historically, by the gradual operation of necessary laws. The external conditions which society has inherited from the past are but the manifestation of inherited internal conditions in the human

[1] Throughout this article, in our statement of Riehl's opinions, we must be understood not as quoting Riehl, but as interpreting and illustrating him.

beings who compose it; the internal conditions and the external are related to each other as the organism and its medium, and development can take place only by the gradual consentaneous development of both.   Take the familiar example of attempts to abolish titles, which have been about as effective as the process of cutting off poppy-heads in a cornfield.   *Jedem Menschen,* says Riehl, *ist sein Zopf angeboren, warum soll denn der sociale Sprachgebrauch nicht auch sein Zopf haben?* — which we may render : " As long as snobbism runs in the blood, why should it not run in our speech ? "   As a necessary preliminary to a purely rational society, you must obtain purely rational men, free from the sweet and bitter prejudices of hereditary affection and antipathy ; which is as easy as to get running streams without springs, or the leafy shade of the forest without the secular growth of trunk and branch.

The historical conditions of society may be compared with those of language.   It must be admitted that the language of cultivated nations is in anything but a rational state ; the great sections of the civilized world are only approximatively intelligible to each other, — and even that, only at the cost of long study ; one word stands for many things, and many words for one thing ; the subtle shades of meaning, and still subtler echoes of association, make language an instrument which scarcely anything short of genius can wield with definiteness and certainty.   Suppose, then, that the effect which has been again and again made to construct a universal language on a rational basis has at length succeeded, and that you have a language which has no uncertainty, no whims of idiom, no cumbrous forms, no fitful simmer of many-hued significance, no hoary archaisms "familiar with forgotten years," — a patent deodorized and non-resonant language, which effects the purpose of communication as perfectly and rapidly as algebraic signs.   Your language may be a perfect medium of expression to science, but will never express *life,* which is a great deal more than science.   With the anomalies and inconveniences of historical language, you will have

parted with its music and its passions, and its vital qualities
as an expression of individual character, with its subtle capa-
bilities of wit, with everything that gives it power over the
imagination; and the next step in simplification will be the
invention of a talking watch, which will achieve the utmost
facility and despatch in the communication of ideas by a
graduated adjustment of ticks, to be represented in writing
by a corresponding arrangement of dots. A melancholy "language of the future!" The sensory and motor nerves, that
run in the same sheath, are scarcely bound together by a
more necessary and delicate union than that which binds men's
affections, imagination, wit, and humor, with the subtle rami-
fications of historical language. Language must be left to
grow in precision, completeness, and unity, as minds grow in
clearness, comprehensiveness, and sympathy. And there is
an analogous relation between the moral tendencies of men
and the social conditions they have inherited. The nature of
European men has its roots intertwined with the past, and can
only be developed by allowing those roots to remain undisturbed while the process of development is going on, until
that perfect ripeness of the seed which carries with it a life
independent of the root. This vital connection with the past
is much more vividly felt on the Continent than in England,
where we have to recall it by an effort of memory and reflection; for though our English life is in its core intensely traditional, Protestantism and commerce have modernized the
face of the land and the aspects of society in a far greater
degree than in any Continental country: —

"Abroad," says Ruskin, "a building of the eighth or tenth century
stands ruinous in the open streets; the children play round it, the
peasants heap their corn in it. The buildings of yesterday nestle about
it, and fit their new stones in its rents, and tremble in sympathy as it
trembles. No one wonders at it, or thinks of it as separate, and of another time; we feel the ancient world to be a real thing, and one with
the new; antiquity is no dream; it is rather the children playing about
the old stones that are the dream. But all is continuous, and the
words 'from generation to generation,' understandable here."

This conception of European society as incarnate history, is the fundamental idea of Riehl's books. After the notable failure of revolutionary attempts conducted from the point of view of abstract democratic and socialistic theories, after the practical demonstration of the evils resulting from a bureaucratic system, which governs by an undiscriminating, dead mechanism, Riehl wishes to urge on the consideration of his countrymen a social policy founded on the special study of the people as they are, — on the natural history of the various social ranks. He thinks it wise to pause a little from theorizing, and see what is the material actually present for theory to work upon. It is the glory of the socialists — in contrast with the democratic doctrinaires who have been too much occupied with the general idea of "the people" to inquire particularly into the actual life of the people — that they have thrown themselves with enthusiastic zeal into the study at least of one social group, namely, the factory operatives; and here lies the secret of their partial success. But unfortunately they have made this special duty of a single fragment of society the basis of a theory which quietly substitutes for the small group of Parisian proletaires or English factory-workers, the society of all Europe, — nay, of the whole world. And in this way they have lost the best fruit of their investigations. For, says Riehl, the more deeply we penetrate into the knowledge of society in its details, the more thoroughly we shall be convinced that *a universal social policy has no validity except on paper*, and can never be carried into successful practice. The conditions of German society are altogether different from those of French, of English, or of Italian society; and to apply the same social theory to these nations indiscriminately, is about as wise a procedure as Triptolemus Yellowley's application of the agricultural directions in Virgil's "Georgics" to his farm in the Shetland Isles.

It is the clear and strong light in which Riehl places this important position, that in our opinion constitutes the suggestive value of his books for foreign as well as German readers. It has not been sufficiently insisted on, that in the various branches of Social Science there is an advance from the general to the special, from the simple to the complex, analogous with that which is found in the series of the sciences, from mathematics to biology. To the laws of quantity, comprised in mathematics and physics, are superadded, in chemistry, laws of quality; to these again are added, in biology, laws of life; and lastly, the conditions of life in general branch out into its special conditions, or natural history, on the one hand, and into its abnormal conditions, or pathology, on the other. And in this series or ramification of the sciences, the more general science will not suffice to solve the problems of the more special. Chemistry embraces phenomena which are not explicable by physics; biology embraces phenomena which are not explicable by chemistry; and no biological generalization will enable us to predict the infinite specialities produced by the complexity of vital conditions. So Social Science, while it has departments which in their fundamental generality correspond to mathematics and physics, — namely, those grand and simple generalizations which trace out the inevitable march of the human race as a whole, and, as a ramification of these, the laws of economical science, — has also, in the departments of government and jurisprudence, which embrace the conditions of social life in all their complexity, what may be called its biology, carrying us on to innumerable special phenomena which outlie the sphere of science, and belong to natural history. And just as the most thorough acquaintance with physics or chemistry or general physiology will not enable you at once to establish the balance of life in your private vivarium, so that your particular society of zoöphytes, molluscs, and echinoderms may feel themselves, as the Germans say, at ease in their skin; so the most complete equipment of theory will not enable a statesman or a political and social reformer to adjust his measures wisely, in the absence of a special acquaintance with the section of society for which he legislates, with the peculiar characteristics of the nation, the province, the class whose well-being he has to consult. In other words, a wise social policy must be based not simply on abstract social science, but on the natural history of social bodies.

Riehl's books are not dedicated merely to the argumentative maintenance of this or of any other position; they are intended chiefly as a contribution to that knowledge of the German people on the importance of which he insists. He is less occupied with urging his own conclusions, than with impressing on his readers the facts which have led him to those conclusions. In the volume entitled " Land und Leute," which, though published last, is properly an introduction to the volume entitled " Die Bürgerliche Gesellschaft," he considers the German people in their physical-geographical relations; he compares the natural divisions of the race, as determined by land and climate and social traditions, with the artificial divisions which are based on diplomacy; and he traces the genesis and influences of what we may call the ecclesiastical geography of Germany, — its partition between Catholicism and Protestantism. He shows that the ordinary antithesis of North and South Germany represents no real ethnographical distinction, and that the natural divisions of Germany, founded on its physical geography, are threefold, — namely, the low plains, the middle mountain region, and the high mountain region, or Lower, Middle, and Upper Germany; and on this primary natural division all the other broad ethnographical distinctions of Germany will be found to rest. The plains of North or Lower Germany include all the seaboard the nation possesses; and this, together with the fact that they are traversed to the depth of six hundred miles by navigable rivers, makes them the natural seat of a trading race. Quite different is the geographical character of Middle Germany. While the northern plains are marked off into great divisions, by such rivers as the Lower Rhine, the Weser, and the Oder, running almost in parallel lines, this central region is cut up like a mosaic by the capricious lines of valleys and rivers. Here is the region in which you find those famous roofs from which the rain-water runs towards two different seas, and the mountain-tops from which you may look into eight or ten German States. The abundance of water-power and the presence of extensive coal-mines allow of a very diversified industrial development in Middle Germany. In Upper Germany, or the high mountain region, we find the same symmetry in the lines of the rivers as in the north; almost all the great Alpine streams flow parallel with the Danube. But the majority of these rivers are neither navigable nor available for industrial objects, and instead of serving for communication, they shut off one great tract from another. The slow development, the simple peasant life of many districts, is here determined by the mountain and the river. In the southeast, however, industrial activity spreads through Bohemia towards Austria, and forms a sort of balance to the industrial districts of the Lower Rhine. Of course, the boundaries of these three regions cannot be very strictly defined; but an approximation to the limits of Middle Germany may be obtained by regarding it as a triangle, of which one angle lies in Silesia, another in Aix-la-Chapelle, and a third at Lake Constance.

This triple division corresponds with the broad distinctions of climate. In the northern plains the atmosphere is damp and heavy; in the southern mountain region it is dry and rare, and there are abrupt changes of temperature, sharp contrasts between the seasons, and devastating storms; but in both these zones men are hardened by conflict with the roughnesses of the climate. In Middle Germany, on the contrary, there is little of this struggle: the seasons are more equable, and the mild, soft air of the valleys tends to make the inhabitants luxurious and sensitive to hardships. It is only in exceptional mountain districts that one is here reminded of the rough, bracing air on the heights of Southern Germany. It is a curious fact that, as the air becomes gradually lighter and rarer, from the North German coast towards Upper Germany, the average of suicides regularly decreases. Mecklenburg has the highest number, then Prussia, while the fewest suicides occur in Bavaria and Austria.

Both the northern and southern regions have still a large extent of waste lands, — downs, morasses, and heaths; and to these are added, in the south, abundance of snow-fields and naked rock; while in Middle Germany culture has almost overspread the face of the land, and there are no large tracts of waste. There is the same proportion in the distribution of forests. Again, in the north we see a monotonous continuity of wheat-fields, potato-grounds, meadow-lands, and vast heaths, and there is the same uniformity of culture over large surfaces in the southern table-lands, and the Alpine pastures. In Middle Germany, on the contrary, there is a perpetual variety of crops within a short space; the diversity of land surface, and the corresponding variety in the species of plants, are an invitation to the splitting up of estates, and this again encourages to the utmost the motley character of the cultivation.

According to this threefold division, it appears that there are certain features common to North and South Germany, in which they differ from Central Germany, and the nature of this difference Riehl indicates by distinguishing the former as Centralized Land, and the latter as Individualized Land; a distinction which is well symbolized by the fact that North and South Germany possess the great lines of railway which are the medium for the traffic of the world, while Middle Germany is far richer in lines for local communication, and possesses the greatest length of railway within the smallest space. Disregarding superficialities, the East Frieslanders, the Schleswig-Holsteiners, the Mecklenburghers, and the Pomeranians are much more nearly allied to the old Bavarians, the Tyrolese, and the Styrians, than any of these are allied to the Saxons, the Thuringians, or the Rhinelanders. Both in North and South Germany original races are still found in large masses, and popular dialects are spoken; you still find there thoroughly peasant districts, thorough villages, and also, at great intervals, thorough cities; you still find there a sense of rank. In Middle Germany, on the contrary, the original races are fused together, or sprinkled hither and thither; the peculiarities of the popular dialects are worn down or confused; there is no very strict line of demarcation between the country and the town population, hundreds of small towns and large villages being hardly distinguishable in their characteristics ; and the sense of rank, as part of the organic structure of society, is almost extinguished. Again, both in the north and south there is still a strong ecclesiastical spirit in the people, and the Pomeranian sees Antichrist in the Pope as clearly as the Tyrolese sees him in Doctor Luther; while in Middle Germany the confessions are mingled, they exist peaceably side by side in very narrow space, and tolerance or indifference has spread itself widely, even in the popular mind. And the analogy, or rather the causal relation between the physical geography of the three regions and the development of the population, goes still further.

"For," observes Riehl, "the striking connection which has been pointed out between the local geological formations in Germany, and the revolutionary disposition of the people, has more than a metaphorical significance. Where the primeval physical revolutions of the globe have been the wildest in their effects, and the most multiform strata have been tossed together or thrown one upon the other, it is a very intelligible consequence that on a land surface thus broken up the population should sooner develop itself into small communities, and that the more intense life generated in these smaller communities should become the most favorable nidus for the reception of modern culture, and with this a susceptibility for its revolutionary ideas; while a people settled in a region where its groups are spread over a large space will persist much more obstinately in the retention of its original character. The people of Middle Germany have none of that exclusive one-sidedness which determines the peculiar genius of great national groups, just as this one-sidedness, or uniformity, is wanting to the geological and geographical character of their land."

This ethnographical outline Riehl fills up with special and typical descriptions, and then makes it the starting-point for a criticism of the actual political condition of Germany. The volume is full of vivid pictures, as well as penetrating glances into the maladies and tendencies of modern society. It would be fascinating as literature, if it were not important for its facts and philosophy. But we can only commend it to our readers, and pass on to the volume entitled "Die Bürgerliche Gesellschaft," from which we have drawn our sketch of the German peasantry. Here Riehl gives us a series of studies in that natural history of the people, which he regards as the proper basis of social policy. He holds that, in European society, there are *three natural ranks, or estates:* the hereditary landed aristocracy, the citizens or commercial class, and the peasantry, or agricultural class. By *natural ranks* he means ranks which have their roots deep in the historical structure of society, and are still, in the present, showing vitality above ground; he means those great social groups which are not only distinguished externally by their vocation, but essentially by their mental character, their habits, their mode of life, — by the principle they represent in the historical development of society. In his conception of the Fourth Estate he differs from the usual interpretation, according to which it is simply equivalent to the proletariat, or those who are dependent on daily wages, whose only capital is their skill or bodily strength — factory operatives, artisans, agricultural laborers, to whom might be added, especially in Germany, the day-laborers with the quill, the literary proletariat. This, Riehl observes, is a valid basis of economical classification, but not of social classification. In his view, the Fourth Estate is a stratum produced by the perpetual abrasion of the other great social groups; it is the sign and result of the decomposition which is commencing in the organic constitution of society. Its elements are derived alike from the aristocracy, the bourgeoisie, and the peasantry. It assembles under its banner the deserters of historical society, and forms them into a terrible army, which is only just awaking to the consciousness of its corporate power The tendency of this Fourth Estate, by the very process of its formation, is to do away with the distinctive historical character of the other estates, and to resolve their peculiar rank and vocation into a uniform social relation, founded on an abstract conception of society. According to Riehl's classification, the day-laborers, whom the political economist designates as the Fourth Estate, belong partly to the peasantry, or agricultural class, and partly to the citizens, or commercial class.

Riehl considers, in the first place, the peasantry and aristocracy as the "forces of social persistence," and, in the second, the bourgeoisie and the Fourth Estate as the "forces of social movement."

The aristocracy, he observes, is the only one among these four groups which is denied by others besides Socialists to have any natural basis as a separate rank. It is admitted that there was once an aristocracy which had an intrinsic ground of existence; but now, it is alleged, this is an historical fossil, an antiquarian relic, venerable because gray with age. In what, it is asked, can consist the peculiar vocation of the aristocracy, since it has no longer the monopoly of the land, of the higher military functions, and of government offices, and since the service of the Court has no longer any political importance? To this Riehl replies, that in great revolutionary crises, the "men of progress" have more than once abolished the aristocracy. But, remarkably enough, the aristocracy has always reappeared. This measure of abolition showed that the nobility were no longer regarded as a real class, for to abolish a real class would be an absurdity. It is quite possible to contemplate a voluntary breaking up of the peasant or citizen class in the socialistic sense, but no man in his senses would think of straightway abolishing citizens and peasants. The aristocracy, then, was regarded as a sort of cancer, or excrescence of society. Nevertheless, not only has it been found impossible to annihilate an hereditary nobility by decree, but, also, the aristocracy of the eighteenth century outlived even the self-destructive acts of its own perversity. A life which was entirely without object, entirely destitute of functions, would not, says Riehl, be so persistent. He has an acute criticism of those who

conduct a polemic against the idea of an hereditary aristocracy, while they are proposing an "aristocracy of talent,"
which, after all, is based on the principle of inheritance.
The Socialists are, therefore, only consistent in declaring
against an aristocracy of talent. "But when they have
turned the world into a great foundling hospital, they will
still be unable to eradicate the 'privileges of birth.'" We
must not follow him in his criticism, however; nor can we
afford to do more than mention hastily his interesting sketch
of the mediæval aristocracy, and his admonition to the German aristocracy of the present day, that the vitality of their
class is not to be sustained by romantic attempts to revive
mediæval forms and sentiments, but only by the exercise of
functions as real and salutary for actual society as those of
the mediæval aristocracy were for the feudal age. "In modern society the divisions of rank indicate *division of labor*,
according to that distribution of functions in the social organism which the historical constitution of society has determined. In this way the principle of differentiation and the
principle of unity are identical."

The elaborate study of the German bourgeoisie, which
forms the next division of the volume, must be passed over;
but we may pause a moment to note Riehl's definition of the
social Philister (Philistine), an epithet for which we have no
equivalent, — not at all, however, for want of the object it represents. Most people, who read a little German, know that
the epithet Philister originated in the *Burschen-leben*, or stu-
dent-life of Germany, and that the antithesis of *Bursch* and
Philister was equivalent to the antithesis of "gown and
town;" but since the word has passed into ordinary language,
it has assumed several shades of significance which have
not yet been merged in a single, absolute meaning; and one
of the questions which an English visitor in Germany will
probably take an opportunity of asking is, "What is the strict
meaning of the word Philister?" Riehl's answer is, that the
Philister is one who is indifferent to all social interests, all
public life, as distinguished from selfish and private interests;

he has no sympathy with political and social events except as they affect his own comfort and prosperity, as they offer him material for amusement or opportunity for gratifying his vanity. He has no social or political creed, but is always of the opinion which is most convenient for the moment. He is always in the majority, and is the main element of unreason and stupidity in the judgment of a "discerning public." It seems presumptuous in us to dispute Riehl's interpretation of a German word, but we must think that, in literature, the epithet Philister has usually a wider meaning than this — includes his definition and something more. We imagine the Philister is the personification of the spirit which judges everything from a lower point of view than the subject demands, — which judges the affairs of the parish from the egotistic or purely personal point of view, which judges the affairs of the nation from the parochial point of view, and does not hesitate to measure the merits of the universe from the human point of view. At least this must surely be the spirit to which Goethe alludes in a passage cited by Riehl himself, where he says that the Germans need not be ashamed of erecting a monument to him as well as to Blücher; for if Blücher had freed them from the French, he (Goethe) had freed them from the nets of the Philister : —

> "Ihr mögt mir immer ungescheut
> Gleich Blüchern Denkmal setzen!
> Von Franzosen hat er euch befreit,
> Ich von Philister-netzen."

Goethe could hardly claim to be the apostle of public spirit; but he is eminently the man who helps us to rise to a lofty point of observation, so that we may see things in their relative proportions.

The most interesting chapters in the description of the Fourth Estate, which concludes the volume, are those on the Aristocratic Proletariat and the Intellectual Proletariat. The Fourth Estate in Germany, says Riehl, has its centre of gravity not, as in England and France, in the day-

laborers and factory operatives, and still less in the degenerate peasantry. In Germany, the *educated* proletariat is
the leaven that sets the mass in fermentation; the dangerous
classes there go about, not in blouses, but in frock-coats;
they begin with the impoverished prince and end in the hun-
griest *littérateur.* The custom that all the sons of a nobleman shall inherit their father's title, necessarily goes on
multiplying that class of aristocrats who are not only without function but without adequate provision, and who shrink
from entering the ranks of the citizens by adopting some
honest calling. The younger son of a prince, says Riehl, is
usually obliged to remain without any vocation; and however
zealously he may study music, painting, literature, or science,
he can never be a regular musician, painter, or man of science; his pursuit will be called a "passion," not a "calling,"
and to the end of his days he remains a dilettante. "But
the ardent pursuit of a fixed practical calling can alone satisfy the active man." Direct legislation cannot remedy this
evil. The inheritance of titles by younger sons is the universal custom, and custom is stronger than law. But if all
government preference for the "aristocratic proletariat" were
withdrawn, the sensible men among them would prefer emigration, or the pursuit of some profession, to the hungry
distinction of a title without rents.

The intellectual proletaires Riehl calls the "church mili-
tant" of the Fourth Estate in Germany. In no other country are they so numerous; in no other country is the trade
in material and industrial capital so far exceeded by the
wholesale and retail trade, the traffic and the usury, in the
intellectual capital of the nation. *Germany yields more intellectual produce than it can use and pay for.*

"This over-production, which is not transient but permanent, nay,
is constantly on the increase, evidences a diseased state of the national
industry, a perverted application of industrial powers, and is a far more
pungent satire on the national condition than all the poverty of operatives and peasants. . . . Other nations need not envy us the preponderance of the intellectual proletariat over the proletaires of manual

labor. For man more easily becomes diseased from over-study than from the labor of the hands ; and it is precisely in the intellectual pro- letariat that there are the most dangerous seeds of disease. This is the group in which the opposition between earnings and wants, be- tween the ideal social position and the real, is the most hopelessly irreconcilable."

We must unwillingly leave our readers to make acquaint- ance for themselves with the graphic details with which Riehl follows up this general statement; but before quitting these admirable volumes, let us say, lest our inevitable omis- sions should have left room for a different conclusion, that Riehl's conservatism is not in the least tinged with the par- tisanship of a class, with a poetic fanaticism for the past, or with the prejudice of a mind incapable of discerning the grander evolution of things to which all social forms are but temporarily subservient. It is the conservatism of a clear- eyed, practical, but withal large-minded man — a little caus- tic, perhaps, now and then, in his epigrams on democratic doctrinaires who have their nostrum for all political and social diseases, and on communistic theories which he regards as " the despair of the individual in his own manhood, re- duced to a system," but nevertheless able and willing to do justice to the elements of fact and reason in every shade of opinion and every form of effort. He is as far as possible from the folly of supposing that the sun will go backward on the dial, because we put the hands of our clock backward ; he only contends against the opposite folly of decreeing that it shall be mid-day, while in fact the sun is only just touch- ing the mountain-tops, and all along the valley men are stum- bling in the twilight.

THREE MONTHS IN WEIMAR.

IT was between three and four o'clock on a fine morning in August, that after a ten hours' journey from Frankfort, I awoke at the Weimar station. No tipsiness can be more dead to all appeals than that which comes from fitful draughts of sleep on a railway journey by night. To the disgust of your wakeful companions, you are totally insensible to the existence of your umbrella, and to the fact that your carpet-bag is stowed under your seat, or that you have borrowed books and tucked them behind the cushion. "What's the odds, so long as one can sleep?" is your philosophic formula; and it is not until you have begun to shiver on the platform in the early morning air that you become alive to property and its duties, — that is, to the necessity of keeping a fast grip upon it. Such was my condition when I reached the station at Weimar. The ride to the town thoroughly roused me, all the more because the glimpses I caught from the carriage window were in startling contrast with my preconceptions. The lines of houses looked rough and straggling, and were often interrupted by trees peeping out from the gardens behind. At last we stopped before the Erbprinz, an inn of long standing, in the heart of the town, and were ushered along heavy-looking in-and-out corridors, such as are found only in German inns, into rooms which overlooked a garden just like one you may see at the back of a farmhouse in many an English village.

A walk in the morning in search of lodgings confirmed the impression that Weimar was more like a market-town than the precinct of a court. "And this is the Athens of the

GRIFF HOUSE, WHERE GEORGE ELIOT LIVED AS A CHILD.

North!" we said.   Materially speaking, it is more like Sparta. The blending of rustic and civic life, the indications of a central government in the midst of very primitive-looking objects, has some distant analogy with the condition of old Lacedæmon. The shops are most of them such as you would see in the back streets of an English provincial town, and the commodities on sale are often chalked on the door-posts. A loud rumbling of vehicles may indeed be heard now and then; but the rumbling is loud, not because the vehicles are many, but because the springs are few. The inhabitants seemed to us to have more than the usual heaviness of *Germanity;* even their stare was slow, like that of herbivorous quadrupeds. We set out with the intention of exploring the town, and at every other turn we came into a street which took us *out* of the town, or else into one that led us back to the market from which we set out. One's first feeling was, How could Goethe live here in this dull, lifeless village? The reproaches cast on him for his worldliness and attachment to court splendor seemed ludicrous enough; and it was inconceivable that the stately Jupiter, in a frock-coat, so familiar to us all through Rauch's statuette, could have habitually walked along these rude streets and among these slouching mortals. Not a picturesque bit of building was to be seen; there was no quaintness, nothing to remind one of historical associations, nothing but the most arid prosaism.

This was the impression produced by a first morning's walk in Weimar, — an impression which very imperfectly represents what Weimar is, but which is worth recording, because it is true as a sort of back view. Our ideas were considerably modified when in the evening we found our way to the Belvedere *chaussée,* a splendid avenue of chestnut-trees, two miles in length, reaching from the town to the summer residence of Belvedere; when we saw the Schloss, and discovered the labyrinthine beauties of the Park; indeed, every day opened to us fresh charms in this quiet little valley and its environs. To any one who loves Nature in her gentle aspects, who delights in the checkered shade on a summer morning, and in a walk on the corn-clad upland at sunset, within sight of a little town nestled among the trees below, I say — come to Weimar. And if you are weary of English unrest, of that society of "eels in a jar," where each is trying to get his head above the other, the somewhat stupid well-being of the Weimarians will not be an unwelcome contrast, for a short time at least. If you care nothing about Goethe and Schiller and Herder and Wieland, why, so much the worse for you, — you will miss many interesting thoughts and associations; still, Weimar has a charm independent of these great names.

First among all its attractions is the Park, which would be remarkably beautiful even among English parks; and it has one advantage over all these, — namely, that it is without a fence. It runs up to the houses and far out into the cornfields and meadows, as if it had a "sweet will" of its own, like a river or a lake, and had not been planned and planted by human will. Through it flows the Ilm, — not a clear stream, it must be confessed, but, like all water, as Novalis says, "an eye to the landscape." Before we came to Weimar we had had dreams of boating on the Ilm, and we were not a little amused at the difference between this vision of our own and the reality. A few water-fowl are the only navigators of the river; and even they seem to confine themselves to one spot, as if they were there purely in the interest of the picturesque. The real extent of the Park is small; but the walks are so ingeniously arranged, and the trees are so luxuriant and various, that it takes weeks to learn the turnings and windings by heart, so as no longer to have the sense of novelty. In the warm weather our great delight was the walk which follows the course of the Ilm, and is overarched by tall trees with patches of dark moss on their trunks, in rich contrast with the transparent green of the delicate leaves, through which the golden sunlight played and checkered the walk before us. On one side of this walk the rocky ground rises to the height of twenty feet or more, and is clothed with mosses and rock-plants. On the other side there are,

every now and then, openings, breaks in the continuity of
shade, which show you a piece of meadow-land with fine
groups of trees; and at every such opening a seat is placed
under the rock, where you may sit and chat away the sunny
hours, or listen to those delicate sounds which one might
fancy came from tiny bells worn on the garment of Silence
to make us aware of her invisible presence. It is along this
walk that you come upon a truncated column, with a serpent
twined round it, devouring cakes, placed on the column as
offerings, a bit of rude sculpture in stone. The inscription
— *Genio loci* — enlightens the learned as to the significance
of this symbol; but the people of Weimar, unedified by classical allusions, have explained the sculpture by a story which
is an excellent example of a modern myth. Once on a time,
say they, a huge serpent infested the Park, and evaded all
attempts to exterminate him, until at last a cunning baker
made some appetizing cakes which contained an effectual
poison, and placed them in the serpent's reach, thus meriting
a place with Hercules, Theseus, and other monster-slayers.
Weimar, in gratitude, erected this column as a memorial of
the baker's feat and its own deliverance. A little farther on
is the Borkenhaus, where Carl August used to play the her-
mit for days together, and from which he used to telegraph
to Goethe in his Gartenhaus. Sometimes we took our shady
walk in the *Stern*, the oldest part of the Park plantations, on
the opposite side of the river, lingering on our way to watch
the crystal brook which hurries on, like a foolish young
maiden, to wed itself with the muddy Ilm. The *Stern*
(Star), a large circular opening among the trees, with walks
radiating from it, has been thought of as the place for the
projected statues of Goethe and Schiller. In Rauch's model
for these statues the poets are draped in togas, Goethe, who
was considerably the shorter of the two, resting his hand on
Schiller's shoulder; but it has been wisely determined to
represent them in their " habit as they lived," so Rauch's
design is rejected. Against classical idealizing in portrait
sculpture, Weimar has already a sufficient warning in the

colossal statue of Goethe, executed after Bettina's design, which the readers of the "Correspondence with a Child" may see engraved as a frontispiece to the second volume. This statue is locked up in an odd structure, standing in the Park, and looking like a compromise between a church and a summer-house. (Weimar does *not* shine in its buildings!) How little real knowledge of Goethe must the mind have that could wish to see him represented as a naked Apollo, with a Psyche at his knee! The execution is as feeble as the sentiment is false; the Apollo-Goethe is a caricature, and the Psyche is simply vulgar. The statue was executed under Bettina's encouragement, in the hope that it would be bought by the King of Prussia; but a breach having taken place between her and her royal friend, a purchaser was sought in the Grand Duke of Weimar, who, after transporting it at enormous expense from Italy, wisely shut it up where it is seen only by the curious.

As autumn advanced and the sunshine became precious, we preferred the broad walk on the higher grounds of the Park, where the masses of trees are finely disposed, leaving wide spaces of meadow which extend on one side to the Belvedere *allée* with its avenue of chestnut-trees, and on the other to the little cliffs which I have already described as forming a wall by the walk along the Ilm. Exquisitely beautiful were the graceful forms of the plane-trees, thrown in golden relief on a background of dark pines. Here we used to turn and turn again in the autumn afternoons, at first bright and warm, then sombre with low-lying purple clouds, and chill with winds that sent the leaves raining from the branches. The eye here welcomes, as a contrast, the white *façade* of a building looking like a small Greek temple, placed on the edge of a cliff, and you at once conclude it to be a bit of pure ornament, a device to set off the landscape; but you presently see a porter seated near the door of the basement story, beguiling the ennui of his sinecure by a book and a pipe, and you learn with surprise that this is another retreat for ducal dignity to unbend and philosophize in. Singularly ill-adapted to such a purpose it seems to beings not ducal. On the other side of the Ilm the Park is bordered by the road leading to the little village of Ober Weimar, — another sunny walk, which has the special attraction of taking one by Goethe's Gartenhaus, his first residence at Weimar. Inside, this Gartenhaus is a homely sort of cottage, such as many an English nobleman's gardener lives in; no furniture is left in it, and the family wish to sell it. Outside, its aspect became to us like that of a dear friend, whose irregular features and rusty clothes have a peculiar charm. It stands, with its bit of garden and orchard, on a pleasant slope, fronting the west; before it the Park stretches one of its meadowy openings to the trees which fringe the Ilm, and between this meadow and the garden hedge lies the said road to Ober Weimar. A grove of weeping birches sometimes tempted us to turn out of this road up to the fields at the top of the slope, on which not only the Gartenhaus, but several other modest villas are placed. From this little height one sees to advantage the plantations of the Park in their autumnal coloring; the town, with its steep-roofed church, and castle clock-tower, painted a gay green; the bushy line of the Belvedere *chaussée*, and Belvedere itself peeping on an eminence from its nest of trees. Here, too, was the place for seeing a lovely sunset, — such a sunset as September sometimes gives us, when the western horizon is like a rippled sea of gold, sending over the whole hemisphere golden vapors, which, as they near the east, are subdued to a deep rose-color.

The Schloss is rather a stately, ducal-looking building, forming three sides of a quadrangle. Strangers are admitted to see a suite of rooms called the Dichter-Zimmer (Poet's Rooms), dedicated to Goethe, Schiller, and Wieland. The idea of these rooms is really a pretty one: in each of them there is a bust of the poet who is its presiding genius, and the walls of the Schiller and Goethe rooms are covered with frescos representing scenes from their works. The Wieland room is much smaller than the other two, and serves as an antechamber to them; it is also decorated more sparingly, but the arabesques on the walls are very tastefully designed, and satisfy one better than the ambitious compositions from Goethe and Schiller.

A more interesting place to visitors is the library, which occupies a large building not far from the Schloss. The principal *Saal*, surrounded by a broad gallery, is ornamented with some very excellent busts and some very bad portraits. Of the busts, the most remarkable is that of Glück, by Houdon, — a striking specimen of the *real* in art. The sculptor has given every scar made by the small-pox; he has left the nose as pug and insignificant, and the mouth as common, as Nature made them; but then he has done what, doubtless, Nature also did, — he has spread over those coarsely cut features the irradiation of genius. A specimen of the opposite style in art is Trippel's bust of Goethe as the young Apollo, also fine in its way. It was taken when Goethe was in Italy; and in the "Italiänische Reise," mentioning the progress of the bust, he says that he sees little likeness to himself, but is not discontented that he should go forth to the world as such a good-looking fellow, — *hübscher Bursch*. This bust, however, is a frank idealization; when an artist tells us that the ideal of a Greek god divides his attention with his immediate subject, we are warned. But one gets rather irritated with idealization in portrait when, as in Dannecker's bust of Schiller, one has been misled into supposing that Schiller's brow was square and massive, while, in fact, it was receding. We say this partly on the evidence of his skull, a cast of which is kept in the library, so that we could place it in juxtaposition with the bust. The story of this skull is curious. When it was determined to disinter Schiller's remains, that they might repose in company with those of Carl August and Goethe, the question of identification was found to be a difficult one, for his bones were mingled with those of ten insignificant fellow-mortals. When, however, the eleven skulls were placed in juxtaposition, a large number of persons who had known Schiller separately and successively fixed upon

the same skull as his, and their evidence was clenched by
the discovery that the teeth of this skull corresponded to the
statement of Schiller's servant, that his master had lost no
teeth, except one, which he specified. Accordingly it was
decided that this was Schiller's skull, and the comparative
anatomist Loder was sent for from Jena to select the bones
which completed the skeleton.[1] The evidence certainly leaves
room for a doubt; but the receding forehead of the skull
agrees with the testimony of persons who knew Schiller, that
he had, as Rauch said to us, a "miserable forehead;" it
agrees, also, with a beautiful miniature of Schiller, taken
when he was about twenty. This miniature is deeply interesting; it shows us a youth whose clearly cut features, with
the mingled fire and melancholy of their expression, could
hardly have been passed with indifference; it has the *langer
Gänsehals* (long goose-neck) which he gives to his Karl
Moor; but instead of the black, sparkling eyes, and the
gloomy, overhanging, bushy eyebrows he chose for his robber
hero, it has the fine wavy auburn locks and the light-blue
eyes which belong to our idea of pure German race. We
may be satisfied that we know at least the *form* of Schiller's
features, for in this particular his busts and portraits are in
striking accordance; unlike the busts and portraits of Goethe,
which are a proof, if any were wanted, how inevitably subjective art is, even when it professes to be purely imitative,
— how the most active perception gives us rather a reflex of
what we think and feel, than the real sum of objects before
us. The Goethe of Rauch or of Schwanthaler is widely different in form, as well as expression, from the Goethe of
Stieler; and Winterberger, the actor, who knew Goethe intimately, told us that to him not one of all the likenesses,
sculptured or painted, seemed to have more than a faint
resemblance to their original. There is, indeed, one likeness,
taken in his old age, and preserved in the library, which is

[1] I tell this story from my recollection of Stahr's account in his "Weimar
und Jena," an account which was confirmed to me by residents in Weimar,
but as I have not the book by me, I cannot test the accuracy of my memory.

startling from the conviction it produces of close resemblance, and Winterberger admitted it to be the best he had seen. It is a tiny miniature painted on a small cup, of Dresden china, and is so wonderfully executed that a magnifying-glass exhibits the perfection of its texture as if it were a flower or a butterfly's wing. It is more like Stieler's portrait than any other; the massive neck, unbent though withered, rises out of his dressing-gown, and supports majestically a head from which one might imagine (though, alas! it never is so in reality) that the discipline of seventy years had purged away all meaner elements than those of the sage and the poet, — a head which might serve as a type of sublime old age. Among the collection of toys and trash, melancholy records of the late Grand Duke's eccentricity, which occupy the upper rooms of the library, there are some precious relics hanging together in a glass case, which almost betray one into sympathy with "holy coat" worship. They are — Luther's gown, the coat in which Gustavus Adolphus was shot, and Goethe's court coat and *Schlafrock*. What a rush of thoughts from the mingled memories of the passionate reformer, the heroic warrior, and the wise singer!

The only one of its great men to whom Weimar has at present erected a statue in the open air is Herder. His statue, erected in 1850, stands in what is called the Herder Platz, with its back to the church in which he preached; in the right hand is a roll bearing his favorite motto, *Licht, Liebe, Leben* (Light, Love, Life), and on the pedestal is the inscription *Von Deutschen aller Länder* (from Germans of all lands). This statue, which is by Schaller of Munich, is very much admired; but, remembering the immortal description in the "Dichtung und Wahrheit," of Herder's appearance when Goethe saw him for the first time at Strasburg, I was disappointed with the parsonic appearance of the statue, as well as of the bust in the library. The part of the town which imprints itself on the memory, next to the Herder Platz, is the Markt, a cheerful square made smart by a new Rath-haus. Twice a week it is crowded with stalls and country people; and it is the very pretty custom for the band to play in the balcony of the Rath-haus about twenty minutes every market-day to delight the ears of the peasantry. A head-dress worn by many of the old women, and here and there by a young one, is, I think, peculiar to Thuringia. Let the fair reader imagine half a dozen of her broadest French sashes dyed black, and attached as streamers to the back of a stiff black skull-cap, ornamented in front with a large bow, which stands out like a pair of donkey's ears; let her further imagine, mingled with the streamers of ribbon, equally broad pendants of a thick woollen texture, something like the fringe of an urn-rug, and she will have an idea of the head-dress in which I have seen a Thuringian damsel figure on a hot summer's day. Two houses in the Markt are pointed out as those from which Tetzel published his indulgences and Luther thundered against them; but it is difficult to one's imagination to conjure up scenes of theological controversy in Weimar, where, from princes down to pastry-cooks, rationalism is taken as a matter of course.

Passing along the Schiller-strasse, a broad, pleasant street, one is thrilled by the inscription, *Hier wohnte Schiller*, over the door of a small house with casts in its bow-window. Mount up to the second story, and you will see Schiller's study very nearly as it was when he worked in it. It is a cheerful room with three windows, two towards the street and one looking on a little garden which divides his house from the neighboring one. The writing-table, which he notes as an important purchase in one of his letters to Körner, and in one of the drawers of which he used to keep rotten apples for the sake of their scent, stands near the last-named window, so that its light would fall on his left hand. On another side of the room is his piano, with his guitar lying upon it; and above these hangs an ugly print of an Italian scene, which has a companion equally ugly on another wall. Strange feelings it awakened in me to run my fingers over the keys of the little piano and call forth its tones, now so queer and feeble, like those of an invalided old woman whose voice could once make a heart beat with fond passion or soothe its angry pulses into calm. The bedstead on which Schiller died has been removed into the study, from the small bedroom behind, which is now empty. A little table is placed close to the head of the bed, with his drinking-glass upon it, and on the wall above the bedstead there is a beautiful sketch of him lying dead. He used to occupy the whole of the second floor. It contains, besides the study and bedroom, an antechamber, now furnished with casts and prints on sale, in order to remunerate the custodiers of the house, and a *salon* tricked out, since his death, with a symbolical cornice, statues, and a carpet worked by the ladies of Weimar.

Goethe's house is much more important-looking, but, to English eyes, far from being the palatial residence which might be expected, from the descriptions of German writers. The entrance hall is indeed rather imposing, with its statues in niches, and its broad staircase, but the rest of the house is not proportionately spacious and elegant. The only part of the house open to the public — and this only on a Friday — is the principal suite of rooms which contain his collection of casts, pictures, cameos, etc. This collection is utterly insignificant, except as having belonged to him ; and one turns away from bad pictures and familiar casts, to linger over the manuscript of the wonderful "Römische Elegein," written by himself in the Italian character. It is to be regretted that a large sum offered for this house by the German Diet was refused by the Goethe family, in the hope, it is said, of obtaining a still larger sum from that mythical English Crœsus always ready to turn fabulous sums into dead capital, who haunts the imagination of Continental people. One of the most fitting tributes a nation can pay to its great dead is to make their habitation, like their works, a public possession, — a shrine where affectionate reverence may be more vividly reminded that the being who has bequeathed to us immortal thoughts or immortal deeds had to endure the daily struggle with the petty details, perhaps with the sordid cares of this working-day world; and it is a sad pity that Goethe's study, bedroom, and library, so fitted to call up that kind of sympathy, because they are preserved just as he left them, should be shut out from all but the specially privileged. We were happy enough to be among these, to look through the mist of rising tears at the dull study with its two small windows, and without a single object chosen for the sake of luxury or beauty; at the dark little bedroom with the bed on which he died, and the arm-chair where he took his morning coffee as he read; at the library with its common deal shelves, and books containing his own paper-marks. In the presence of this hardy simplicity, the contrast suggests itself of the study at Abbotsford, with its elegant Gothic fittings, its delicious easy-chair, and its oratory of painted glass.

We were very much amused at the privacy with which people keep their shops at Weimar. Some of them have not so much as their names written up; and there is so much indifference of manner towards customers that one might suppose every shopkeeper was a salaried functionary employed by government. The distribution of commodities, too, is carried on according to a peculiar Weimarian logic; we bought our lemons at a ropemaker's, and should not have felt ourselves very unreasonable if we had asked for shoes at a stationer's. As to competition, I should think a clever tradesman or artificer is almost as free from it at Weimar as Æsculapius or Vulcan in the days of old Olympus. Here is an illustration. Our landlady's husband was called the "*süsser* Rabenhorst," by way of distinguishing him from a brother of his who was the reverse of sweet. This Rabenhorst, who was not sweet, but who nevertheless dealt in sweets, for he was a confectioner, was so utter a rogue that any transaction with him was avoided almost as much as if he had been the Evil One himself, yet so clever a rogue that he always managed to keep on the windy side of the law. Nevertheless, he had so many dainties in the confectionery line — *so viel Süssigkeiten und Leckerbissen* — that people bent on giving a fine entertainment were at last constrained to say, "After all, I must go to Rabenhorst;" and so he got abundant custom, in spite of general detestation.

A very fair dinner is to be had at several *tables d'hôte* in Weimar for ten or twelve groschen (a shilling or fifteen pence). The Germans certainly excel us in their *Mehlspeise*, or farinaceous puddings, and in their mode of cooking vegetables; they are bolder and more imaginative in their combination of sauces, fruits, and vegetables with animal food, and they are faithful to at least one principle of dietetics, — variety. The only thing at table we have any pretext for being supercilious about is the quality and dressing of animal food. The meat at a *table d'hôte* in Thuringia, and even Berlin, except in the very first hotels, bears about the same relation to ours as horse-flesh probably bears to German beef and mutton; and an Englishman with a bandage over his eyes would often be sorely puzzled to guess the kind of flesh he was eating. For example, the only flavor we could ever discern in hare, which is a very frequent dish, was that of the more or less disagreeable fat which predominated in the dressing; and roast meat seems to be considered an extravagance rarely admissible. A melancholy sight is a flock of Weimarian sheep, followed or led by their shepherd. They are as dingy as London sheep, and far more skinny; indeed, an Englishman who dined with us said the sight of the sheep had set him against mutton. Still, the variety of dishes you get for ten groschen is something marvellous to those who have been accustomed to English charges; and among the six courses it is not a great evil to find a dish or two the reverse of appetizing. I suppose, however, that the living at *tables d'hôte* gives one no correct idea of the mode in which the people live at home. The basis of the national food seems to be raw ham and sausage, with a copious superstratum of *Blaukraut, Sauerkraut*, and black bread. Sausage seems to be to the German what potatoes were to the Irish, — the *sine quâ non* of bodily sustenance. Goethe asks the Frau von Stein to send him *so eine Wurst* when he wants to have a make-shift dinner away from home; and in his letters to

Kestner he is enthusiastic about the delights of dining on *Blaukraut* and *Leberwurst* (blue cabbage and liver sausage). If *Kraut* and *Wurst* may be called the solid prose of Thuringian diet, fish and *Kuchen* (generally a heavy kind of fruit tart) are the poetry : the German appetite disports itself with these as the English appetite does with ices and whipped creams.

At the beginning of August, when we arrived in Weimar, almost every one was away — "at the Baths," of course — except the tradespeople. As birds nidify in the spring, so Germans wash themselves in the summer : their *Waschungstrieb* acts strongly only at a particular time of the year ; during all the rest, apparently, a decanter and a sugar-basin or pie-dish are an ample toilet-service for them. We were quite contented, however, that it was not yet the Weimar "season," fashionably speaking, since it was the very best time for enjoying something far better than Weimar gayeties, — the lovely Park and environs. It was pleasant, too, to see the good bovine citizens enjoying life in their quiet fashion. Unlike our English people, they take pleasure into their calculations, and seem regularly to set aside part of their time for recreation. It is understood that something is to be done in life besides business and housewifery : the women take their children and their knitting to the *Erholung,* or walk with their husbands to Belvedere, or in some other direction where a cup of coffee is to be had. The *Erholung,* by the way, is a pretty garden, with shady walks, abundant seats, an orchestra, a ball-room, and a place for refreshments. The higher classes are subscribers and visitors here as well as the *bourgeoisie ;* but there are several resorts of a similar kind frequented by the latter exclusively. The reader of Goethe will remember his little poem, "Die Lustigen von Weimar," which still indicates the round of amusements in this simple capital : the walk to Belvedere or Tiefurt ; the excursion to Jena, or some other trip, not made expensive by distance ; the round game at cards ; the dance ; the theatre ; and so many other enjoyments to be had by a people not bound to give dinner-parties and "keep up a position."

It is charming to see how real an amusement the theatre is to the Weimar people. The greater number of places are occupied by subscribers, and there is no fuss about toilet or escort. The ladies come alone, and slip quietly into their places without need of "protection," — a proof of civilization perhaps more than equivalent to our pre-eminence in patent locks and carriage springs ; and after the performance is over you may see the same ladies following their servants, with lanterns, through streets innocent of gas, in which an oil-lamp, suspended from a rope slung across from house to house, occasionally reveals to you the shafts of a cart or omnibus, conveniently placed for you to run upon them.

A yearly autumn festival at Weimar is the *Vogelschiessen*, or Bird-shooting; but the reader must not let his imagination wander at this word into fields and brakes. The bird here concerned is of wood, and the shooters, instead of wandering over breezy down and common, are shut up, day after day, in a room clouded with tobacco-smoke, that they may take their turn at shooting with the rifle from the window of a closet about the size of a sentinel's box. However, this is a mighty enjoyment to the Thuringian yeomanry, and an occasion of profit to our friend Punch, and other itinerant performers ; for while the *Vogelschiessen* lasts, a sort of fair is held in the field where the marksmen assemble.

Among the quieter every-day pleasures of the Weimarians, perhaps the most delightful is the stroll on a bright afternoon or evening to the Duke's summer residence of Belvedere, about two miles from Weimar. As I have said, a glorious avenue of chestnut-trees leads all the way from the town to the entrance of the grounds, which are open to all the world as much as to the Duke himself. Close to the palace and its subsidiary buildings there is an inn, for the accommodation of the good people who come to take dinner or any other meal here, by way of holiday-making. A sort of pavilion stands on a spot commanding a lovely view of Weimar and its valley, and here the Weimarians constantly come on summer and autumn evenings to smoke a cigar or drink a cup of coffee. In one wing of the little palace, which is made smart by wooden cupolas, with gilt pinnacles, there is a saloon, which I recommend to the imitation of tasteful people in their country-houses. It has no decoration but that of natural foliage: ivy is trained at regular intervals up the pure white walls, and all round the edge of the ceiling, so as to form pilasters and a cornice; ivy again, trained on trellis-work, forms a blind to the window, which looks towards the entrance court; and beautiful ferns, arranged in tall baskets, are placed here and there against the walls. The furniture is of light cane-work. Another pretty thing here is the Natur-Theater, — a theatre constructed with living trees, trimmed into walls and side scenes. We pleased ourselves for a little while with thinking that this was one of the places where Goethe acted in his own dramas, but we afterwards learned that it was not made until his acting days were over. The inexhaustible charm of Belvedere, however, is the grounds, which are laid out with a taste worthy of a first-rate landscape-gardener. The tall and graceful limes, plane-trees, and weeping birches, the little basins of water here and there, with fountains playing in the middle of them, and with a fringe of broad-leaved plants, or other tasteful bordering round them, the gradual descent towards the river, and the hill clothed with firs and pines on the opposite side, forming a fine dark background for the various and light foliage of the trees that ornament the gardens, — all this we went again and again to enjoy, from the time when everything was of a vivid green until the Virginian creepers which festooned the silver stems of the birches were bright scarlet, and the touch of autumn had turned all the green to gold. One of the spots to linger in is at a semicircular seat against an artificial rock, on which are placed large glass globes of different colors. It is wonderful to see with what minute perfection the scenery around is painted in these globes. Each is like a pre-Raphaelite picture, with every little detail of gravelly walk, mossy bank, and delicately leaved, interlacing boughs presented in accurate miniature.

In the opposite direction to Belvedere lies Tiefurt, with its small park and tiny château, formerly the residence of the Duchess Amalia, the mother of Carl August, and the friend and patroness of Wieland, but now apparently serving as little else than a receptacle for the late Duke Carl Friedrich's rather childish collections. In the second story there is a suite of rooms, so small that the largest of them does not take up as much space as a good dining-table, and each of these doll-house rooms is crowded with prints, old china, and all sorts of knick-knacks and *rococo* wares. The park is a little paradise. The Ilm is seen here to the best advantage: it is clearer than at Weimar, and winds about gracefully between the banks, on one side steep, and curtained with turf and shrubs, or fine trees. It was here, at a point where the bank forms a promontory into the river, that Goethe and his Court friends got up the performance of an operetta, "Die Fischerin," by torchlight. On the way to Tiefurt lies the Webicht, a beautiful wood, through which run excellent carriage-roads and grassy footpaths. It was a rich enjoyment to skirt this wood along the Jena road, and see the sky arching grandly down over the open fields on the other side of us, the evening red flushing the west over the town, and the stars coming out as if to relieve the sun in its watch; or to take the winding road through the wood, under its tall, overarching trees, now bending their mossy trunks forward, now standing with the stately erectness of lofty pillars; or to saunter along the grassy footpaths where the sunlight streamed through the fairy-like foliage of the silvery-barked birches.

Stout pedestrians who go to Weimar will do well to make a walking excursion, as we did, to Ettersburg, a more distant summer residence of the Grand Duke, interesting to us beforehand as the scene of private theatricals and *sprees* in the Goethe days. We set out on one of the brightest and hottest mornings that August ever bestowed, and it required some resolution to trudge along the shadeless *chaussée*, which formed the first two or three miles of our way. One compensating pleasure was the sight of the beautiful mountain-ash trees in full berry, which, alternately with cherry-trees, border the road for a considerable distance. At last we rested from our broiling walk on the borders of a glorious pine wood, so extensive that the trees in the distance form a complete wall with their trunks, and so give one a twilight very welcome on a summer's noon. Under these pines you tread on a carpet of the softest moss, so that you hear no sound of a footstep, and all is as solemn and still as in the crypt of a cathedral. Presently we passed out of the pine wood into one of limes, beeches, and other trees of transparent and light foliage; and from this again we emerged into the open space of the Ettersburg Park in front of the Schloss, which is finely placed on an eminence commanding a magnificent view of the far-reaching woods. Prince Pückler Muskau has been of service here by recommending openings to be made in the woods, in the taste of the English parks. The Schloss, which is a favorite residence of the Grand Duke, is a house of very moderate size, and no pretension of any kind. Its stuccoed walls, and doors long unacquainted with fresh paint, would look distressingly shabby to the owner of a villa at Richmond or Twickenham; but much beauty is procured here at slight expense, by the tasteful disposition of creepers on the balustrades, and pretty vases full of plants ranged along the steps, or suspended in the little piazza beneath them. A walk through a beech-wood took us to the *Mooshütte*, in front of which stands the famous beech from whence Goethe denounced Jacobi's " Woldemar." The bark is covered with initials cut by him and his friends.

People who only allow themselves to be idle under the pretext of hydropathizing, may find all the apparatus necessary to satisfy their conscience at Bercka, a village seated in a lovely valley about six miles from Weimar. Now and then a Weimar family takes lodgings here for the summer, retiring from the quiet of the capital to the deeper quiet of Bercka; but generally the place seems not much frequented. It would be difficult to imagine a more peace-inspiring scene than this little valley. The hanging woods; the soft coloring and graceful outline of the uplands; the village, with its roofs and spire of a reddish-violet hue, muffled in luxuriant trees, the white Kurhaus glittering on a grassy slope; the avenue of poplars contrasting its pretty primness with the wild, bushy outline of the wood-covered hill, which rises abruptly from the smooth, green meadows; the clear, winding stream, now sparkling in the sun, now hiding itself under soft gray willows, — all this makes an enchanting picture. The walk to Bercka and back was a favorite expedition with us and a few Weimar friends; for the road thither is a pleasant one, leading at first through open, cultivated fields, dotted here and there with villages, and then through wooded hills, — the outskirts of the Thuringian Forest. We used not to despise the fine plums which hung in tempting abundance by the roadside; but we afterwards found that we had been deceived in supposing ourselves free to pluck them, as if it were the golden age, and that we were liable to a penalty of ten groschen for our depredations.

But I must not allow myself to be exhaustive on pleasures which seem monotonous when told, though in enjoying them one is as far from wishing them to be more various as from wishing for any change in the sweet sameness of successive summer days. I will only advise the reader who has yet to make excursions in Thuringia to visit Jena, less for its traditions than for its fine scenery, which makes it, as Goethe says, a delicious place in spite of its dull, ugly streets; and exhort him, above all, to brave the discomforts of a *Postwagen* for the sake of getting to Ilmenau. Here he will find the grandest pine-clad hills, with endless walks under their solemn shades; beech-woods where every tree is a picture; an air that he will breathe with as conscious a pleasure as if he were taking iced water on a hot day; baths *ad libitum*, with a *douche* lofty and tremendous enough to invigorate the giant Cormoran; and more than all, one of the most interesting relics of Goethe, who had a great love for Ilmenau. This is the small wooden house, on the height called the Kickelhahn, where he often lived in his long retirements here, and where you may see written by his own hand, near the window-frame, those wonderful lines, — perhaps the finest expression yet given to the sense of resignation inspired by the sublime calm of Nature, —

> " Ueber allen Gipfeln
> Ist Ruh,
> In allen Wipfeln
> Spürest du
> Kaum einen Hauch;
> Die Vögelein schweigen im Walde,
> Warte nur, balde
> Ruhest du auch."

ADDRESS TO WORKING–MEN, BY FELIX HOLT.

FELLOW-WORKMEN: I am not going to take up your time by complimenting you. It has been the fashion to compliment kings and other authorities when they have come into power, and to tell them that, under their wise and beneficent rule, happiness would certainly overflow the land. But the end has not always corresponded to that beginning. If it were true that we who work for wages had more of the wisdom and virtue necessary to the right use of power than has been shown by the aristocratic and mercantile classes, we should not glory much in that fact, or consider that it carried with it any near approach to infallibility.

In my opinion there has been too much complimenting of that sort; and whenever a speaker, whether he is one of ourselves or not, wastes our time in boasting or flattery, I say, let us hiss him. If we have the beginning of wisdom, which is, to know a little truth about ourselves, we know that as a body we are neither very wise nor very virtuous. And to prove this, I will not point specially to our own habits and doings, but to the general state of the country. Any nation that had within it a majority of men — and we are the majority — possessed of much wisdom and virtue, would not tolerate the bad practices, the commercial lying and swindling, the poisonous adulteration of goods, the retail cheating, and the political bribery which are carried on boldly in the midst of us. A majority has the power of creating a public opinion. We could groan and hiss before we had the franchise: if we had groaned and hissed in the right place, if we had discerned better between good and evil, if the multitude of us artisans, and factory hands, and miners, and laborers of all sorts, had been skilful, faithful, well-judging, industrious, sober, — and I don't see how there can be wisdom and virtue anywhere without these qualities, — we should have made an audience that would have shamed the other classes out of their share in the national vices. We should have had better members of Parliament, better religious teachers, honester tradesmen, fewer foolish demagogues, less impudence in infamous and brutal men; and we should not have had among us the abomination of men calling themselves religious while living in splendor on ill-gotten gains. I say, it is not possible for any society in which there is a very large body of wise and virtuous men to be as vicious as our society is, — to have as low a standard of right and wrong, to have so much belief in falsehood, or to have so degrading, barbarous a notion of what pleasure is, or of what justly raises a man above his fellows. Therefore let us have done with this nonsense about our being much better than the rest of our countrymen, or the pretence that that was a reason why we ought to have such an extension of the franchise as has been given to us. The reason for our having the franchise, as I want presently to show, lies somewhere else than in our personal good qualities, and does not in the least lie in any high betting chance that a delegate is a better man than a duke, or that a Sheffield grinder is a better man than any one of the firm he works for.

However, we have got our franchise now. We have been sarcastically called in the House of Commons the future masters of the country; and if that sarcasm contains any truth, it seems to me that the first thing we had better think of is, our heavy responsibility, — that is to say, the terrible risk we run of working mischief and missing good, as others have done before us. Suppose certain men, discontented with the irrigation of a country which depended for all its prosperity on the right direction being given to the waters of a great river, had got the management of the irrigation before they were quite sure how exactly it could be altered for the better, or whether they could command the necessary agency for such an alteration. Those men would have a difficult and dangerous business on their hands; and the more sense, feeling, and knowledge they had, the more they would be likely to tremble rather than to triumph. Our situation is not altogether unlike theirs. For general prosperity and well-being is a vast crop, that like the corn in Egypt can be come at, not at all by hurried snatching, but only by a well-judged patient process; and whether our political power will be any good to us now we have got it, must depend entirely on the means and materials, — the knowledge, ability, and honesty we have at command. These three things are the only conditions on which we can get any lasting benefit, as every clever workman among us knows: he knows that for an article to be worth much there must be a good invention or plan to go upon, there must be a well-prepared material, and there must be skilful and honest work in carrying out the plan. And by this test we may try those who want to be our leaders. Have they anything to offer us besides indignant talk? When they tell us we ought to have this, that, or the other thing, can they explain to us any reasonable, fair, safe way of getting it? Can they argue in favor of a particular change by showing us pretty closely how the change is likely to work? I don't want to decry a just indignation; on the contrary, I should like it to be more thorough and general. A wise man, more than two thousand years ago, when he was asked what would most tend to lessen injustice in the world, said, "If every bystander felt as indignant at a wrong as if he himself were the sufferer." Let us cherish such indignation. But the long-growing evils of a great nation are a tangled business, asking for a good deal more than indignation in order to be got rid of. Indignation is a fine war-horse, but the war-horse must be ridden by a man: it must be ridden by rationality, skill, courage, armed with the right weapons, and taking definite aim.

We have reason to be discontented with many things, and, looking back either through the history of England to much earlier generations or to the legislation and administrations of later times, we are justified in saying that many of the evils under which our country now suffers are the consequences of folly, ignorance, neglect, or self-seeking in those who, at different times, have wielded the powers of rank, office, and money. But the more bitterly we feel this, the more loudly we utter it, the stronger is the obligation we lay on ourselves to beware, lest we also, by a too hasty wresting of measures which seem to promise an immediate partial relief, make a worse time of it for our own generation, and leave a bad inheritance to our children. The deepest curse of wrong-doing, whether of the foolish or wicked sort, is that its effects are difficult to be undone. I suppose there is hardly anything more to be shuddered at than that part of the history of disease which shows how, when a man injures his constitution by a life of vicious excess, his children and grandchildren inherit diseased bodies and minds, and how the effects of that unhappy inheritance continue to spread beyond our calculation. This is only one example of the law by which human lives are linked together; another example of what we complain of when we point to our pauperism, to the brutal ignorance of multitudes among our fellow-countrymen, to the weight of taxation laid on us by blamable wars, to the wasteful channels made for the public money, to the expense and trouble of getting justice, and call these the effects of bad rule. This is the law that we all bear the yoke of, — the law of no man's making, and which no man can undo. Everybody now sees an example of it in the case of Ireland. We who are living now are sufferers by the wrong-doing of those who lived before us; we are the sufferers by each other's wrong-doing; and the children who come after us are and will be sufferers from the same causes. Will any man say he does n't care for that law — it is nothing to him — what he wants is to better himself? With what face then will he complain of any injury? If he says that in politics or in any sort of social action he will not care to know what are likely to be the consequences to others besides himself, he is defending the very worst doings that have brought about his discontent. He might as well say that there is no better rule needful for men than that each should tug and drive for what will please him, without caring how that tugging will act on the fine wide-spread network of society in which he is fast meshed. If any man taught that as a doctrine, we should know him for a fool. But there are men who act upon it; every scoundrel, for example, whether he is a rich religious scoundrel who lies and cheats on a large scale, and will perhaps come and ask you to send him to Parliament, or a poor pocket-picking scoundrel, who will steal your loose pence while you are listening round the platform. None of us are so ignorant as not to know that a society, a nation, is held together by just the opposite doctrine and action, — by the dependence of men on each other and the sense they have of a common interest in preventing injury. And we working-men are, I think, of all classes the last that can afford to forget this; for if we did we should be much like sailors cutting away the timbers of our own ship to warm our grog with. For what else is the meaning of our trades-unions? What else is the meaning of every flag we carry, every procession we make, every crowd we collect for the sake of making some protest on behalf of our body as receivers of wages, if not this: that it is our interest to stand by each other, and that this being the common interest, no one of us will try to make a good bargain for himself without considering what will be good for his fellows? And every member of a union believes that the wider he can spread his union, the stronger and surer will be the effect of it. So I think I shall be borne out in saying that a working-man who can put two and two together, or take three from four and see what will be the remainder, can understand that a society, to be well off, must be made up chiefly of men who consider the general good as well as their own.

Well, but taking the world as it is — and this is one way we must take it when we want to find out how it can be improved — no society is made up of a single class: society stands before us like that wonderful piece of life, the human body, with all its various parts depending on one another, and with a terrible liability to get wrong because of that delicate dependence. We all know how many diseases the human body is apt to suffer from, and how difficult it is even for the doctors to find out exactly where the seat or beginning of the disorder is. That is because the body is made up of so many various parts, all related to each other, or likely all to feel the effect if any one of them goes wrong. It is somewhat the same with our old nations or societies. No society ever stood long in the world without getting to be composed of different classes. Now, it is all pretence to say that there is no such thing as class interest. It is clear that if any particular number of men get a particular benefit from .any existing institution, they are likely to band together, in order to keep up that benefit and increase it, until it is perceived to be unfair and injurious to another large number, who get knowledge and strength enough to set up a resistance. And this, again, has been part of the history of every great society since history began. But the simple reason for this being, that any large body of men is likely to have more of stupidity, narrowness, and greed than of far-sightedness and generosity, it is plain that the number who resist unfairness and injury are in danger of becoming injurious in their turn. And in this way a justifiable resistance has become a damaging convulsion, making everything worse instead of better. This has been seen so often that we ought to profit a little by the experience. So long as there is selfishness in men; so long as they have not found out for themselves institutions which express and carry into practice the truth, that the highest interest of mankind must at last be a common and not a divided interest; so long as the gradual operation of steady causes has not made that truth a part of every man's knowledge and feeling, just as we now not only know that it is good for our health to be cleanly, but feel that cleanliness is only another word for comfort, which is the under side or lining of all pleasure, — so long, I say, as men wink at their own knowingness, or hold their heads high because they have got an advantage over their fellows, so long class interest will be in danger of making itself felt injuriously. No set of men will get any sort of power without being in danger of wanting more than their right share. But, on the other hand, it is just as certain that no set of men will get angry at having less than their right share, and set up a claim on that ground, without falling into just the same danger of exacting too much, and exacting it in wrong ways. It's human nature we have got to work with all round, and nothing else. That seems like saying something very commonplace, — nay, obvious; as if one should say that where there are hands there are mouths. Yet, to hear a good deal of the speechifying and to see a good deal of the action that go forward, one might suppose it was forgotten.

But I come back to this : that, in our old society, there are old institutions, and among them the various distinctions and inherited advantages of classes, which have shaped themselves along with all the wonderful, slow-growing system of things made up of our laws, our commerce, and our stores of all sorts, whether in material objects, such as buildings and machinery, or in knowledge, such as scientific thought and professional skill. Just as in that case I spoke of before, the irrigation of a country, which must absolutely have its water distributed or it will bear no crop; there are the old channels, the old banks, and the old pumps, which must be used as they are until new and better have been prepared, or the structure of the old has been gradually altered. But it would be fool's work to batter down a pump only because a better might be made, when you had no machinery ready for a new one : it would be wicked work, if villages lost their crops by it. Now the only safe way by which society can be steadily improved and our worst evils reduced, is not by any attempt to do away directly with the actually existing class distinctions and advantages, as if everybody could have the same sort of work, or lead the same sort of life (which none of my hearers are stupid enough to suppose), but by the turning of class interests into class functions or duties. What I mean is, that each class should be urged by the surrounding conditions to perform its particular work under the strong pressure of responsibility to the nation at large ; that our public affairs should be got into a state in which there should be no impunity for foolish or faithless conduct. In this way the public judgment would sift out incapability and dishonesty from posts of high charge, and even personal ambition would necessarily become of a worthier sort, since the desires of the most selfish men must be a good deal shaped by the opinions of those around them ; and for one person to put on a cap and bells, or to go about dishonest or paltry ways of getting rich that he may spend a vast sum of money in having more finery than his neighbors, he must be pretty sure of a crowd who will applaud him. Now, changes can only be good in proportion as they help to bring about this sort of result ; in proportion as they put knowledge in the place of ignorance, and fellow-feeling in the place of selfishness. In the course of that substitution class distinctions must inevitably change their character, and represent the varying duties of men, not their varying interests. But this end will not come by impatience. "Day will not break the sooner because we get up before the twilight." Still less will it come by mere undoing, or change merely as change. And moreover, if we believed that it would be unconditionally hastened by our getting the franchise, we should be what I call superstitious men, believing in magic, or the production of a result by hocus-pocus Our getting the franchise will greatly hasten that good end in proportion only as every one of us has the knowledge, the foresight, the conscience, that will make him well-judging and scrupulous in the use of it. The nature of things in this world has been determined for us beforehand, and in such a way that no ship can be expected to sail well on a difficult voyage, and reach the right port, unless it is well manned : the nature of the winds and the waves, of the timbers, the sails, and the cordage, will not accommodate itself to drunken, mutinous sailors.

You will not suspect me of wanting to preach any cant to you, or of joining in the pretence that everything is in a fine way, and need not be made better. What I am striving to keep in our minds is the care, the precaution, with which we should go about making things better, so that the public order may not be destroyed, so that no fatal shock may be given to this society of ours, this living body in which our lives are bound up. After the Reform Bill of 1832 I was in an election riot, which showed me clearly, on a small scale, what public disorder must always be; and I have never forgotten that the riot was brought about chiefly by the agency of dishonest men who professed to be on the people's side. Now, the danger hanging over change is great, just in proportion as it tends to produce such disorder by giving any large number of ignorant men, whose notions of what is good are of a low and brutal sort, the belief that they have got power into their hands, and may do pretty much as they like. If any one can look round us and say that he sees no signs of any such danger now, and that our national condition is running along like a clear broadening stream, safe not to get choked with mud, I call him a cheerful man: perhaps he does his own gardening, and seldom takes exercise far away from home. To us who have no gardens, and often walk abroad, it is plain that we can never get into a bit of a crowd but we must rub clothes with a set of roughs, who have the worst vices of the worst rich, — who are gamblers, sots, libertines, knaves, or else mere sensual simpletons and victims. They are the ugly crop that has sprung up while the stewards have been sleeping; they are the multiplying brood begotten by parents who have been left without all teaching save that of a too craving body, without all well-being save the fading delusions of drugged beer and gin. They are the hideous margin of society, at one edge drawing toward it the undesigning ignorant poor, at the other darkening imperceptibly into the lowest criminal class. Here is one of the evils which cannot be got rid of quickly, and against which any of us who have got sense, decency, and instruction have need to watch.

That these degraded fellow-men could really get the mastery in a persistent disobedience to the laws and in a struggle to subvert order, I do not believe; but wretched calamities must come from the very beginning of such a struggle, and the continuance of it would be a civil war, in which the inspiration on both sides might soon cease to be even a false notion of good, and might become the direct savage impulse of ferocity.   We have all to see to it that we do not help to rouse what I may call the savage beast in the breasts of our generation, — that we do not help to poison the nation's blood, and make richer provision for bestiality to come.   We know well enough that oppressors have sinned in this way, — that oppression has notoriously made men mad; and we are determined to resist oppression.   But let us, if possible, show that we can keep sane in our resistance, and shape our means more and more reasonably toward the least harmful, and therefore the speediest, attainment of our end.   Let us, I say, show that our spirits are too strong to be driven mad, but can keep that sober determination which alone gives mastery over the adaptation of means.   And a first guarantee of this sanity will be to act as if we understood that the fundamental duty of a government is to preserve order, to enforce obedience of the laws.   It has been held hitherto that a man can be depended on as a guardian of order only when he has much money and comfort to lose.   But a better state of things would be, that men who had little money and not much comfort should still be guardians of order, because they had sense to see that disorder would do no good, and had a heart of justice, pity, and fortitude, to keep them from making more misery only because they felt some misery themselves.   There are thousands of artisans who have already shown this fine spirit, and have endured much with patient heroism.   If such a spirit spread, and penetrated us all, we should soon become the masters of the country in the best sense and to the best ends.   For, the public order being preserved, there can be no government in future that will not be determined by our insistence on our fair and practicable demands. It is only by disorder that our demands will be choked, that we shall find ourselves lost among a brutal rabble, with all the intelligence of the country opposed to us, and see government in the shape of guns that will sweep us down in the ignoble martyrdom of fools.

It has been a too common notion that to insist much on the preservation of order is the part of a selfish aristocracy and a selfish commercial class, because among these, in the nature of things, have been found the opponents of change. I am a Radical; and what is more, I am not a Radical with a title, or a French cook, or even an entrance into fine society. I expect great changes, and I desire them. But I don't expect them to come in a hurry, by mere inconsiderate sweeping. A Hercules with a big besom is a fine thing for a filthy stable, but not for weeding a seed-bed, where his besom would soon make a barren floor.

That is old-fashioned talk, some one may say. We know all that.

Yes, when things are put in an extreme way, most people think they know them ; but, after all, they are comparatively few who see the small degrees by which those extremes are arrived at, or have the resolution and-self control to resist the little impulses by which they creep on surely toward a fatal end. Does anybody set out meaning to ruin himself, or to drink himself to death, or to waste his life so that he becomes a despicable old man, a superannuated nuisance, like a fly in winter. Yet there are plenty, of whose lot this is the pitiable story. Well now, supposing us all to have the best intentions, we working-men, as a body, run some risk of bringing evil on the nation in that unconscious manner — half hurrying, half pushed in a jostling march toward an end we are not thinking of. For just as there are many things which we know better and feel much more strongly than the richer, softer-handed classes can know or feel them ; so there are many things — many precious benefits — which we, by the very fact of our privations, our lack of leisure and in-struction, are not so likely to be aware of and take into our account. Those precious benefits form a chief part of what I may call the common estate of society : a wealth over and above buildings, machinery, produce, shipping, and so on, though closely connected with these ; a wealth of a more delicate kind, that we may more unconsciously bring into danger, doing harm and not knowing that we do it. I mean that treasure of knowledge, science, poetry, refinement of thought, feeling, and manners, great memories and the interpretation of great records, which is carried on from the minds of one generation to the minds of another. This is something distinct from the indulgences of luxury and the pursuit of vain finery ; and one of the hardships in the lot of working-men is that they have been for the most part shut out from sharing in this treasure. It can make a man's life very great, very full of delight, though he has no smart furniture and no horses : it also yields a great deal of discovery that corrects error, and of invention that lessens bodily pain, and must at least make life easier for all.

Now the security of this treasure demands, not only the preservation of order, but a certain patience on our part with many institutions and facts of various kinds, especially touching the accumulation of wealth, which from the light we stand in, we are more likely to discern the evil than the good of. It is constantly the task of practical wisdom not to say, "This is good, and I will have it," but to say, "This is the less of two unavoidable evils, and I will bear it." And this treasure of knowledge, which consists in the fine activity, the exalted vision of many minds, is bound up at present with conditions which have much evil in them. Just as in the case of material wealth and its distribution we are obliged to take the selfishness and weaknesses of human nature into account, and however we insist that men might act better, are forced, unless we are fanatical simpletons, to consider how they are likely to act ; so in this matter of the wealth that is carried in men's minds, we have to reflect that the too absolute predominance of a class whose wants have been of a common sort, who are chiefly struggling to get better and more food, clothing, shelter, and bodily recreation, may lead to hasty measures for the sake of having things more fairly shared, which, even if they did not fail of their object, would at last debase the life of the nation. Do anything which will throw the classes who hold the treasures of knowledge — nay, I may say, the treasures of refined needs — into the background, cause them to withdraw from public affairs, stop too suddenly any of the sources by which their leisure and ease are furnished, rob them of the chances by which they may be influential and pre-eminent, and you do something as short-sighted as the acts of France and Spain when in jealousy and wrath, not altogether unprovoked, they drove from among them races and classes that held the traditions of handicraft and agriculture. You injure your own inheritance and the inheritance of your children. You may truly say that this which I call the common estate of society has been anything but common to you; but the same may be said, by many of us, of the sunlight and the air, of the sky and the fields, of parks and holiday games. Nevertheless, that these blessings exist makes life worthier to us, and urges us the more to energetic, likely means of getting our share in them; and I say, let us watch carefully, lest we do anything to lessen this treasure which is held in the minds of men, while we exert ourselves, first of all, and to the very utmost, that we and our children may share in all its benefits. Yes; exert ourselves to the utmost, to break the yoke of ignorance. If we demand more leisure, more ease in our lives, let us show that we don't deserve the reproach of wanting to shirk that industry which, in some form or other, every man, whether rich or poor, should feel himself as much bound to as he is bound to decency. Let us show that we want to have some time and strength left to us, that we may use it, not for brutal indulgence, but for the rational exercise of the faculties which make us men. Without this no political measures can benefit us. No political institution will alter the nature of Ignorance, or hinder it from producing vice and misery. Let Ignorance start how it will, it must run the same round of low appetites, poverty, slavery, and superstition. Some of us know this well, — nay, I will say, feel it, — for knowledge of this kind cuts deep; and to us it is one of the most painful facts belonging to our condition that there are numbers of our fellow-workmen who are so far from feeling in the same way, that they never use the imperfect opportunities already offered them for giving their children some schooling, but turn their little ones of tender age into bread-winners, often at cruel tasks, exposed to the horrible infection of childish vice. Of course, the causes of these hideous things go a long way back. Parents' misery has made parents' wickedness. But we who are still blessed with the hearts of fathers and the consciences of men, — we who have some knowledge of the curse entailed on broods of creatures in human shape, whose enfeebled bodies and dull perverted minds are mere centres of uneasiness in whom even appetite is feeble and joy impossible, — I say we are bound to use all the means at our command to help in putting a stop to this horror. Here, it seems to me, is a way in which we may use extended co-operation among us to the most momentous of all purposes, and make conditions of enrolment that would strengthen all educational measures. It is true enough that there is a low sense of parental duties in the nation at large, and that numbers who have no excuse in bodily hardship seem to think it a light thing to beget children, to bring human beings with all their tremendous possibilities into this difficult world, and then take little heed how they are disciplined and furnished for the perilous journey they are sent on without any asking of their own. This is a sin, shared in more or less by all classes; but there are sins which, like taxation, fall the heaviest on the poorest, and none have such galling reasons as we working-men to try and rouse to the utmost the feeling of responsibility in fathers and mothers. We have been urged into co-operation by the pressure of common demands. In war men need each other more; and where a given point has to be defended, fighters inevitably find themselves shoulder to shoulder. So fellowship grows, so grow the rules of fellowship, which gradually shape themselves to thoroughness as the idea of a common good becomes more complete. We feel a right to say, If you will be one of us, you must make such and such a contribution, you must renounce such and such a separate advantage, you must set your face against such and such an infringement. If we have any false ideas about our common good, our rules will be wrong, and we shall be co-operating to damage each other. But, now, here is a part of our good, without which everything else we strive for will be worthless, — I mean the rescue of our children. Let us demand from the members of our unions that they fulfil their duty as parents in this definite matter, which rules can reach. Let us demand that they send their children to school, so as not to go on recklessly, breeding a moral pestilence among us, just as strictly as we demand that they pay their contributions to a common fund, understood to be for a common benefit. While we watch our public men, let us watch one another as to this duty, which is also public, and more momentous even than obedience to sanitary regulations. While we resolutely declare against the wickedness in high places, let us set ourselves also against the wickedness in low places, not quarrelling which came first, or which is the worse of the two, — not trying to settle the miserable precedence of plague or famine, but insisting unflinchingly on remedies once ascertained, and summoning those who hold the treasure of knowledge to remember that they hold it in trust, and that with them lies the task of searching for new remedies, and finding the right methods of applying them.

To find right remedies and right methods. Here is the great function of knowledge: here the life of one man may make a fresh era straight away, in which a sort of suffering that has existed shall exist no more. For the thousands of years down to the middle of the sixteenth century that human limbs had been hacked and amputated, nobody knew how to stop the bleeding except by searing the ends of the vessels with red-hot iron. But then came a man named Ambrose Paré, and said, "Tie up the arteries!" That was a fine word to utter. It contained the statement of a method, — a plan by which a particular evil was forever assuaged. Let us try to discern the men whose words carry that sort of kernel, and choose such men to be our guides and representatives, — not choose platform swaggerers, who bring us nothing but the ocean to make our broth with.

To get the chief power into the hands of the wisest, which means to get our life regulated according to the truest principles mankind is in possession of, is a problem as old as the very notion of wisdom. The solution comes slowly, because men collectively can only be made to embrace principles, and to act on them, by the slow stupendous teaching of the world's events. Men will go on planting potatoes, and nothing else but potatoes, till a potato disease comes and forces them to find out the advantage of a varied crop. Selfishness, stupidity, sloth, persist in trying to adapt the world to their desires, till a time comes when the world manifests itself as too decidedly inconvenient to them. Wisdom stands outside of man and urges itself upon him, like the marks of the changing seasons, before it finds a home within him, directs his actions, and from the precious effects of obedience begets a corresponding love.

But while still outside of us, wisdom often looks terrible, and wears strange forms, wrapped in the changing conditions of a struggling world. It wears now the form of wants and just demands in a great multitude of British men : wants and demands urged into existence by the forces of a maturing world. And it is in virtue of this — in virtue of this presence of wisdom on our side as a mighty fact, physical and moral, which must enter into and shape the thoughts and actions of mankind — that we working-men have obtained the suffrage. Not because we are an excellent multitude, but because we are a needy multitude.

But now, for our own part, we have seriously to consider this outside wisdom which lies in the supreme unalterable nature of things, and watch to give it a home within us and obey it. If the claims of the unendowed multitude of working-men hold within them principles which must shape the future, it is not less true that the endowed classes, in their inheritance from the past, hold the precious material without which no worthy, noble future can be moulded. Many of the highest uses of life are in their keeping; and if privilege has often been abused, it has also been the nurse of excellence. Here again we have to submit ourselves to the great law of inheritance. If we quarrel with the way in which the labors and earnings of the past have been preserved and handed down, we are just as bigoted, just as narrow, just as wanting in that religion which keeps an open ear and an obedient mind to the teachings of fact, as we accuse those of being, who quarrel with the new truths and new needs which are disclosed in the present. The deeper insight we get into the causes of human trouble, and the ways by which men are made better and happier, the less we shall be inclined to the unprofitable spirit and practice of reproaching classes as such in a wholesale fashion. Not all the evils of our condition are such as we can justly blame others for; and, I repeat, many of them are such as no changes of institutions can quickly remedy. To discern between the evils that energy can remove and the evils that patience must bear, makes the difference between manliness and childishness, between good sense and folly. And more than that, without such discernment, seeing that we have grave duties toward our own body and the country at large, we can hardly escape acts of fatal rashness and injustice.

I am addressing a mixed assembly of workmen, and some of you may be as well or better fitted than I am to take up this office. But they will not think it amiss in me that I have tried to bring together the considerations most likely to be of service to us in preparing ourselves for the use of our new opportunities. I have avoided touching on special questions. The best help toward judging well on these is to approach them in the right temper without vain expectation, and with a resolution which is mixed with temperance.

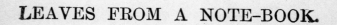

LEAVES FROM A NOTE-BOOK.

LEAVES FROM A NOTE–BOOK.

AUTHORSHIP.

TO lay down in the shape of practical moral rules courses of conduct only to be made real by the rarest states of motive and disposition, tends not to elevate, but to degrade the general standard, by turning that rare attainment from an object of admiration into an impossible prescription, against which the average nature first rebels and then flings out ridicule. It is for art to present images of a lovelier order than the actual, gently winning the affections, and so determining the taste. But in any rational criticism of the time which is meant to guide a practical reform, it is idle to insist that action ought to be this or that, without considering how far the outward conditions of such change are present, even supposing the inward disposition towards it. Practically, we must be satisfied to aim at something short of perfection, — and at something very much further off it in one case than in another. While the fundamental conceptions of morality seem as stationary through ages as the laws of life, so that a moral manual written eighteen centuries ago still admonishes us that we are low in our attainments, it is quite otherwise with the degree to which moral conceptions have penetrated the various forms of social activity, and made what may be called the special conscience of each calling, art, or industry. While on some points of social duty public opinion has reached a tolerably high standard, on others a public opinion is not yet born; and there are even some functions and practices with regard to which men far above the line in honorableness of nature feel hardly any scrupulosity, though their consequent behavior is easily shown to be as injurious as bribery, or any other slowly poisonous procedure which degrades the social vitality.

Among those callings which have not yet acquired anything near a full-grown conscience in the public mind is Authorship. Yet the changes brought about by the spread of instruction and the consequent struggles of an uneasy ambition are, or at least might well be, forcing on many minds the need of some regulating principle with regard to the publication of intellectual products, which would override the rule of the market, — a principle, that is, which should be derived from a fixing of the author's vocation according to those characteristics in which it differs from the other bread-winning professions. Let this be done, if possible, without any cant, which would carry the subject into Utopia, away from existing needs. The guidance wanted is a clear notion of what should justify men and women in assuming public authorship, and of the way in which they should be determined by what is usually called success. But the forms of authorship must be distinguished; journalism, for example, carrying a necessity for that continuous production which in other kinds of writing is precisely the evil to be fought against, and judicious careful compilation, which is a great public service, holding in its modest diligence a guarantee against those deductions of vanity and idleness which draw many a young gentleman into reviewing, instead of the sorting and copying which his small talents could not rise to with any vigor and completeness.

A manufacturer goes on producing calicoes as long and as fast as he can find a market for them; and in obeying this indication of demand he gives his factory its utmost usefulness to the world in general and to himself in particular. Another manufacturer buys a new invention of some light kind likely to attract the public fancy, is successful in finding a multitude who will give their testers for the transiently desirable commodity, and before the fashion is out, pockets a considerable sum: the commodity was colored with a green which had arsenic in it that damaged the factory workers and the purchasers. What then? These, he contends (or does not know or care to contend), are superficial effects, which it is folly to dwell upon while we have epidemic diseases and bad government.

The first manufacturer we will suppose blameless. Is an author simply on a par with him, as to the rules of production?

The author's capital is his brain-power, — power of invention, power of writing. The manufacturer's capital, in fortunate cases, is being continually reproduced and increased. Here is the first grand difference between the capital which is turned into calico and the brain capital which is turned into literature. The calico scarcely varies in appropriateness of quality; no consumer is in danger of getting too much of it, and neglecting his boots, hats, and flannel shirts in consequence. That there should be large quantities of the same sort in the calico manufacture is an advantage: the sameness is desirable, and nobody is likely to roll his person in so many folds of calico as to become a mere bale of cotton goods, and nullify his senses of hearing and touch, while his morbid passion for Manchester shirtings makes him still cry "More!" The wise manufacturer gets richer and richer, and the consumers he supplies have their real wants satisfied and no more.

Let it be taken as admitted that all legitimate social activity must be beneficial to others besides the agent. To write prose or verse as a private exercise and satisfaction is not social activity; nobody is culpable for this any more than for learning other people's verse by heart, if he does not neglect his proper business in consequence. If the exercise made him sillier or secretly more self-satisfied, that, to be sure, would be a roundabout way of injuring society; for though a certain mixture of silliness may lighten existence, we have at present more than enough.

But man or woman who publishes writings inevitably assumes the office of teacher or influencer of the public mind. Let him protest as he will that he only seeks to amuse, and has no pretension to do more than while away an hour of leisure or weariness, — "the idle singer of an empty day," — he can no more escape influencing the moral taste, and with it the action of the intelligence, than a setter of fashions in furniture and dress can fill the shops with his designs and leave the garniture of persons and houses unaffected by his industry.

For a man who has a certain gift of writing to say, "I will make the most of it while the public likes my wares, as long as the market is open and I am able to supply it at a money profit, such profit being the sign of liking," he should have a belief that his wares have nothing akin to the arsenic green in them, and also that his continuous supply is secure from a degradation in quality which the habit of consumption encouraged in the buyers may hinder them from marking their sense of by rejection, so that they complain, but pay, and read while they complain. Unless he has that belief, he is on a level with the manufacturer who gets rich by fancy wares colored with arsenic green. He really cares for nothing but his income. He carries on authorship on the principle of the gin-palace; and bad literature of the sort called amusing is spiritual gin.

A writer capable of being popular can only escape this social culpability by first of all getting a profound sense that literature is good for nothing if it is not admirably good; he must detest bad literature too heartily to be indifferent about producing it if only other people don't detest it. And if he has this sign of the divine afflatus within him, he must make up his mind that he must not pursue authorship as a vocation with a trading determination to get rich by it. It is in the highest sense lawful for him to get as good a price as he honorably can for the best work he is capable of; but not for him to force or hurry his production, or even do over again what has already been done, either by himself or others, so as to render his work no real contribution, for the sake of bringing up his income to the fancy pitch. An author who would keep a pure and noble conscience, and with that a developing instead of degenerating intellect and taste, must cast out of his aims the aim to be rich. And therefore he must keep his expenditure low, — he must make for himself no dire necessity to earn sums in order to pay bills.

In opposition to this, it is common to cite Walter Scott's case, and cry, "Would the world have got as much innocent (and therefore salutary) pleasure out of Scott, if he had not brought himself under the pressure of money-need ?" I think it would — and more; but since it is impossible to prove what would have been, I confine myself to replying that Scott was not justified in bringing himself into a position where severe consequences to others depended on his retaining or not retaining his mental competence. Still less is Scott to be taken as an example to be followed in this matter, even if it were admitted that money-need served to press at once the best and the most work out of him; any more than a great navigator who has brought his ship to port in spite of having taken a wrong and perilous route, is to be followed as to his route by navigators who are not yet as-certained to be great.

But after the restraints and rules which must guide the acknowledged author, whose power of making a real contri-bution is ascertained, comes the consideration, How or on what principle are we to find a check for that troublesome disposition to authorship arising from the spread of what is called Education, which turns a growing rush of vanity and ambition into this current ? The well-taught — an increasing number — are almost all able to write essays on given themes, which demand new periodicals to save them from lying in cold obstruction. The ill-taught — also an increasing num-ber — read many books, seem to themselves able to write others surprisingly like what they read, and probably supe-rior, since the variations are such as please their own fancy, and such as they would have recommended to their favorite authors : these ill-taught persons are perhaps idle and want to give themselves " an object ; " or they are short of money, and feel disinclined to get it by a commoner kind of work :

or they find a facility in putting sentences together which gives them more than a suspicion that they have genius, which, if not very cordially believed in by private confidants, will be recognized by an impartial public; or, finally, they observe that writing is sometimes well paid, and some times a ground of fame or distinction, and without any use of punctilious logic, they conclude to become writers themselves.

As to these ill-taught persons, whatever medicines of a spiritual sort can be found good against mental emptiness and inflation, such medicines are needful for *them*. The contempt of the world for their productions only comes after their disease has wrought its worst effects. But what is to be said to the well-taught, who have such an alarming equality in their power of writing "like a scholar and a gentleman"? Perhaps they too can only be cured by the medicine of higher ideals in social duty, and by a fuller representation to themselves of the processes by which the general culture is furthered or impeded.

JUDGMENTS ON AUTHORS.

In endeavoring to estimate a remarkable writer who aimed at more than temporary influence, we have first to consider what was his individual contribution to the spiritual wealth of mankind. Had he a new conception? Did he animate long-known but neglected truths with new vigor, and cast fresh light on their relation to other admitted truths? Did he impregnate any ideas with a fresh store of emotion, and in this way enlarge the area of moral sentiment? Did he, by a wise emphasis here, and a wise disregard there, give a more useful or beautiful proportion to aims or motives? And even where his thinking was most mixed with the sort of mistake which is obvious to the majority, as well as that which can only be discerned by the instructed, or made manifest by the progress of things, has it that salt of a noble enthusiasm which should rebuke our critical discrimination if its correctness is inspired with a less admirable habit of feeling ?

This is not the common or easy course to take in estimating a modern writer. It requires considerable knowledge of what he has himself done, as well as of what others have done before him, or what they were doing contemporaneously ; it requires deliberate reflection as to the degree in which our own prejudices may hinder us from appreciating the intellectual or moral bearing of what on a first view offends us. An easier course is to notice some salient mistakes, and take them as decisive of the writer's incompetence; or to find out that something apparently much the same as what he has said in some connection not clearly ascertained had been said by somebody else, though without great effect, until this new effect of discrediting the other's originality had shown itself as an adequate final cause ; or to pronounce from the point of view of individual taste that this writer for whom regard is claimed is repulsive, wearisome, not to be borne except by those dull persons who are of a different opinion.

Elder writers who have passed into classics were doubtless treated in this easy way when they were still under the misfortune of being recent, — nay, are still dismissed with the same rapidity of judgment by daring ignorance. But people who think that they have a reputation to lose in the matter of knowledge have looked into cyclopædias and histories of philosophy or literature, and possessed themselves of the duly balanced epithets concerning the immortals. They are not left to their own unguided rashness, or their own unguided pusillanimity. And it is this sheeplike flock who have no direct impressions, no spontaneous delight, no genuine objection or self-confessed neutrality in relation to the writers become classic, — it is these who are incapable of passing a genuine judgment on the living. Necessarily. The susceptibility they have kept active is a susceptibility to their own reputation for passing the right judgment, not the susceptibility to qualities in the object of judgment. Who learns to discriminate shades of color by considering what is expected of him ? The habit of expressing borrowed judgments stupefies the sensibilities, which are the only foundation of genuine judgments, just as the constant reading and retailing of results from other men's observations through the microscope, without ever looking through the lens one's self, is an instruction in some truths and some prejudices, but is no instruction in observant susceptibility ; on the contrary, it breeds a habit of inward seeing according to verbal statement, which dulls the power of outward seeing according to visual evidence.

On this subject, as on so many others, it is difficult to strike the balance between the educational needs of passivity or receptivity, and independent selection. We should learn nothing without the tendency to implicit acceptance; but there must clearly be a limit to such mental submission, else we should come to a standstill. The human mind would be no better than a dried specimen, representing an unchangeable type. When the assimilation of new matter ceases, decay must begin. In a reasoned self-restraining deference there is as much energy as in rebellion ; but among the less capable, one must admit that the superior energy is on the side of the rebels. And certainly a man who dares to say that he finds an eminent classic feeble here, extravagant there, and in general overrated, may chance to give an opinion which has some genuine discrimination in it concerning a new work or a living thinker, — an opinion such as can hardly ever be got from the reputed judge who is a correct echo of the most approved phrases concerning those who have been already canonized.

STORY-TELLING.

WHAT is the best way of telling a story? Since the standard must be the interest of the audience, there must be several or many good ways rather than one best. For we get interested in the stories life presents to us through divers orders and modes of presentation. Very commonly our first awakening to a desire of knowing a man's past or future comes from our seeing him as a stranger in some unusual or pathetic or humorous situation, or manifesting sòme remarkable characteristics. We make inquiries in consequence, or we become observant and attentive whenever opportunities of knowing more may happen to present themselves without our search. You have seen a refined face among the prisoners picking tow in jail ; you afterwards see the same unforgetable face in a pulpit : he must be of dull fibre who would not care to know more about a life which showed such contrasts, though he might gather his knowledge in a fragmentary and unchronological way.

Again, we have heard much, or at least something not quite common, about a man whom we have never seen, and hence we look round with curiosity when we are told that he is present ; whatever he says or does before us is charged with a meaning due to our previous hearsay knowledge about him, gathered either from dialogue of which he was expressly and emphatically the subject, or from incidental remark, or from general report either in or out of print.

These indirect ways of arriving at knowledge are always the most stirring even in relation to impersonal subjects. To see a chemical experiment gives an attractiveness to a definition of chemistry, and fills it with a significance which it would never have had without the pleasant shock of an unusual sequence, such as the transformation of a solid into gas, and *vice versa*. To see a word for the first time either as substantive or adjective in a connection where we care about knowing its complete meaning, is the way to vivify its meaning in our recollection. Curiosity becomes the more eager from the incompleteness of the first information. Moreover, it is in this way that memory works in its incidental revival of events : some salient experience appears in inward vision, and in consequence the antecedent facts are retraced from what is regarded as the beginning of the episode in which that experience made a more or less strikingly memorable part. "Ah! I remember addressing the mob from the hustings at Westminster, — you would n't have thought that I could ever have been in such a position. Well, how I came there was in this way;" and then follows a retrospective narration.

The modes of telling a story founded on these processes of outward and inward life derive their effectiveness from the superior mastery of images and pictures in grasping the attention, — or, one might say with more fundamental accuracy, from the fact that our earliest, strongest impressions, our most intimate convictions, are simply images added to more or less of sensation. These are the primitive instruments of thought. Hence it is not surprising that early poetry took this way, — telling a daring deed, a glorious achievement, without caring for what went before. The desire for orderly narration is a later, more reflective birth. The presence of the Jack in the box affects every child : it is the more reflective lad, the miniature philosopher, who wants to know how he got there.

The only stories life presents to us in an orderly way are those of our autobiography, or the career of our companions from our childhood upwards, or perhaps of our own children. But it is a great art to make a connected strictly relevant narrative of such careers as we can recount from the beginning. In these cases the sequence of associations is almost sure to overmaster the sense of proportion. Such narratives *ab ovo* are summer's-day stories for happy loungers ; not the cup of self-forgetting excitement to the busy who can snatch an hour of entertainment.

But the simple opening of a story with a date and necessary account of places and people, passing on quietly towards the more rousing elements of narrative and dramatic presentation, without need of retrospect, has its advantages, which have to be measured by the nature of the story. Spirited narrative, without more than a touch of dialogue here and there, may be made eminently interesting, and is suited to the novelette. Examples of its charm are seen in the short tales in which the French have a mastery never reached by the English, who usually demand coarser flavors than are given by that delightful gayety which is well described by La Fontaine [1] as not anything that provokes fits of laughter, but a certain charm, an agreeable mode of handling, which lends attractiveness to all subjects, even the most serious. And it is this sort of gayety which plays around the best French novelettes. But the opening chapters of the "Vicar of Wakefield" are as fine as anything that can be done in this way.

Why should a story not be told in the most irregular fashion that an author's idiosyncrasy may prompt, provided that he gives us what we can enjoy? The objections to Sterne's wild way of telling "Tristram Shandy" lie more solidly in the quality of the interrupting matter than in the fact of interruption. The dear public would do well to reflect that they are often bored from the want of flexibility in their own minds. They are like the topers of "one liquor."

HISTORIC IMAGINATION.

THE exercise of a veracious imagination in historical picturing seems to be capable of a development that might help the judgment greatly with regard to present and future events. By veracious imagination, I mean the working out in detail of the various steps by which a political or social change was reached, using all extant evidence and supplying deficiencies by careful analogical creation. How triumphant opinions originally spread; how institutions arose; what were the conditions of great inventions, discoveries, or theoretic conceptions; what circumstances affecting individual lots are attendant on the decay of long-established systems, — all these grand elements of history require the illumination of special imaginative treatment. But effective truth in this

[1] "Je n'appelle pas gayeté ce qui excite le rire, mais un certain charme, un air agréable qu'on peut donner à toutes sortes de sujets, mesme les plus sérieux." — *Preface to Fables.*

application of art requires freedom from the vulgar coercion of conventional plot, which is become hardly of higher influence on imaginative representation than a detailed "order" for a picture sent by a rich grocer to an eminent painter, — allotting a certain portion of the canvas to a rural scene, another to a fashionable group, with a request for a murder in the middle distance, and a little comedy to relieve it. A slight approximation to the veracious glimpses of history artistically presented, which I am indicating, but applied only to an incident of contemporary life, is "Un Paquet de Lettres" by Gustave Droz. For want of such real, minute vision of how changes come about in the past, we fall into ridiculously inconsistent estimates of actual movements, condemning in the present what we belaud in the past, and pronouncing impossible processes that have been repeated again and again in the historical preparation of the very system under which we live. A false kind of idealization dulls our perception of the meaning in words when they relate to past events which have had a glorious issue; for lack of comparison no warning image rises to check scorn of the very phrases which in other associations are consecrated.

Utopian pictures help the reception of ideas as to constructive results, but hardly so much as a vivid presentation of how results have been actually brought about, especially in religious and social change. And there is the pathos, the heroism, often accompanying the decay and final struggle of old systems, which has not had its share of tragic commemoration. What really took place in and around Constantine before, upon, and immediately after his declared conversion? Could a momentary flash be thrown on Eusebius in his sayings and doings as an ordinary man in bishop's garments? Or on Julian and Libanius? There has been abundant writing on such great turning-points, but not such as serves to instruct the imagination in true comparison. I want something different from the abstract treatment which belongs to grave history from a doctrinal point of view, and something different from the schemed picturesqueness of ordinary

historical fiction.   I want brief, severely conscientious repro-
ductions, in their concrete incidents, of pregnant movements
in the past.

VALUE IN ORIGINALITY.

THE supremacy given in European cultures to the literatures of Greece and Rome has had an effect almost equal to
that of a common religion in binding the Western nations
together.   It is foolish to be forever complaining of the consequent uniformity, as if there were an endless power of
originality in the human mind.   Great and precious origination must always be comparatively rare, and can only exist
on condition of a wide, massive uniformity.   When a multitude of men have learned to use the same language in speech
and writing, then and then only can the greatest masters of
language arise.   For in what does their mastery consist ?
They use words which are already a familiar medium of
understanding and sympathy in such a way as greatly to enlarge the understanding and sympathy.   Originality of this
order changes the wild grasses into world-feeding grain.
Idiosyncrasies are pepper and spices of questionable aroma.

TO THE PROSAIC ALL THINGS ARE PROSAIC.

" Is the time we live in prosaic ? "   " That depends : it
must certainly be prosaic to one whose mind takes a prosaic
stand in contemplating it."   " But it is precisely the most
poetic minds that most groan over the vulgarity of the present, its degenerate sensibility to beauty, eagerness for mate-
rialistic explanation, noisy triviality."   " Perhaps they would
have had the same complaint to make about the age of Elizabeth, if, living then, they had fixed their attention on its
more sordid elements, or had been subject to the grating influence of its every-day meannesses, and had sought refuge
from them in the contemplation of whatever suited their
taste in a former age."

"DEAR RELIGIOUS LOVE."

WE get our knowledge of perfect Love by glimpses and in fragments chiefly, — the rarest only among us knowing what it is to worship and caress, reverence and cherish, divide our bread and mingle our thoughts at one and the same time, under inspiration of the same object. Finest aromas will so often leave the fruits to which they are native and cling elsewhere, leaving the fruit empty of all but its coarser structure!

WE MAKE OUR OWN PRECEDENTS.

IN the times of national mixture, when modern Europe was, as one may say, a-brewing, it was open to a man who did not like to be judged by the Roman law to choose which of certain other codes he would be tried by. So, in our own times, they who openly adopt a higher rule than their neighbors do thereby make act of choice as to the laws and precedents by which they shall be approved or condemned; and thus it may happen that we see a man morally pilloried for a very customary deed, and yet having no right to complain, inasmuch as in his foregoing deliberative course of life he had referred himself to the tribunal of those higher conceptions, before which such a deed is without question condemnable.

BIRTH OF TOLERANCE.

TOLERANCE first comes through equality of struggle, as in the case of Arianism and Catholicism in the early times, — Valens, Eastern and Arian, Valentinian, Western and Catholic, alike publishing edicts of tolerance; or it comes from a common need of relief from an oppressive predominance, as when James II. published his Act of Tolerance towards non-Anglicans, being forced into liberality towards the Dissenters by the need to get it for the Catholics. Community of interest is the root of justice; community of suffering, the root of pity; community of joy, the root of love.

ENVELOPED in a common mist, we seem to walk in clearness ourselves, and behold only the mist that enshrouds others.

SYMPATHETIC people are often incommunicative about themselves : they give back reflected images which hide their own depths.

THE pond said to the ocean, " Why do you rage so ? The wind is not so very violent, — nay, it is already fallen. Look at me. I rose into no foaming waves, and am already smooth again."

FELIX QUI NON POTUIT.

MANY feel themselves very confidently on safe ground when they say : It must be good for man to know the Truth. But it is clearly not good for a particular man to know some particular truth, as irremediable treachery in one whom he cherishes, — better that he should die without knowing it.

Of scientific truth, is it not conceivable that some facts as to the tendency of things affecting the final destination of the race might be more hurtful when they had entered into the human consciousness than they would have been if they had remained purely external in their activity ?

DIVINE GRACE A REAL EMANATION.

THERE is no such thing as an impotent or neutral deity, if the deity be really believed in, and contemplated either in prayer or meditation. Every object of thought reacts on the mind that conceives it, still more on that which habitually contemplates it. In this we may be said to solicit help from a generalization or abstraction. Wordsworth had this truth in his consciousness when he wrote (in the Prelude), —

> "Nor general truths, which are themselves a sort
> Of elements and agents, Under-powers,
> Subordinate helpers of the living mind " —

not indeed precisely in the same relation, but with a meaning which involves that wider moral influence.

"A FINE EXCESS." — FEELING IS ENERGY.

ONE can hardly insist too much, in the present stage of thinking, on the efficacy of feeling in stimulating to ardent co-operation, quite apart from the conviction that such co-operation is needed for the achievement of the end in view. Just as hatred will vent itself in private curses no longer believed to have any potency, and joy, in private singing far out among the woods and fields, so sympathetic feeling can only be satisfied by joining in the action which expresses it, though the added "Bravo!" the added push, the added penny, is no more than a grain of dust on a rolling mass. When students take the horses out of a political hero's carriage, and draw him home by the force of their own muscle, the struggle in each is simply to draw or push, without consideration whether his place would not be as well filled by somebody else, or whether his one arm be really needful to the effect. It is under the same inspiration that abundant help rushes towards the scene of a fire, rescuing imperilled lives, and laboring with generous rivalry in carrying buckets. So the old blind King John of Bohemia at the battle of Crécy begged his vassals to lead him into the fight that he might strike a good blow, though his own stroke, possibly fatal to himself, could not turn by a hair's-breadth the imperious course of victory.

The question, "Of what use is it for me to work towards an end confessedly good?" comes from that sapless kind of reasoning which is falsely taken for a sign of supreme mental activity, but is really due to languor, or incapability of that mental grasp which makes objects strongly present, and to a lack of sympathetic emotion. In the "Spanish Gypsy" Fedalma says, —

> "The grandest death! to die in vain — for Love
> Greater than sways the forces of the world"[1] —

---

[1] *Vide* what Demosthenes says ("De Coronâ") about Athens pursuing the same course, though she had known from the beginning that her heroic resistance would be in vain.

referring to the image of the disciples throwing themselves, consciously in vain, on the Roman spears. I really believe and mean this — not as a rule of general action, but as a possible grand instance of determining energy in human sympathy, which even in particular cases, where it has only a magnificent futility, is more adorable, or as we say divine, than unpitying force, or than a prudent calculation of results. Perhaps it is an implicit joy in the resources of our human nature which has stimulated admiration for acts of self-sacrifice which are vain as to their immediate end. Marcus Curtius was probably not imagined as concluding to himself that he and his horse would so fill up the gap as to make a smooth *terra firma*. The impulse and act made the heroism, not the correctness of adaptation. No doubt the passionate inspiration which prompts and sustains a course of self-sacrificing labor in the light of soberly estimated results gathers the highest title to our veneration, and makes the supreme heroism. But the generous leap of impulse is needed too, to swell the flood of sympathy in us beholders, that we may not fall completely under the mastery of calculation, which in its turn may fail of ends for want of energy got from ardor. We have need to keep the sluices open for possible influxes of the rarer sort.

IMPRESSIONS OF THEOPHRASTUS SUCH

LOOKING INWARD.

IT is my habit to give an account to myself of the characters I meet with; can I give any true account of my
own? I am a bachelor, without domestic distractions of any
sort, and have all my life been an attentive companion to
myself, flattering my nature agreeably on plausible occasions,
reviling it rather bitterly when it mortified me; and in general remembering its doings and sufferings with a tenacity
which is too apt to raise surprise, if not disgust, at the care-
less inaccuracy of my acquaintances, who impute to me opinions I never held, express their desire to convert me to my
favorite ideas, forget whether I have ever been to the East,
and are capable of being three several times astonished at
my never having told them before of my accident in the
Alps, causing me the nervous shock which has ever since
notably diminished my digestive powers. Surely I ought to
know myself better than these indifferent outsiders can
know me; nay, better even than my intimate friends, to
whom I have never breathed those items of my inward experience which have chiefly shaped my life.

Yet I have often been forced into the reflection that even
the acquaintances who are as forgetful of my biography and
tenets as they would be if I were a dead philosopher, are
probably aware of certain points in me which may not be included in my most active suspicion. We sing an exquisite
passage out of tune, and innocently repeat it for the greater
pleasure of our hearers. Who can be aware of what his foreign accent is in the ears of a native? And how can a man
be conscious of that dull perception which causes him to

mistake altogether what will make him agreeable to a particular woman, and to persevere eagerly in a behavior which she is privately recording against him ? I have had some confidences, from my female friends, as to their opinion of other men, whom I have observed trying to make themselves amiable ; and it has occurred to me that, though I can hardly be so blundering as Lippus, and the rest of those mistaken candidates for favor whom I have seen ruining their chance by a too elaborate personal canvass, I must still come under the common fatality of mankind, and share the liability to be absurd without knowing that I am absurd. It is in the nature of foolish reasonings to seem good to the foolish reasoner. Hence, with all possible study of myself, with all possible effort to escape from the pitiable illusion which makes men laugh, shriek, or curl the lip at Folly's likeness, in total unconsciousness that it resembles themselves, I am obliged to recognize that, while there are secrets in me unguessed by others, these others have certain items of knowledge about the extent of my powers, and the figure I make with them, which in turn are secrets unguessed by me. When I was a lad I danced a hornpipe with arduous scrupulosity, and while suffering pangs of pallid shyness, was yet proud of my superiority as a dancing-pupil, imagining for myself a high place in the estimation of beholders; but I can now picture the amusement they had in the incongruity of my solemn face and ridiculous legs. What sort of hornpipe am I dancing now ?

Thus, if I laugh at you, O fellow-men ! if I trace with curious interest your labyrinthine self-delusions, note the inconsistencies in your zealous adhesions, and smile at your helpless endeavors in a rashly chosen part, it is not that I feel myself aloof from you ; the more intimately I seem to discern your weaknesses, the stronger to me is the proof that I share them. How otherwise could I get the discernment ? — for even what we are averse to, what we vow not to entertain, must have shaped or shadowed itself within us as a possibility, before we can think of exorcising it. No man can know his brother simply as a spectator. Dear blunderers, I am one of you. I wince at the fact, but I am not ignorant of it, that I too am laughable on unsuspected occasions ; nay, in the very tempest and whirlwind of my anger, I include myself under my own indignation. If the human race has a bad reputation, I perceive that I cannot escape being compromised. And thus, while I carry in myself the key to other men's experience, it is only by observing others that I can so far correct my self-ignorance as to arrive at the certainty that I am liable to commit myself unawares, and to manifest some incompetency, which I know no more of than the blind man knows of his image in the glass.

Is it then possible to describe one's self at once faithfully and fully ? In all autobiography there is, nay, ought to be, an incompleteness which may have the effect of falsity. We are each of us bound to reticence by the piety we owe to those who have been nearest to us and have had a mingled influence over our lives, by the fellow-feeling which should restrain us from turning our volunteered and picked confessions into an act of accusation against others, who have no chance of vindicating themselves; and most of all by that reverence for the higher efforts of our common nature, which commands us to bury its lowest fatalities, its invincible remnants of the brute, its most agonizing struggles with temptation, in unbroken silence. But the incompleteness which comes of self-ignorance may be compensated by self-betrayal. A man who is affected to tears in dwelling on the generosity of his own sentiments makes me aware of several things not included under those terms. Who has sinned more against those three duteous reticences than Jean Jacques ? Yet half our impressions of his character come not from what he means to convey, but from what he unconsciously enables us to discern.

This *naïve* veracity of self-presentation is attainable by the slenderest talent on the most trivial occasions. The least lucid and impressive of orators may be perfectly successful in showing us the weak points of his grammar.

Hence I too may be so far like Jean Jacques as to communicate more than I am aware of. I am not, indeed, writing an autobiography, or pretending to give an unreserved description of myself, but only offering some slight confessions in an apologetic light, to indicate that if in my absence you dealt as freely with my unconscious weaknesses as I have dealt with the unconscious weaknesses of others, I should not feel myself warranted by common-sense in regarding your freedom of observation as an exceptional case of evil-speaking, or as malignant interpretation of a character which really offers no handle to just objection, or even as an unfair use, for your amusement, of disadvantages which, since they are mine, should be regarded with more than ordinary tenderness. Let me at least try to feel myself in the ranks with my fellow-men. It is true, that I would rather not hear either your well-founded ridicule or your judicious strictures. Though not averse to finding fault with myself, and conscious of deserving lashes, I like to keep the scourge in my own discriminating hand. I never felt myself sufficiently meritorious to like being hated, as a proof of my superiority, or so thirsty for improvement as to desire that all my acquaintances should give me their candid opinion of me. I really do not want to learn from my enemies ; I prefer having none to learn from. Instead of being glad when men use me despitefully, I wish they would behave better, and find a more amiable occupation for their intervals of business. In brief, after a close intimacy with myself for a longer period than I choose to mention, I find within me a permanent longing for approbation, sympathy, and love.

Yet I am a bachelor, and the person I loved best has never loved me, or known that I loved her. Though continually in society, and caring about the joys and sorrows of my neighbors, I feel myself, so far as my personal lot is concerned, uncared for and alone. "Your own fault, my dear fellow ! " said Minutius Felix, one day that I had incautiously mentioned this uninteresting fact. And he was right, in senses other than he intended. Why should I

expect to be admired, and have my company doted on?
I have done no services to my country beyond those of every
peaceable, orderly citizen; and as to intellectual contribution,
my only published work was a failure, so that I am spoken
of to inquiring beholders as "the author of a book you have
probably not seen." (The work was a humorous romance,
unique in its kind, and I am told is much tasted in a Cher-
okee translation, where the jokes are rendered with all the
serious eloquence characteristic of the red races.) This
sort of distinction, as a writer nobody is likely to have read,
can hardly counteract an indistinctness in my articulation,
which the best-intentioned loudness will not remedy. Then,
in some quarters, my awkward feet are against me, the length
of my upper lip, and an inveterate way I have of walking
with my head foremost and my chin projecting. One can
become only too well aware of such things by looking in the
glass, or in that other mirror, held up to nature in the frank
opinions of street-boys, or of our Free People travelling by
excursion-train; and no doubt they account for the half-
suppressed smile which I have observed on some fair faces
when I have first been presented before them. This direct-
perspective judgment is not to be argued against. But I am
tempted to remonstrate when the physical points I have
mentioned are apparently taken to warrant unfavorable inferences concerning my mental quickness. With all the
increasing uncertainty which modern progress has thrown
over the relations of mind and body, it seems tolerably clear
that wit cannot be seated in the upper lip, and that the balance of the haunches in walking has nothing to do with the
subtle discrimination of ideas. Yet strangers evidently do
not expect me to make a clever observation, and my good
things are as unnoticed as if they were anonymous pictures.
I have indeed had the mixed satisfaction of finding that
when they were appropriated by some one else they were
found remarkable, and even brilliant. It is to be borne in
mind that I am not rich, have neither stud nor cellar, and
no very high connections such as give to a look of imbecility

a certain prestige of inheritance through a titled line; just as "the Austrian lip" confers a grandeur of historical associations on a kind of feature which might make us reject an advertising footman. I have now and then done harm to a good cause by speaking for it in public, and have discovered too late that my attitude on the occasion would more suitably have been that of negative beneficence. Is it really to the advantage of an opinion that I should be known to hold it? And as to the force of my arguments, that is a secondary consideration with audiences who have given a new scope to the *ex pede Herculem* principle, and from awkward feet infer awkward fallacies. Once, when zeal lifted me on my legs, I distinctly heard an enlightened artisan remark, "Here's a rum cut!" — and doubtless he reasoned in the same way as the elegant Glycera, when she politely puts on an air of listening to me, but elevates her eyebrows and chills her glance in sign of predetermined neutrality; both have their reasons for judging the quality of my speech beforehand.

This sort of reception to a man of affectionate disposition, who has also the innocent vanity of desiring to be agreeable, has naturally a depressing if not embittering tendency; and in early life I began to seek for some consoling point of view, some warrantable method of softening the hard peas I had to walk on, some comfortable fanaticism which might supply the needed self-satisfaction. At one time I dwelt much on the idea of compensation, — trying to believe that I was all the wiser for my bruised vanity, that I had the higher place in the true spiritual scale, and even that a day might come when some visible triumph would place me in the French heaven of having the laughers on my side. But I presently perceived that this was a very odious sort of self-cajolery. Was it in the least true that I was wiser than several of my friends who made an excellent figure, and were perhaps praised a little beyond their merit? Is the ugly, unready man in the corner, outside the current of conversation, really likely to have a fairer view of things than the agreeable talker, whose success strikes the unsuccessful as a repulsive example of forwardness and conceit ? And as to compensation in future years, would the fact that I myself got it reconcile me to an order of things in which I could see a multitude with as bad a share as mine, who, instead of getting their corresponding compensation, were getting beyond the reach of it in old age ? What could be more contemptible than the mood of mind which makes a man measure the justice of divine or human law by the agreeableness of his own shadow and the ample satisfaction of his own desires ?

I dropped a form of consolation which seemed to be encouraging me in the persuasion that my discontent was the chief evil in the world, and my benefit the soul of good in that evil. May there not be at least a partial release from the imprisoning verdict that a man's philosophy is the formula of his personality ? In certain branches of science we can ascertain our personal equation, the measure of difference between our own judgments and an average standard : may there not be some corresponding correction of our personal partialities in moral theorizing ? If a squint, or other ocular defect, disturbs my vision, I can get instructed in the fact, be made aware that my condition is abnormal, and either through spectacles or diligent imagination I can learn the average appearance of things : is there no remedy or corrective for that inward squint which consists in a dissatisfied egoism, or other want of mental balance ? In my conscience I saw that the bias of personal discontent was just as misleading and odious as the bias of self-satisfaction. Whether we look through the rose-colored glass or the indigo, we are equally far from the hues which the healthy human eye beholds in heaven above and earth below. I began to dread ways of consoling which were really a flattering of native illusions, a feeding-up into monstrosity of an inward growth already disproportionate; to get an especial scorn for that scorn of mankind which is a transmuted disappointment of preposterous claims; to watch with peculiar alarm lest what I called my philosophic estimate of the human lot in general, should be a mere prose lyric expressing my own pain and consequent bad temper. The standing-ground worth striving after seemed to be some Delectable Mountain whence I could see things in proportions as little as possible determined by that self-partiality which certainly plays a necessary part in our bodily sustenance, but has a starving effect on the mind.

Thus I finally gave up any attempt to make out that I preferred cutting a bad figure, and that I liked to be despised, because in this way I was getting more virtuous than my successful rivals; and I have long looked with suspicion on all views which are recommended as peculiarly consolatory to wounded vanity, or other personal disappointment. The consolations of egoism are simply a change of attitude, or a resort to a new kind of diet, which soothes and fattens it. Fed in this way, it is apt to become a monstrous spiritual pride, or a chuckling satisfaction that the final balance will not be against those who now eclipse us. Examining the world in order to find consolation is very much like looking carefully over the pages of a great book in order to find our own name, if not in the text, at least in a laudatory note; whether we find what we want or not, our preoccupation has hindered us from a true knowledge of the contents. But an attention fixed on the main theme, or various matter of the book, would deliver us from that slavish subjection to our own self-importance. And I had the mighty volume of the world before me. Nay, I had the struggling action of a myriad lives around me, each single life as dear to itself as mine to me. Was there no escape here from this stupidity of a murmuring self-occupation? Clearly enough, if anything hindered my thought from rising to the force of passionately interested contemplation, or my poor pent-up pond of sensitiveness from widening into a beneficent river of sympathy, it was my own dulness; and though I could not make myself the reverse of shallow all at once, I had at least learned where I had better turn my attention.

Something came of this alteration in my point of view, though I admit that the result is of no striking kind. It is unnecessary for me to utter modest denials, since none have assured me that I have a vast intellectual scope, or — what is more surprising, considering I have done so little — that I might, if I chose, surpass any distinguished man whom they wish to depreciate. I have not attained any lofty peak of magnanimity, nor would I trust beforehand in my capability of meeting a severe demand for moral heroism. But that I have at least succeeded in establishing a habit of mind which keeps watch against my self-partiality, and promotes a fair consideration of what touches the feelings or the fortunes of my neighbors, seems to be proved by the ready confidence with which men and women appeal to my interest in their experience. It is gratifying to one, who would above all things avoid the insanity of fancying himself a more momentous or touching object than he really is, to find that nobody expects from him the least sign of such mental aberration, and that he is evidently held capable of listening to all kinds of personal outpouring, without the least disposition to become communicative in the same way. This confirmation of the hope that my bearing is not that of the self-flattering lunatic is given me in ample measure. My acquaintances tell me unreservedly of their triumphs and their piques; explain their purposes at length, and reassure me with cheerfulness as to their chances of success; insist on their theories, and accept me as a dummy with whom they rehearse their side of future discussions; unwind their coiled-up griefs in relation to their husbands, or recite to me examples of feminine incomprehensibleness as typified in their wives; mention frequently the fair applause which their merits have wrung from some persons, and the attacks to which certain oblique motives have stimulated others. At the time when I was less free from superstition about my own power of charming, I occasionally, in the glow of sympathy which embraced me and my confiding friend on the subject of his satisfaction or resentment, was urged to hint at a corresponding experience in my own case: but the signs of a rapidly lowering pulse and spreading nervous depression in my previously vivacious interlocutor warned me that I was acting on that dangerous misreading, "Do as you are done by." Recalling the true version of the Golden Rule, I could not wish that others should lower my spirits as I was lowering my friend's. After several times obtaining the same result from a like experiment, in which all the circumstances were varied except my own personality, I took it as an established inference that these fitful signs of a lingering belief in my own importance were generally felt to be abnormal, and were something short of that sanity which I aimed to secure. Clearness on this point is not without its gratifications, as I have said. While my desire to explain myself in private ears has been quelled, the habit of getting interested in the experience of others has been continually gathering strength, and I am really at the point of finding that this world would be worth living in without any lot of one's own. Is it not possible for me to enjoy the scenery of the earth without saying to myself I have a cabbage-garden in it? But this sounds like the lunacy of fancying one's self everybody else, and being unable to play one's own part decently, — another form of the disloyal attempt to be independent of the common lot, and to live without a sharing of pain.

Perhaps I have made self-betrayals enough already, to show that I have not arrived at that non-human independence. My conversational reticences about myself turned into garrulousness on paper; as the sea-lion plunges and swims the more energetically, because his limbs are of a sort to make him shambling on land. The act of writing, in spite of past experience, brings with it the vague, delightful illusion of an audience nearer to my idiom than the Cherokees, and more numerous than the visionary One for whom many authors have declared themselves willing to go through the pleasing punishment of publication. My illusion is of a more liberal kind, and I imagine a far-off, hazy, multitudinous assemblage, as in a picture of Paradise, making an approving chorus to the sentences and paragraphs of which I myself particularly enjoy the writing. The haze is a necessary condition. If any physiognomy becomes distinct in the foreground, it is fatal. The countenance is sure to be one bent on discountenancing my innocent intentions: it is pale-eyed, incapable of being amused when I am amused, or indignant at what makes me indignant; it stares at my presumption, pities my ignorance, or is manifestly preparing to expose the various instances in which I unconsciously disgrace myself. I shudder at this too corporeal auditor, and turn toward another point of the compass where the haze is unbroken. Why should I not indulge this remaining illusion, since I do not take my approving choral paradise as a warrant for setting the press to work again and making some thousand sheets of superior paper unsalable? I leave my manuscripts to a judgment outside my imagination; but I will not ask to hear it, or request my friend to pronounce before I have been buried decently, what he really thinks of my parts, and to state candidly whether my papers would be most usefully applied in lighting the cheerful domestic fire. It is too probable that he will be exasperated at the trouble I have given him of reading them; but the consequent clearness and vivacity with which he could demonstrate to me that the fault of my manuscripts, as of my one published work, is simply flatness, and not that surpassing subtilty which is the preferable ground of popular neglect — this verdict, however instructively expressed, is a portion of earthly discipline of which I will not beseech my friend to be the instrument. Other persons, I am aware, have not the same cowardly shrinking from a candid opinion of their performances, and are even importunately eager for it; but I have convinced myself, in numerous cases, that such exposers of their own back to the smiter were of too hopeful a disposition to believe in the scourge, and really trusted in a pleasant anointing, an outpouring of balm without any previous wounds. I am of a less trusting disposition, and will only ask my friend to use his judgment in insuring me against posthumous mistake.

Thus I make myself a character to write, and keep the

pleasing, inspiring illusion of being listened to, though I may sometimes write about myself. What I have already said on this too familiar theme has been meant only as a preface, to show that in noting the weaknesses of my acquaintances I am conscious of my fellowship with them. That a gratified sense of superiority is at the root of barbarous laughter may be at least half the truth. But there is a loving laughter in which the only recognized superiority is that of the ideal self, the God within, holding the mirror and the scourge for our own pettiness as well as our neighbors'.

LOOKING BACKWARD.

MOST of us, who have had decent parents, would shrink from wishing that our father and mother had been somebody else whom we never knew; yet it is held no impiety — rather, a graceful mark of instruction — for a man to wail that he was not the son of another age and another nation. of which also he knows nothing except through the easy process of an imperfect imagination and a flattering fancy.

But the period thus looked back on with a purely admiring regret, as perfect enough to suit a superior mind, is always a long way off; the desirable contemporaries are hardly nearer than Leonardo da Vinci, most likely they are the fellow-citizens of Pericles, or, best of all, of the Æolic lyrists, whose sparse remains suggest a comfortable contrast with our redundance. No impassioned personage wishes he had been born in the age of Pitt, that his ardent youth might have eaten the dearest bread, dressed itself with the longest coat-tails and shortest waist, or heard the loudest grumbling at the heaviest war-taxes; and it would be really something original in polished verse if one of our young writers declared he would gladly be turned eighty-five, that he might have known the joy and pride of being an Englishman when there were fewer reforms and plenty of highwaymen, fewer discoveries and more faces pitted with the small-pox, when laws were made to keep up the price of corn, and the troublesome Irish were more miserable. Three-quarters of a century ago is not a distance that lends much enchantment to the view. We are familiar with the average men of that period, and are still consciously encumbered with its bad contrivances and mistaken acts. The lords and gentlemen painted by young Lawrence talked and wrote their nonsense in a tongue we thoroughly understand; hence their times are not much flattered, not much glorified, by the yearnings of that modern sect of Flagellants who make a ritual of lashing — not themselves, but all their neighbors. To me, however, that parental time, the time of my father's youth, never seemed prosaic, for it came to my imagination first through his memories, which made a wondrous perspective to my little daily world of discovery. And, for my part, I can call no age absolutely unpoetic: how should it be so, since there are always children to whom the acorns and the swallow's eggs are a wonder, — always these human passions and fatalities, through which Garrick as Hamlet in bob-wig and knee-breeches moved his audience, more than some have since done in velvet tunic and plume? But every age since the golden may be made more or less prosaic by minds that attend only to its vulgar and sordid elements, of which there was always an abundance, even in Greece and Italy, the favorite realms of the retrospective optimists. To be quite fair toward the ages, a little ugliness as well as beauty must be allowed to each of them, a little implicit poetry even to those which echoed loudest with servile, pompous, and trivial prose.

Such impartiality is not in vogue at present. If we acknowledge our obligation to the ancients, it is hardly to be done without some flouting of our contemporaries, who, with all their faults, must be allowed the merit of keeping the world habitable for the refined eulogists of the blameless past. One wonders whether the remarkable originators who first had the notion of digging wells, or of churning for butter, and who were certainly very useful to their own time as well as ours, were left quite free from invidious comparison with predecessors who let the water and the milk alone; or whether some rhetorical nomad, as he stretched himself on the grass with a good appetite for contemporary butter, became loud on the virtue of ancestors who were uncorrupted by the produce of the cow; nay, whether, in a high flight of imaginative self-sacrifice (after swallowing the butter), he even wished himself earlier born and already eaten for the sustenance of a generation more *naïve* than his own.

I have often had the fool's hectic of wishing about the unalterable; but with me that useless exercise has turned chiefly on the conception of a different self, and not, as it usually does in literature, on the advantage of having been born in a different age, and more especially in one where life is imagined to have been altogether majestic and graceful. With my present abilities, external proportions, and generally small provision for ecstatic enjoyment, where is the ground for confidence that I should have had a preferable career in such an epoch of society? An age in which every department has its awkward-squad seems in my mind's eye to suit me better. I might have wandered by the Strymon under Philip and Alexander without throwing any new light on method or organizing the sum of human knowledge; on the other hand, I might have objected to Aristotle as too much of a systematizer, and have preferred the freedom of a little self-contradiction as offering more chances of truth. I gather, too, from the undeniable testimony of his disciple Theophrastus, that there were boors, ill-bred persons, and detractors, even in Athens, of species remarkably corresponding to the English, and not yet made endurable by being classic; and altogether, with my present fastidious nostril, I feel that I am the better off for possessing Athenian life solely as an inodorous fragment of antiquity. As to Sappho's Mitylene, while I am convinced that the Lesbian capital held some plain men of middle stature and slow conversational powers, the addition of myself to their number, though clad in the majestic folds of the himation and without cravat, would hardly have made a sensation among the accomplished fair ones who were so precise in adjusting their own drapery about their delicate ankles. Whereas, by being another sort of person in the present age, I might have given it some needful theoretic clew; or I might have poured forth poetic strains which would have anticipated theory, and seemed a voice from "the prophetic soul of the wide world dreaming of things to come;" or I might have been one of those benignant lovely souls who, without astonishing the public and posterity, make a happy difference in the lives close around them, and in this way lift the average of earthly joy: in some form or other I might have been so filled from the store of universal existence, that I should have been freed from that empty wishing which is like a child's cry to be inside a golden cloud, its imagination being too ignorant to figure the lining of dimness and damp.

On the whole, though there is some rash boasting about enlightenment, and an occasional insistence on an originality which is that of the present year's corn-crop, we seem too much disposed to indulge, and to call by complimentary names, a greater charity for other portions of the human race than for our contemporaries. All reverence and gratitude for the worthy dead on whose labors we have entered, all care for the future generations whose lot we are preparing; but some affection and fairness for those who are doing the actual work of the world, some attempt to regard them with the same freedom from ill-temper, whether on private or public grounds, as we may hope will be felt by those who will call us ancient! Otherwise, the looking before and after, which is our grand human privilege, is in danger of turning to a sort of other-worldliness, breeding a more illogical indifference or bitterness than was ever bred by the ascetic's contemplation of heaven. Except on the ground of a primitive golden age and continuous degeneracy, I see no rational footing for scorning the whole present population of the globe; unless I scorn every previous generation from whom they have inherited their diseases of mind and body, and by consequence scorn my own scorn, which is equally an inheritance of mixed ideas and feelings, concocted for me in the boiling caldron of this universally contemptible life — and so on, scorning to infinity. This may represent some actual states of mind, for it is a narrow prejudice of mathematicians to suppose that ways of thinking are to be driven out of the field by being reduced to an absurdity. The Absurd is taken as an excellent juicy thistle by many constitutions.

Reflections of this sort have gradually determined me not to grumble at the age in which I happen to have been born — a natural tendency certainly older than Hesiod. Many ancient beautiful things are lost, many ugly modern things have arisen; but invert the proposition, and it is equally true. I at least am a modern, with some interest in advocating tolerance; and notwithstanding an inborn beguilement which carries my affection and regret continually into an imagined past, I am aware that I must lose all sense of moral proportion unless I keep alive a stronger attachment to what is near, and a power of admiring what I best know and understand. Hence this question of wishing to be rid of one's contemporaries associates itself with my filial feeling, and calls up the thought that I might as justifiably wish that I had had other parents than those whose loving tones are my earliest memory, and whose last parting first taught me the meaning of death. I feel bound to quell such a wish, as blasphemy.

Besides, there are other reasons why I am contented that my father was a country parson, born much about the same time as Scott and Wordsworth; notwithstanding certain qualms I have felt at the fact that the property on which I am living was saved out of tithe before the period of commutation, and without the provisional transfiguration into a modus. It has sometimes occurred to me, when I have been taking a slice of excellent ham, that, from a too tenable point of view, I was breakfasting on a small, squealing, black pig which, more than half a century ago, was the unwilling representative of spiritual advantages, not otherwise acknowledged by the grudging farmer or dairyman who parted with him. One enters on a fearful labyrinth in tracing compound interest backward, and such complications of thought have reduced the flavor of the ham; but since I have nevertheless eaten it, the chief effect has been to moderate the severity of my radicalism (which was not part of my paternal inheritance) and to raise the assuaging reflection, that if the pig and the parishioner had been intelligent enough to anticipate my historical point of view, they would have seen themselves and the rector in a light that would have made tithe voluntary. Notwithstanding such drawbacks, I am rather fond of the mental furniture I got by having a father who was well acquainted with all ranks of his neighbors, and am thankful that he was not one of those aristocratic clergymen who could not have sat down to a meal with any family in the parish except my lord's, — still more, that he was not an earl or a marquis. A chief misfortune of high birth is that it usually shuts a man out from the large sympathetic knowledge of human experience which comes from contact with various classes on their own level, and in my father's time that entail of social ignorance had not been disturbed as we see it now. To look always from overhead at the crowd of one's fellow-men must be in many ways incapacitating, even with the best will and intelligence. The serious blunders it must lead to in the effort to manage them for their good, one may see clearly by the mistaken ways people take of flattering and enticing those whose associations are alike their own. Hence I have always thought that the most fortunate Britons are those whose experience has given them a practical share in many aspects of the national lot, who have lived long among the mixed commonalty, roughing it with them under difficulties, knowing how their food tastes to them, and getting acquainted with their notions and motives, not by inference from traditional types in literature or from philosophical theories, but from daily fellowship and observation. Of course such experience is apt to get antiquated, and my father might find himself much at a loss among a mixed rural population of the present day; but he knew very well what could be wisely expected from the miners, the weavers, the field-laborers, and farmers of his own time, — yes, and from the aristocracy, for he had been brought up in close contact with them, and had been companion to a young nobleman who was deaf and dumb. "A clergyman, lad," he used to say to me, "should feel in himself a bit of every class;" and this theory had a felicitous agreement with his inclination and practice, which certainly answered in making him beloved by his parishioners. They grumbled at their obligation towards him; but what then? It was natural to grumble at any demand for payment, tithe included, but also natural for a rector to desire his tithe and look well after the levying. A Christian pastor who did not mind about his money was not an ideal prevalent among the rural minds of fat central England, and might have seemed to introduce a dangerous laxity of supposition about Christian laymen who happened to be creditors. My father was none the less beloved because he was understood to be of a saving disposition; and how could he save without getting his tithe? The sight of him was not unwelcome at any door, and he was remarkable among the clergy of his district for having no lasting feud with rich or poor in his parish. I profited by his popularity; and for months after my mother's death, when I was a little fellow of nine, I was taken care of first at one homestead, and then at another, — a variety which I enjoyed much more than my stay at the Hall, where there was a tutor. Afterward, for several years, I was my father's constant companion in his out-door business, riding by his side on my little pony, and listening to the lengthy dialogues he held with Darby or Joan, the one on the road or in the field, the other outside or inside her door. In my earliest remembrance of him his hair was already gray, for I was his youngest as well as his only surviving child; and it seemed to me that advanced age was appropriate to a father, as indeed in all respects I considered him a parent so much to my honor, that the mention of my relationship to him was likely to secure me regard among those to whom I was otherwise a stranger, — my father's stories from his life including so many names of distant persons, that my imagination placed no limit to his acquaintanceship. He was a pithy talker, and his sermons bore marks of his own composition. It is true, they must have been already old when I began to listen to them, and they were no more than a year's supply, so that they recurred as regularly as the Collects. But though this system has been much ridiculed, I am prepared to defend it as equally sound with that of a liturgy; and even if my researches had shown me that some of my father's early sermons had been copied out from the works of elder divines, this would only have been another proof of his good judgment. One may prefer fresh eggs, though laid by a fowl of the meanest understanding; but why fresh sermons?

Nor can I be sorry, though myself given to meditative if not active innovation, that my father was a Tory who had not exactly a dislike to innovators and dissenters, but a slight opinion of them as persons of ill-founded self-confidence; whence my young ears gathered many details concerning those who might perhaps have called themselves the more advanced thinkers in our nearest market-town, tending to convince me that their characters were quite as mixed as those of the thinkers behind them. This circumstance of my rearing has at least delivered me from certain mistakes of classification which I observe in many of my superiors, who have apparently no affectionate memories of a goodness mingled with what they now regard as outworn prejudices. Indeed my philosophical notions, such as they are, continually carry me back to the time when the fitful gleams of a spring day used to show me my own shadow as that of a small boy on a small pony, riding by the side of a larger cob-mounted shadow over the breezy uplands which we used to dignify with the name of hills, or along by-roads, with broad grassy borders and hedgerows reckless of utility, on our way to outlying hamlets, whose groups of inhabitants were as distinctive to my imagination as if they had belonged to different regions of the globe. From these we sometimes rode onward to the adjoining parish, where also my father officiated, for he was a pluralist, but — I hasten to add — on the smallest scale; for his own extra living was a poor vicarage, with hardly fifty parishioners, and its church would have made a very shabby barn, — the gray, worm-eaten wood of its pews and pulpit, with their doors only half-hanging on the hinges, being exactly the color of a lean mouse which I once observed as an interesting member of the scant congregation, and conjectured to be the identical Church-mouse I had heard referred to as an example of extreme poverty; for I was a precocious boy, and often reasoned after the fashion of my elders, arguing that Jack and Jill were real personages in our parish, and that if I could identify Jack I should find on him the mark of a broken crown.

Sometimes when I am in a crowded London drawing-room (for I am a town-bird now, acquainted with smoky eaves, and tasting Nature in the parks), quick flights of memory take me back among my father's parishioners, while I am still conscious of elbowing men who wear the same evening uniform as myself; and I presently begin to wonder what varieties of history lie hidden under this monotony of aspect. Some of them, perhaps, belong to families with many quarterings; but how many "quarterings" of diverse contact with their fellow-countrymen enter into their qualifications to be parliamentary leaders, professors of social science, or journalistic guides of the popular mind? Not that I feel myself a person made competent by experience; on the contrary, I argue that since an observation of different ranks has still left me practically a poor creature, what must be the condition of those who object even to read about the life of other British classes than their own? But of my elbowing neighbors with their crush-hats I usually imagine that the most distinguished among them have probably had a far more instructive journey into manhood than mine. Here, perhaps, is a thought-worn physiognomy, seeming at the present moment to be classed as a mere species of white cravat and swallow-tail, which may once, like Faraday's, have shown itself in curiously dubious embryonic form leaning against a cottage-lintel, in small corduroys, and hungrily eating a bit of brown bread and bacon; *there* is a pair of eyes, now too much wearied by the gas-light of public assemblies,

that once perhaps learned to read their native England
through the same alphabet as mine — not within the boundaries of an ancestral park, never even being driven through
the country town five miles off, but — among the midland
villages and markets, along by the tree-studded hedgerows,
and where the heavy barges seem in the distance to float
mysteriously among the rushes and the feathered grass.
Our vision, both real and ideal, has since then been filled
with far other scenes, — among eternal snows and stupendous
sun-scorched monuments of departed empires, within the
scent of the long orange-groves, and where the temple of
Neptune looks out over the siren-haunted sea. But my eyes
at least have kept their early affectionate joy in our native
landscape, which is one deep root of our national life and
language.

And I often smile at my consciousness that certain conservative prepossessions have mingled themselves for me
with the influences of our midland scenery, from the tops of
the elms down to the buttercups and the little wayside
vetches. Naturally enough! That part of my father's prime
to which he oftenest referred had fallen on the days when
the great wave of political enthusiasm and belief in a speedy
regeneration of all things had ebbed, and the supposed millennial initiative of France was turning into a Napoleonic empire — the sway of an Attila, with a mouth speaking proud
things, in a jargon half-revolutionary, half-Roman. Men
were beginning to shrink timidly from the memory of their
own words, and from the recognition of the fellowships they
had formed ten years before ; and even reforming Englishmen, for the most part, were willing to wait for the perfection of society, if only they could keep their throats perfect,
and help to drive away the chief enemy of mankind from
our coasts. To my father's mind the noisy teachers of revolutionary doctrine were, to speak mildly, a variable mixture
of the fool and the scoundrel; the welfare of the nation lay
in a strong government which could maintain order; and I
was accustomed to hear him utter the word "government"

in a tone that charged it with awe, and made it part of my effective religion, — in contrast with the word " rebel," which seemed to carry the stamp of evil in its syllables, and, lit by the fact that Satan was the first rebel, made an argument dispensing with more detailed inquiry. I gathered that our national troubles in the first two decades of this century were not at all due to the mistakes of our administrators, and that England, with its fine Church and Constitution, would have been exceedingly well off if every British subject had been thankful for what was provided, and had minded his own business — if, for example, numerous Catholics of that period had been aware how very modest they ought to be, considering they were Irish. The times, I heard, had often been bad; but I was constantly hearing of "bad times" as a name for actual evenings and mornings, when the godfathers who gave them that name appeared to me remarkably comfortable. Altogether, my father's England seemed to me lovable, laudable, full of good men, and having good rulers, from Mr. Pitt on to the Duke of Wellington, until he was for emancipating the Catholics; and it was so far from prosaic to me, that I looked into it for a more exciting romance than such as I could find in my own adventures, which consisted mainly in fancied crises calling for the resolute wielding of domestic swords and fire-arms against unapparent robbers, rioters, and invaders, who, it seemed, in my father's prime, had more chance of being real. The morris-dancers had not then dwindled to a ragged and almost vanished rout (owing the traditional name probably to the historic fancy of our superannuated groom); also the good old king was alive and well, which made all the more difference, because I had no notion what he was and did — only understanding in general that, if he had been still on the throne, he would have hindered everything that wise persons thought undesirable.

Certainly that elder England — with its frankly salable boroughs, so cheap compared with the seats obtained under the reformed method, and its boroughs kindly presented by noblemen desirous to encourage gratitude; its prisons, with a miscellaneous company of felons and maniacs, and without any supply of water; its bloated, idle charities; its non-resident, jovial clergy; its militia-balloting; and, above all, its blank ignorance of what we, its posterity, should be thinking of it — has great differences from the England of to-day. Yet we discern a strong family likeness. Is there any country which shows at once as much stability and as much susceptibility to change as ours? Our national life is like that scenery which I early learned to love, not subject to great convulsions, but easily showing more or less delicate (sometimes melancholy) effects from minor changes. Hence our midland plains have never lost their familiar expression and conservative spirit for me; yet at every other mile, since I first looked on them, some sign of world-wide change, some new direction of human labor, has wrought itself into what one may call the speech of the landscape — in contrast with those grander and vaster regions of the earth which keep an indifferent aspect in the presence of men's toil and devices. What does it signify that a liliputian train passes over a viaduct amidst the abysses of the Apennines, or that a caravan, laden with a nation's offerings, creeps across the unresting sameness of the desert, or that a petty cloud of steam sweeps for an instant over the face of an Egyptian colossus, immovably submitting to its slow burial beneath the sand? But our woodlands and pastures, our hedge-parted cornfields and meadows, our bits of high common where we used to plant the windmills, our quiet little rivers here and there fit to turn a mill-wheel, our villages along the old coach-roads, are all easily alterable lineaments that seem to make the face of our mother-land sympathetic with the laborious lives of her children. She does not take their ploughs and wagons contemptuously, but rather makes every hovel and every sheepfold, every railed bridge or fallen tree-trunk, an agreeably noticeable incident; not a mere speck in the midst of unmeasured vastness, but a piece of our social history in pictorial writing.

Our rural tracts, where no Babel-chimney scales the heavens, are without mighty objects to fill the soul with the sense of an outer world unconquerably aloof from our efforts. The wastes are playgrounds (and let us try to keep them such for the children's children, who will inherit no other sort of demesne); the grasses and reeds nod to each other over the river, but we have cut a canal close by; the very heights laugh with corn in August, or lift the plough-team against the sky in September. Then comes a crowd of burly navvies with pickaxes and barrows; and while hardly a wrinkle is made in the fading mother's face, or a new curve of health in the blooming girl's, the hills are cut through or the breaches between them spanned, we choose our level, and the white steam-pennon flies along it.

But because our land shows this readiness to be changed, all signs of permanence upon it raise a tender attachment instead of awe: some of us, at least, love the scanty relics of our forests, and are thankful if a bush is left of the old hedgerow. A crumbling bit of wall where the delicate ivy-leaved toad-flax hangs its light branches, or a bit of gray thatch with patches of dark moss on its shoulder and a troop of grass-stems on its ridge, is a thing to visit. And then the tiled roof of cottage and homestead; of the long cow-shed where generations of the milky mothers have stood patiently; of the broad-shouldered barns, where the old-fashioned flail once made resonant music, while the watch-dog barked at the timidly venturesome fowls, making pecking raids on the out-flying grain, — the roofs that have looked out from among the elms and walnut-trees, or beside the yearly group of hay and corn stacks, or below the square stone steeple, gathering their gray or ochre-tinted lichens and their olive-green mosses under all ministries — let us praise the sober harmonies they give to our landscape, helping to unite us pleasantly with the elder generations, who tilled the soil for us before we were born, and paid heavier and heavier taxes, with much grumbling, but without that deepest root of corruption — the self-indulgent despair which cuts down and consumes, and never plants.

But I check myself. Perhaps this England of my affections is half-visionary — a dream in which things are connected according to my well-fed, lazy mood, and not at all
by the multitudinous links of graver, sadder fact, such as
belong everywhere to the story of human labor. Well, well,
the illusions that began for us when we were less acquainted
with evil have not lost their value when we discern them to
be illusions. They feed the ideal Better; and in loving them
still, we strengthen the precious habit of loving something
not visibly, tangibly existent, but a spiritual product of our
visible, tangible selves.

I cherish my childish loves, the memory of that warm
little nest where my affections were fledged. Since then I
have learned to care for foreign countries, for literatures
foreign and ancient, for the life of Continental towns dozing
round old cathedrals, for the life of London, half-sleepless
with eager thought and strife, with indigestion, or with hunger; and now my consciousness is chiefly of the busy, anxious, metropolitan sort. My system responds sensitively to
the London weather-signs, political, social, literary; and my
bachelor's hearth is imbedded where, by much craning of
head and neck, I can catch sight of a sycamore in the Square
garden. I belong to the "Nation of London." Why? There
have been many voluntary exiles in the world; and probably
in the very first exodus of the patriarchal Aryans — for I am
determined not to fetch my examples from races whose talk
is of uncles and no fathers —some of those who sallied forth
went for the sake of a loved companionship, when they
would willingly have kept sight of the familiar plains, and
of the hills to which they had first lifted up their eyes.

HOW WE ENCOURAGE RESEARCH.

THE serene and beneficent goddess Truth, like other deities whose disposition has been too hastily inferred from that of the men who have invoked them, can hardly be well pleased with much of the worship paid to her even in this milder age, when the stake and the rack have ceased to form part of her ritual. Some cruelties still pass for service done in her honor; no thumb-screw is used, no iron boot, no scorching of flesh, but plenty of controversial bruising, laceration, and even life-long maiming. Less than formerly; but so long as this sort of Truth-worship has the sanction of a public that can often understand nothing in a controversy except personal sarcasm or slanderous ridicule, it is likely to continue. The sufferings of its victims are often as little regarded as those of the sacrificial pig offered in old time, with what we now regard as a sad miscalculation of effects.

One such victim is my old acquaintance, Merman.

Twenty years ago Merman was a young man of promise, a conveyancer with a practice which had certainly budded, but, like Aaron's rod, seemed not destined to proceed further in that marvellous activity. Meanwhile he occupied himself in miscellaneous periodical-writing, and in a multifarious study of moral and physical science. What chiefly attracted him in all subjects were the vexed questions, which have the advantage of not admitting the decisive proof or disproof that renders many ingenious arguments superannuated. Not that Merman had a wrangling disposition: he put all his doubts, queries, and paradoxes deferentially; contended without unpleasant heat, and only with a sonorous eagerness, against the personality of Homer; expressed himself civilly though firmly on the origin of language; and had tact enough to drop at the right moment such subjects as the ultimate reduction of all the so-called elementary substances, his own total scepticism concerning Manetho's chronology, or even the relation between the magnetic condition of the earth and the outbreak of revolutionary tendencies. Such flexibility was naturally much helped by his amiable feeling toward woman, whose nervous system, he was convinced, would not bear the continuous strain of difficult topics; and also by his willingness to contribute a song whenever the same desultory charmer proposed music. Indeed, his tastes were domestic enough to beguile him into marriage when his resources were still very moderate and partly uncertain. His friends wished that so ingenious and agreeable a fellow might have more prosperity than they ventured to hope for him; their chief regret on his account being that he did not concentrate his talent, and leave off forming opinions on at least half a dozen of the subjects over which he scattered his attention, especially now that he had married "a nice little woman" (the generic name for acquaintances' wives when they are not markedly disagreeable). He could not, they observed, want all his various knowledge and Laputan ideas for his periodical-writing which brought him most of his bread, and he would do well to use his talents in getting a specialty that would fit him for a post. Perhaps these well-disposed persons were a little rash in presuming that fitness for a post would be the surest ground for getting it; and, on the whole, in now looking back on their wishes for Merman, their chief satisfaction must be that those wishes did not contribute to the actual result.

For in an evil hour Merman did concentrate himself. He had for many years taken into his interest the comparative history of the ancient civilizations, but it had not preoccupied him so as to narrow his generous attention to everything else. One sleepless night, however (his wife has more than once narrated to me the details of an event memorable to her as the beginning of sorrows), after spending some hours over the epoch-making work of Grampus, a new idea seized him with regard to the possible connection of certain symbolic monuments common to widely scattered races. Merman started up in bed. The night was cold; and the sudden withdrawal of warmth made his wife first dream of a snow-ball, and then cry,

"What is the matter, Proteus?"

"A great matter, Julia. That fellow Grampus, whose book is cried up as a revelation, is all wrong about the Magicodumbras and the Zuzumotzis, and I have got hold of the right clew."

"Good gracious! does it matter so much? Don't drag the clothes, dear."

"It signifies this, Julia, that if I am right I shall set the world right; I shall regenerate history; I shall win the mind of Europe to a new view of social origins; I shall bruise the head of many superstitions."

"Oh no, dear, don't go too far into things. Lie down again. You have been dreaming. What are the Madicojumbras and Zuzitotzums? I never heard you talk of them before. What use can it be, troubling yourself about such things?"

"That is the way, Julia! That is the way wives alienate their husbands, and make any hearth pleasanter to him than his own."

"What *do* you mean, Proteus?"

"Why, if a woman will not try to understand her husband's ideas, or at least to believe that they are of more value than she can understand, — if she is to join anybody who happens to be against him, and suppose he is a fool because others contradict him, — there is an end of our happiness. That is all I have to say."

"Oh no, Proteus, dear. I do believe what you say is right. That is my only guide. I am sure I never have any opinions in any other way, — I mean about subjects. Of course there are many little things that would tease you, that you like me to judge of for myself.   I know I said once that I did not want you to sing 'Oh, ruddier than the cherry,' because it was not in your voice.   But I cannot remember ever differing from you about *subjects*.   I never in my life thought any one cleverer than you."

Julia Merman was really " a nice little woman," not one of the stately Dians sometimes spoken of in those terms. Her black silhouette had a very infantine aspect; but she had discernment and wisdom enough to act on the strong hint of that memorable conversation, never again giving her husband the slightest ground for suspecting that she thought treasonably of his ideas in relation to the Magicodumbras and Zuzumotzis, or in the least relaxed her faith in his infallibility because Europe was not also convinced of it.   It was well for her that she did not increase her troubles in this way; but to do her justice, what she was chiefly anxious about was to avoid increasing her husband's troubles.

Not that these were great in the beginning.   In the first development and writing out of his scheme, Merman had a more intense kind of intellectual pleasure than he had ever known before.   His face became more radiant, his general view of human prospects more cheerful.   Foreseeing that truth as presented by himself would win the recognition of his contemporaries, he excused with much liberality their rather rough treatment of other theorists, whose basis was less perfect.   His own periodical-criticisms had never before been so amiable; he was sorry for that unlucky majority whom the spirit of the age, or some other prompting more definite and local, compelled to write without any particular ideas. The possession of an original theory, which has not yet been assailed, must certainly sweeten the temper of a man who is not beforehand ill-natured.   And Merman was the reverse of ill-natured.

But the hour of publication came; and to half a dozen persons, described as the learned world of two hemispheres, it became known that Grampus was attacked.   This might have been a small matter; for who or what on earth, that is good for anything, is not assailed by ignorance, stupidity, or malice, and sometimes even by just objection ? But on examination it appeared that the attack might possibly be held damaging, unless the ignorance of the author were well exposed, and his pretended facts shown to be chimeras of that remarkably hideous kind begotten by imperfect learning on the more feminine element of original incapacity. Grampus himself did not immediately cut open the volume which Merman had been careful to send him, not without a very lively and shifting conception of the possible effects which the explosive gift might produce on the too eminent scholar — effects that must certainly have set in on the third day from the despatch of the parcel. But in point of fact Grampus knew nothing of the book until his friend Lord Narwhal sent him an American newspaper containing a spirited article by the well-known Professor Sperm N. Whale, which was rather equivocal in its bearing, the passages quoted from Merman being of rather a telling sort, and the paragraphs which seemed to blow defiance being unaccountably feeble, coming from so distinguished a Cetacean. Then, by another post, arrived letters from Butzkopf and Dugong, both men whose signatures were familiar to the Teutonic world, in the "Selten-erscheinender Monat-schrift," or Hyrick for the insertion of Split Hairs, asking their Master whether he meant to take up the combat, because, in the contrary case, both were ready.

Thus America and Germany were roused, though England was still drowsy; and it seemed time now for Grampus to find Merman's book under the heap, and cut it open. For his own part, he was perfectly at ease about his system; but this is a world in which the truth requires defence, and specious falsehood must be met with exposure. Grampus having once looked through the book, no longer wanted any urging to write the most crushing of replies. This, and nothing less than this, was due from him to the cause of sound inquiry; and the punishment would cost him little pains. In three weeks from that time the palpitating Merman saw his book announced in the programme of the leading Review. No need for Grampus to put his signature. Who else had his vast yet microscopic knowledge, who else his power of epithet? This article — in which Merman was pilloried and as good as mutilated, for he was shown to have neither ear nor nose for the subtleties of philological and archæological study — was much read and more talked of; not because of any interest in the system of Grampus, or any precise conception of the danger attending lax views of the Magicodumbras and Zuzumotzis, but because the sharp epigrams with which the victim was lacerated, and the soaring fountains of acrid mud which were shot upward and poured over the fresh wounds, were found amusing in recital. A favorite passage was one in which a certain kind of socialist was described as a creature of the walrus kind, having a phantasmal resemblance to higher animals when seen by ignorant minds in the twilight, dabbling or hobbling in first one element and then the other, without parts or organs suited to either; in fact, one of Nature's impostors, who could not be said to have any artful pretences, since a congenital incompetence to all precision of aim and movement made their every action a pretence — just as a being born in doeskin gloves would necessarily pass a judgment on surfaces, but we all know what his judgment would be worth. In drawing-room circles, and for the immediate hour, this ingenious comparison was as damaging as the showing-up of Merman's mistakes, and the mere smattering of linguistic and historical knowledge which he had presumed to be a sufficient basis for theorizing; but the more learned cited his blunders aside to each other, and laughed the laugh of the initiated. In fact, Merman's was a remarkable case of sudden notoriety. In London drums and clubs he was spoken of abundantly as one who had written ridiculously about the Magicodumbras and Zuzumotzis : the leaders of conversation, whether Christians, Jews, infidels, or of any other confession, except the confession of ignorance, pronouncing him shallow and indiscreet, if not presumptuous and absurd. He was heard of at Warsaw, and even Paris took knowledge of him. M. Cachalot had not read either Grampus or Merman, but heard of their dispute in time to insert a paragraph upon it in his brilliant work, " L'Orient au Point de Vue Actuel," in which he was dispassionate enough to speak of Grampus as possessing a *coup d'œil presque français* in matters of historical interpretation, and of Merman as nevertheless an objector *qui mérite d'être connu.* M. Porpesse, also, availing himself of M. Cachalot's knowledge, reproduced it in an article with certain additions, which it is only fair to distinguish as his own, implying that the vigorous English of Grampus was not always as correct as a Frenchman could desire, while Merman's objections were more sophistical than solid. Presently, indeed, there appeared an able *extrait* of Grampus's article in the valuable " Rapporteur Scientifique et Historique," and Merman's mistakes were thus brought under the notice of certain Frenchmen who are among the masters of those who know on Oriental subjects. In a word, Merman, though not extensively read, was extensively read about.

Meanwhile, how did he like it ? Perhaps nobody, except his wife, for a moment reflected on that. An amused society considered that he was severely punished, but did not take the trouble to imagine his sensations ; indeed, this would have been a difficulty for persons less sensitive and excitable than Merman himself. Perhaps that popular comparison of the walrus had truth enough to bite and blister on thorough application, even if exultant ignorance had not applauded it. But it is well known that the walrus, though not in the least a malignant animal, if allowed to display its remarkably plain person and blundering performances at ease in any element it chooses, becomes desperately savage, and musters alarming auxiliaries when attacked or hurt. In this characteristic, at least, Merman resembled the walrus. And now he concentrated himself with a vengeance. That his counter-theory was fundamentally the right one he had a genuine conviction, whatever collateral mistakes he might have committed ; and his bread would not cease to be bitter to him until he had convinced his contemporaries that Grampus had used his

minute learning as a dust-cloud to hide sophistical evasions —
that, in fact, minute learning was an obstacle to clear-sighted
judgment, more especially with regard to the Magicodumbras
and Zuzumotzis, and that the best preparation in this matter
was a wide survey of history, and a diversified observation of
men.   Still, Merman was resolved to muster all the learning
within his reach, and he wandered day and night through
many wildernesses of German print; he tried compendious
methods of learning Oriental tongues, and, so to speak, getting at the marrow of languages independently of the bones,
for the chance of finding details to corroborate his own views,
or possibly even to detect Grampus in some oversight or tex-
tual tampering.   All other work was neglected ; rare clients
were sent away, and amazed editors found this maniac indifferent to his chance of getting book-parcels from them.   It
was many months before Merman had satisfied himself that
he was strong enough to face round upon his adversary.   But
at last he had prepared sixty condensed pages of eager argument, which seemed to him worthy to rank with the best
models of controversial writing.   He had acknowledged his
mistakes, but had restated his theory, so as to show that it was
left intact in spite of them ; and he had even found cases in
which Ziphius, Microps, Scrag Whale the explorer, and other
Cetaceans of unanswerable authority, were decidedly at issue
with Grampus.   Especially a passage cited by this last from
that greatest of fossils, Megalosaurus, was demonstrated by
Merman to be capable of three different interpretations, all
preferable to that chosen by Grampus, who took the words
in their most literal sense; for (1) the incomparable Saurian,
alike unequalled in close observation and far-glancing comprehensiveness, might have meant those words ironically ;
(2) *motzis* was probably a false reading for *potzis*, in which
case its bearing was reversed; and (3) it is known that in
the age of the Saurians there were conceptions about the *motzis* which entirely remove it from the category of things comprehensible in an age when Saurians run ridiculously small :
all which views were godfathered by names quite fit to be

ranked with that of Grampus. In fine, Merman wound up his rejoinder by sincerely thanking the eminent adversary, without whose fierce assault he might not have undertaken a revision, in the course of which he had met with unexpected and striking confirmations of his own fundamental views. Evidently Merman's anger was at white heat.

The rejoinder being complete, all that remained was to find a suitable medium for its publication. This was not so easy. Distinguished mediums would not lend themselves to contradictions of Grampus; or if they would, Merman's article was too long and too abstruse, while he would not consent to leave anything out of an article which had no superfluities, — for all this happened years ago, when the world was a different stage. At last, however, he got his rejoinder printed, and not on hard terms, since the medium, in every sense modest, did not ask him to pay for its insertion.

But if Merman expected to call out Grampus again, he was mistaken. Everybody felt it too absurd that Merman should undertake to correct Grampus in matters of erudition, and an eminent man has something else to do than to refute a petty objector twice over. What was essential had been done: the public had been enabled to form a true judgment of Merman's incapacity. The Magicodumbras and Zuzumotzis were but subsidiary elements in Grampus's system, and Merman might now be dealt with by younger members of the Master's school. But he had at least the satisfaction of finding that he had raised a discussion which would not be let die. The followers of Grampus took it up with an ardor and industry of research worthy of their exemplar. Butzkopf made it the subject of an elaborate *Einleitung* to his important work "Die Bedeutung des Ægyptischen Labyrinthes;" and Dugong, in a remarkable address which he delivered to a learned society in Central Europe, introduced Merman's theory with so much power of sarcasm that it became a theme of more or less derisive allusion to men of many tongues. Merman with his Magicodumbras and Zuzumotzis was on the way to become a proverb, being used illustratively by many able journalists, who took those names of questionable things to be Merman's own invention—"than which," said one of the graver guides, "we can recall few more melancholy examples of speculative aberration." Naturally, the subject passed into popular literature, and figured very commonly in advertised programmes. The fluent Loligo, the formidable Shark, and a younger member of his remarkable family, known as S. Catulus, made a special reputation by their numerous articles, eloquent, lively, or abusive, all on the same theme, under titles ingeniously varied, alliterative, sonorous, or boldly fanciful — such as, "Moments with Mr. Merman," "Mr. Merman and the Magicodumbras," "Greenland Grampus and Proteus Merman," "Grampian Heights and their Climbers, or the New Excelsior." They tossed him on short sentences; they swathed him in paragraphs of winding imagery; they found him at once a mere plagiarist and a theorizer of unexampled perversity, ridiculously wrong about *potzis* and ignorant of Pali; they hinted, indeed, at certain things which to their knowledge he had silently brooded over in his boyhood, and seemed tolerably well assured that this preposterous attempt to gainsay an incomparable Cetacean of world-wide fame had its origin in a peculiar mixture of bitterness and eccentricity which, rightly estimated and seen in its definite proportions, would furnish the best key to his argumentation. All alike were sorry for Merman's lack of sound learning; but how could their readers be sorry? Sound learning would not have been amusing; and as it was, Merman was made to furnish these readers with amusement at no expense of trouble on their part. Even burlesque-writers looked into his book to see where it could be made use of; and those who did not know him were desirous of meeting him at dinner, as one likely to feed their comic vein.

On the other hand, he made a serious figure in sermons under the name of "Some" or "Others," who had attempted presumptuously to scale eminences too high and arduous for human ability, and had given an example of ignominious failure, edifying to the humble Christian.

All this might be very advantageous for able persons, whose superfluous fund of expression needed a paying investment; but the effect on Merman himself was unhappily not so transient as the busy writing and speaking of which he had become the occasion. His certainty that he was right naturally got stronger in proportion as the spirit of resistance was stimulated. The scorn and unfairness with which he felt himself to have been treated, by those really competent to appropriate his ideas, had galled him and made a chronic sore; and the exultant chorus of the incompetent seemed a pouring of vinegar on his wound. His brain became a registry of the foolish and ignorant objections made against him, and of continually amplified answers to these objections. Unable to get his answers printed, he had recourse to that more primitive mode of publication, oral transmission, or button-holding, now generally regarded as a troublesome survival; and the once pleasant, flexible Merman was on the way to be shunned as a bore. His interest in new acquaintances turned chiefly on the possibility that they would care about the Magicodumbras and Zuzumotzis; that they would listen to his complaints and exposures of unfairness, and not only accept copies of what he had written on the subject, but send him appreciative letters in acknowledgment. Repeated disappointment of such hopes tended to embitter him; and not the less because after awhile the fashion of mentioning him died out, allusions to his theory were less understood, and people could only pretend to remember it. And all the while Merman was perfectly sure that his very opponents, who had knowledge enough to be capable judges, were aware that his book, whatever errors of statement they might detect in it, had served as a sort of divining-rod, pointing out hidden sources of historical interpretation; nay, his jealous examination discerned in a new work by Grampus himself a certain shifting of ground, which — so poor Merman declared — was the sign of an intention gradually to appropriate the views of the man he had attempted to brand as an ignorant impostor.

And Julia ? And the housekeeping, — the rent, food, and clothing, which controversy can hardly supply, unless it be of the kind that serves as a recommendation to certain posts ? Controversial pamphlets have been known to earn large plums ; but nothing of the sort could be expected from unpractical heresies about the Magicodumbras and Zuzumotzis, — painfully the contrary. Merman's reputation as a sober thinker, a safe writer, a sound lawyer, was irretrievably injured ; the distractions of controversy had caused him to neglect useful editorial connections, and indeed his dwindling care for miscellaneous subjects made his contributions too dull to be desirable. Even if he could now have given a new turn to his concentration, and applied his talents so as to be ready to show himself an exceptionally qualified lawyer, he would only have been like an architect in competition, too late with his superior plans : he would not have had an opportunity of showing his qualification. He was thrown out of the course. The small capital which had filled up deficiencies of income was almost exhausted, and Julia, in the effort to make supplies equal to wants, had to use much ingenuity in diminishing the wants. The brave and affectionate woman, whose small outline, so unimpressive against an illuminated background, held within it a good share of feminine heroism, did her best to keep up the charm of home and soothe her husband's excitement, — parting with the best jewel among her wedding presents in order to pay rent, without ever hinting to her husband that this sad result had come of his undertaking to convince people who only laughed at him. She was a resigned little creature, and reflected that some husbands took to drinking and others to forgery ; hers had only taken to the Magicodumbras and Zuzumotzis, and was not unkind — only a little more indifferent to her and the two children than she had ever expected he would be ; his mind was eaten up with "subjects," and constantly a little angry, not with her, but with everybody else, especially those who were celebrated.

This was the sad truth. Merman felt himself ill-used by

the world, and thought very much worse of the world in consequence. The gall of his adversaries' ink had been sucked into his system and ran in his blood. He was still in the prime of life, but his mind was aged by that eager, monotonous construction which comes of feverish excitement on a single topic, and uses up the intellectual strength.

Merman had never been a rich man, but he was now conspicuously poor, and in need of the friends who had power or interest which he believed they could exert on his behalf. Their omitting or declining to give this help could not seem to him so clearly as to them an inevitable consequence of his having become impracticable, or at least of his passing for a man whose views were not likely to be safe and sober. Each friend in turn offended him, though unwillingly, and was suspected of wishing to shake him off. It was not altogether so ; but poor Merman's society had undeniably ceased to be attractive, and it was difficult to help him. At last the pressure of want urged him to try for a post far beneath his earlier prospects, and he gained it. He holds it still, for he has no vices, and his domestic life has kept up a sweetening current of motive around and within him. Nevertheless, the bitter flavor mingling itself with all topics, the premature weariness and withering, are irrevocably there. It is as if he had gone through a disease which alters what we call the constitution. He has long ceased to talk eagerly of the ideas which possess him, or to attempt making proselytes. The dial has moved onward, and he himself sees many of his former guesses in a new light. On the other hand, he has seen what he foreboded, that the main idea which was at the root of his too rash theorizing has been adopted by Grampus and received with general respect, no reference being heard to the ridiculous figure this important conception made when ushered in by the incompetent " Others."

Now and then, on rare occasions, when a sympathetic *tête-à-tête* has restored some of his old expansiveness, he will tell a companion in a railway-carriage, or other place of meeting favorable to autobiographical confidences, what has been the course of things in his particular case, as an example of the justice to be expected of the world. The companion usually allows for the bitterness of a disappointed man, and is secretly disinclined to believe that Grampus was to blame.

A MAN SURPRISED AT HIS ORIGINALITY.

AMONG the many acute sayings of La Rochefoucauld, there is hardly one more acute than this: "La plus grande ambition n'en a pas la moindre apparence lorsqu'elle se rencontre dans une impossibilité absolue d'arriver où elle aspire." Some of us might do well to use this hint in our treatment of acquaintances and friends, from whom we are expecting gratitude because we are so very kind in thinking of them, inviting them, and even listening to what they say — considering how insignificant they must feel themselves to be. We are often fallaciously confident in supposing that our friend's state of mind is appropriate to our moderate estimate of his importance, — almost as if we imagined the humble mollusk (so useful as an illustration) to have a sense of his own exceeding softness and low place in the scale of being. Your mollusk, on the contrary, is inwardly objecting to every other grade of solid, rather than to himself. Accustomed to observe what we think an unwarrantable conceit exhibiting itself in ridiculous pretensions and forwardness to play the lion's part, in obvious self-complacency and loud peremptoriness, we are not on the alert to detect the egoistic claims of a more exorbitant kind, often hidden under an apparent neutrality or an acquiescence in being put out of the question.

Thoughts of this kind occurred to me yesterday, when I saw the name of Lentulus in the obituary. The majority of his acquaintances, I imagine, have always thought of him as a man justly unpretending and as nobody's rival; but some of them have perhaps been struck with surprise at his reserve in praising the works of his contemporaries, and have now and then felt themselves in need of a key to his remarks on men of celebrity in various departments. He was a man of fair position, deriving his income from a business in which he did nothing, at leisure to frequent clubs and at ease in giving dinners, — well-looking, polite, and generally acceptable in society as a part of what we may call its bread-crumb, the neutral basis needful for the plums and spice. Why, then, did he speak of the modern Maro or the modern Flaccus with a peculiarity in his tone of assent to other people's praise which might almost have led you to suppose that the eminent poet had borrowed money of him and showed an indisposition to repay? He had no criticism to offer, no sign of objection more specific than a slight cough, a scarcely perceptible pause before assenting, and an air of self-control in his utterance — as if certain considerations had determined him not to inform against the so-called poet, who, to his knowledge, was a mere versifier. If you had questioned him closely, he would perhaps have confessed that he did think something better might be done in the way of Eclogues and Georgics, or of Odes and Epodes, and that to his mind poetry was something very different from what had hitherto been known under that name.

For my own part, being of a superstitious nature, given readily to imagine alarming causes, I immediately, on first getting these mystic hints from Lentulus, concluded that he held a number of entirely original poems, or at the very least a revolutionary treatise on poetics, in that melancholy manuscript state to which works excelling all that is ever printed are necessarily condemned; and I was long timid in speaking of the poets when he was present. For what might not Lentulus have done, or be profoundly aware of, that would make my ignorant impressions ridiculous? One cannot well be sure of the negative in such a case, except through certain positives that bear witness to it; and those witnesses are not always to be got hold of. But time wearing on, I perceived that the attitude of Lentulus toward the philosophers was essentially the same as his attitude toward the poets; nay, there was something so much more decided in his mode of closing his mouth after brief speech on the former, there was such an air of rapt consciousness in his private hints as to his conviction that all thinking hitherto had been an elaborate mistake, and as to his own power of conceiving a sound basis for a lasting superstructure, that I began to believe less in the poetical stores, and to infer that the line of Lentulus lay rather in the rational criticism of our beliefs and in systematic construction. In this case I did not figure to myself the existence of formidable manuscripts ready for the press; for great thinkers are known to carry their theories growing within their minds long before committing them to paper, and the ideas which made a new passion for them when their locks were jet or auburn, remain perilously unwritten, an inwardly developing condition of their successive selves, until the locks are gray or scanty. I only meditated improvingly on the way in which a man of exceptional faculties, and even carrying within him some of that fierce refiner's fire which is to purge away the dross of human error, may move about in society totally unrecognized, regarded as a person whose opinion is superfluous, and only rising into a power in emergencies of threatened black-balling. Imagine a Descartes or a Locke being recognized for nothing more than a good fellow and a perfect gentleman; what a painful view does such a picture suggest of impenetrable dulness in the society around them!

I would at all times rather be reduced to a cheaper estimate of a particular person, if by that means I can get a more cheerful view of my fellow-men generally; and I confess that, in a certain curiosity which led me to cultivate Lentulus's acquaintance, my hope leaned to the discovery that he was a less remarkable man than he had seemed to imply. It would have been a grief to discover that he was bitter or malicious; but by finding him to be neither a mighty poet, nor a revolutionary poetical critic, nor an epoch-making philosopher, my admiration for the poets and thinkers whom he rated so low would recover all its buoyancy, and I should not be left to trust to that very suspicious sort of merit which constitutes an exception in the history of mankind, and recommends itself as the total abolitionist of all previous claims on our confidence. You are not greatly surprised at the infirm logic of the coachman who would persuade you to engage him by insisting that any other would be sure to rob you in the matter of hay and corn, thus demanding a difficult belief in him as the sole exception from the frailties of his calling; but it is rather astonishing that the whole-sale decriers of mankind and its performances should be even more unwary in their reasoning than the coachman, since each of them not merely confides in your regarding himself as an exception, but overlooks the almost certain fact that you are wondering whether he inwardly excepts *you*. Now, conscious of entertaining some common opin-ions which seemed to fall under the mildly intimated but sweeping ban of Lentulus, my self-complacency was a little concerned.

Hence I deliberately attempted to draw out Lentulus in private dialogue, for it is the reverse of injury to a man to offer him that hearing which he seems to have found nowhere else. And for whatever purposes silence may be equal to gold, it cannot be safely taken as an indication of specific ideas. I sought to know why Lentulus was more than indif-ferent to the poets, and what was that new poetry which he had either written or, as to its principles, distinctly conceived. But I presently found that he knew very little of any partic-ular poet, and had a general notion of poetry as the use of artificial language to express unreal sentiments; he instanced "The Giaour," "Lalla Rookh," "The Pleasures of Hope," and "Ruin seize thee, ruthless King," — adding, "and plenty more." On my observing that he probably preferred a larger, simpler style, he emphatically assented. "Have you not," said I, "written something of that order?" "No, but I often compose as I go along. I see how things might be written as fine as Ossian, only with true ideas. The world has no notion what poetry will be."

It was impossible to disprove this, and I am always glad
to believe that the poverty of our imagination is no measure
of the world's resources. Our posterity will no doubt get
fuel in ways that we are unable to devise for them. But
what this conversation persuaded me of was, that the birth
with which the mind of Lentulus was pregnant could not be
poetry, though I did not question that he composed as he
went along, and that the exercise was accompanied with a
great sense of power. This is a frequent experience in
dreams, and much of our waking experience is but a dream
in the daylight. Nay, for what I saw, the compositions
might be fairly classed as Ossianic. But I was satisfied that
Lentulus could not disturb my grateful admiration for the
poets of all ages by eclipsing them, or by putting them under
a new electric light of criticism.

Still, he had himself thrown the chief emphasis of his
protest and his consciousness of corrective illumination on
the philosophic thinking of our race ; and his tone in assuring
me that everything which had been done in that way was
wrong, that Plato, Robert Owen, and Dr. Tuffle, who wrote
in the "Regulator," were all equally mistaken, gave my
superstitious nature a thrill of anxiety. After what had
passed about the poets, it did not seem likely that Lentulus
had all systems by heart; but who could say he had not
seized that thread which may somewhere hang out loosely
from the web of things, and be the clew of unravelment ?
We need not go far to learn that a prophet is not made by
erudition. Lentulus at least had not the bias of a school ;
and if it turned out that he was in agreement with any celebrated thinker, ancient or modern, the agreement would
have the value of an undesigned coincidence not due to forgotten reading. It was therefore with renewed curiosity
that I engaged him on this large subject, the universal
erroneousness of thinking up to the period when Lentulus
began that process. And here I found him more copious
than on the theme of poetry. He admitted that he did contemplate writing down his thoughts, but his difficulty was

their abundance. Apparently he was like the wood-cutter entering the thick forest, and saying, "Where shall I begin?" The same obstacle appeared in a minor degree to cling about his verbal exposition, and accounted perhaps for his rather helter-skelter choice of remarks bearing on the number of unaddressed letters sent to the post-office; on what logic really is, as tending to support the buoyancy of human mediums and mahogany tables; on the probability of all miracles under all religions when explained by hidden laws, and my unreasonableness in supposing that their profuse occurrence at half a guinea an hour in recent times was anything more than a coincidence; on the hap-hazard way in which marriages are determined — showing the baselessness of social and moral schemes; and on his expectation that he should offend the scientific world when he told them what he thought of electricity as an agent.

No man's appearance could be graver or more gentleman-like than that of Lentulus as we walked along the Mall, while he delivered these observations, understood by himself to have a regenerative bearing on human society. His wrist-bands and black gloves, his hat and nicely clipped hair, his laudable moderation in beard, and his evident discrimination in choosing his tailor, all seemed to excuse the prevalent estimate of him as a man untainted with heterodoxy, and likely to be so unencumbered with opinions that he would always be useful as an assenting and admiring listener. Men of science, seeing him at their lectures, doubtless flattered themselves that he came to learn from them; the philosophic ornaments of our time, expounding some of their luminous ideas in the social circle, took the meditative gaze of Lentulus for one of surprise, not unmixed with a just reverence at such close reasoning toward so novel a conclusion; and those who are called men of the world considered him a good fellow, who might be asked to vote for a friend of their own, and would have no troublesome notion to make him unaccommodating. You perceive how very much they were all mistaken, except in qualifying him as a good fellow.

This Lentulus certainly was, in the sense of being free from envy, hatred, and malice; and such freedom was all the more remarkable an indication of native benignity, because of his gaseous, illimitably expansive conceit. Yes, conceit; for that his enormous and contentedly ignorant confidence in his own rambling thoughts was usually clad in a decent silence, is no reason why it should be less strictly called by the name directly implying a complacent self-estimate unwarranted by performance. Nay, the total privacy in which he enjoyed his consciousness of inspiration was the very condition of its undisturbed, placid nourishment and gigantic growth. Your audibly arrogant man exposes himself to tests; in attempting to make an impression on others, he may possibly (not always) be made to feel his own lack of definiteness; and the demand for definiteness is to all of us a needful check on vague depreciation of what others do, and vague ecstatic trust in our own superior ability. But Lentulus was at once so unreceptive, and so little gifted with the power of displaying his miscellaneous deficiency of information, that there was really nothing to hinder his astonishment at the spontaneous crop of ideas which his mind secretly yielded. If it occurred to him that there were more meanings than one for the word "motive," since it sometimes meant the end aimed at, and sometimes the feeling that prompted the aiming, and that the word "cause" was also of changeable import, he was naturally struck with the truth of his own perception, and was convinced that if this vein were well followed out much might be made of it. Men were evidently in the wrong about cause and effect; else why was society in the confused state we behold? And as to motive, Lentulus felt that when he came to write down his views he should look deeply into this kind of subject, and show up thereby the anomalies of our social institutions; meanwhile the various aspects of "motive" and "cause" flitted about among the motley crowd of ideas which he regarded as original, and pregnant with reformative efficacy. For his unaffected good-will made him regard all his insight as only valuable because it tended toward reform.

The respectable man had got into his illusory maze of discoveries, by letting go that clew of conformity in his thinking which he had kept fast hold of in his tailoring and manners. He regarded heterodoxy as a power in itself, and took his inacquaintance with doctrines for a creative dissidence. But his epitaph needs not to be a melancholy one. His benevolent disposition was more effective for good, than his silent presumption for harm. He might have been mischievous but for the lack of words; instead of being astonished at his inspirations in private, he might have clad his addled originalities, disjointed commonplaces, blind denials, and balloon-like conclusions in that mighty sort of language which would have made a new Koran for a knot of followers. I mean no disrespect to the ancient Koran, but one would not desire the roc to lay more eggs, and give us a whole wing-flapping brood to soar and make twilight.

Peace be with Lentulus, for he has left us in peace. Blessed is the man who, having nothing to say, abstains from giving us wordy evidence of the fact, — from calling on us to look through a heap of millet-seed, in order to be sure that there is no pearl in it.

A TOO DEFERENTIAL MAN.

A LITTLE unpremeditated insincerity must be indulged under the stress of social intercourse. The talk even of an honest man must often represent merely his wish to be inoffensive or agreeable, rather than his genuine opinion or feeling on the matter in hand. His thought, if uttered, might be wounding; or he has not the ability to utter it with exactness, and snatches at a loose paraphrase; or he has really no genuine thought on the question, and is driven to fill up the vacancy by borrowing the remarks in vogue. These are the winds and currents we have all to steer among, and they are often too strong for our truthfulness or our wit. Let us not bear too hardly on each other for this common incidental frailty, or think that we rise superior to it by dropping all considerateness and deference.

But there are studious, deliberate forms of insincerity which it is fair to be impatient with — Hinze's, for example. From his name you might suppose him to be German; in fact, his family is Alsatian, but has been settled in England for more than one generation. He is the superlatively deferential man, and walks about with murmured wonder at the wisdom and discernment of everybody who talks to him. He cultivates the low-toned *tête-a-tête*, keeping his hat carefully in his hand, often stroking it, while he smiles with downcast eyes, as if to relieve his feelings under the pressure of the remarkable conversation which it is his honor to enjoy at the present moment. I confess to some rage on hearing him yesterday talking to Felicia, who is certainly a clever woman, and without any unusual desire to show her cleverness, occasionally says something of her own, or makes an allusion which is not quite common. Still, it must happen to her, as to every one else, to speak of many subjects on which the best things were said long ago; and in conversation with a person who has been newly introduced, those well-worn themes naturally recur as a further development of salutations and preliminary media of understanding, such as pipes, chocolate, or mastic-chewing, which serve to confirm the impression that our new acquaintance is on a civilized footing, and has enough regard for formulas to save us from shocking outbursts of individu-alism, to which we are always exposed with the tamest bear or baboon. Considered purely as a matter of information, it cannot any longer be important for us to learn that a British subject, included in the last census, holds Shakspeare to be supreme in the presentation of character; still, it is as admis-sible for any one to make this statement about himself as to rub his hands and tell you that the air is brisk, if only he will let it fall as a matter of course, with a parenthetic light-ness, and not announce his adhesion to a commonplace with an emphatic insistence, as if it were a proof of singular in-sight. We mortals should chiefly like to talk to each other out of good-will and fellowship, not for the sake of hearing revelations or being stimulated by witticisms; and I have usually found that it is the rather dull person who appears to be disgusted with his contemporaries because they are not always strikingly original, and to satisfy whom the party at a country-house should have included the prophet Isaiah, Plato, Francis Bacon, and Voltaire. It is always your heaviest bore who is astonished at the tameness of modern celebrities; naturally, for a little of his company has reduced them to a state of flaccid fatigue. It is right and meet that there should be an abundant utterance of good sound commonplaces. Part of an agreeable talker's charm is that he lets them fall continually with no more than their due emphasis. Giving a pleasant voice to what we are all well assured of, makes a sort of wholesome air for more special and dubious remark to move in.

Hence it seemed to me far from unbecoming in Felicia that in her first dialogue with Hinze, previously quite a stranger to her, her observations were those of an ordinarily refined and well-educated woman on standard subjects, and might have been printed in a manual of polite topics and creditable opinions. She had no desire to astonish a man of whom she had heard nothing particular. It was all the more exasperating to see and hear Hinze's reception of her well-bred conformities. Felicia's acquaintances knew her as the suitable wife of a distinguished man, a sensible, vivacious, kindly disposed woman, helping her husband with graceful apologies written and spoken, and making her receptions agreeable to all comers. But you would have imagined that Hinze had been prepared by general report to regard this introduction to her as an opportunity comparable to an audience of the Delphic Sibyl. When she had delivered herself on the changes in Italian travel, on the difficulty of reading Ariosto in these busy times, on the want of equilibrium in French political affairs, and on the pre-eminence of German music, he would know what to think. Felicia was evidently embarrassed by his reverent wonder, and, in dread lest she should seem to be playing the oracle, became somewhat confused, stumbling on her answers rather than choosing them. But this made no difference to Hinze's rapt attention and subdued eagerness of inquiry. He continued to put large questions, bending his head slightly, that his eyes might be a little lifted in awaiting her reply.

"What, may I ask, is your opinion as to the state of Art in England?"

"Oh," said Felicia, with a light deprecatory laugh, "I think it suffers from two diseases — bad taste in the patrons, and want of inspiration in the artists."

"That is true indeed," said Hinze, in an undertone of deep conviction. "You have put your finger with strict accuracy on the causes of decline. To a cultivated taste like yours this must be particularly painful."

"I did not say there was actual decline," said Felicia,

with a touch of brusquerie.   " I don't set myself up as the great personage whom nothing can please."

" That would be too severe a misfortune for others," says my complimentary ape. "You approve, perhaps, of Rosemary's 'Babes in the Wood,' as something fresh and *naïve* in sculpture ? "

" I think it enchanting."

" Does he know that ?   Or *will* you permit me to tell him ? "

" Heaven forbid ! It would be an impertinence in me to praise a work of his, to pronounce on its quality ; and that I happen to like it can be of no consequence to him."

Here was an occasion for Hinze to smile down on his hat and stroke it — Felicia's ignorance that her praise was inestimable being peculiarly noteworthy to an observer of mankind.   Presently he was quite sure that her favorite author was Shakspeare, and wished to know what she thought of Hamlet's madness.   When she had quoted Wilhelm Meister on this point, and had afterward testified that " Lear " was beyond adequate presentation, that " Julius Cæsar " was an effective acting play, and that a poet may know a good deal about human nature while knowing little of geography, Hinze appeared so impressed with the plenitude of these revelations that he recapitulated them, weaving them together with threads of compliment : " As you very justly observed ; " and " It is most true, as you say ; " and " It were well if others noted what you have remarked."

Some listeners, incautious in their epithets, would have called Hinze an " ass."   For my part, I would never insult that intelligent and unpretending animal, who no doubt brays with perfect simplicity and substantial meaning to those acquainted with his idiom, and if he feigns more submission than he feels, has weighty reasons for doing so ; I would never, I say, insult that historic and ill-appreciated animal, the ass, by giving his name to a man whose continuous pretence is so shallow in its motive, so unexcused by any sharp appetite, as this of Hinze's.

But perhaps you would say that his adulatory manner was originally adopted under strong promptings of self-interest, and that his absurdly overacted deference to persons from whom he expects no patronage is the unreflecting persistence of habit — just as those who live with the deaf will shout to everybody else.

And you might indeed imagine that in talking to Tulpian, who has considerable interest at his disposal, Hinze had a desired appointment in his mind. Tulpian is appealed to on innumerable subjects, and if he is unwilling to express himself on any one of them, says so with instructive copiousness ; he is much listened to, and his utterances are registered and reported with more or less exactitude. But I think he has no other listener who comports himself as Hinze does — who, figuratively speaking, carries about a small spoon, ready to pick up any dusty crumb of opinion that the eloquent man may have let drop. Tulpian, with reverence be it said, has some rather absurd notions, such as a mind of large discourse often finds room for. They slip about among his higher conceptions and multitudinous acquirements, like disreputable characters at a national celebration in some vast cathedral, where to the ardent soul all is glorified by rainbow-light and grand associations ; any vulgar detective knows them for what they are. But Hinze is especially fervid in his desire to hear Tulpian dilate on his crotchets, and is rather troublesome to bystanders in asking them whether they have read the various fugitive writings in which these crotchets have been published. If an expert is explaining some matter on which you desire to know the evidence, Hinze teases you with Tulpian's guesses, and asks the expert what he thinks of them.

In general, Hinze delights in the citation of opinions, and would hardly remark that the sun shone, without an air of respectful appeal or fervid adhesion. The "Iliad," one sees, would impress him little, if it were not for what Mr. Fugleman has lately said about it ; and if you mention an image or sentiment in Chaucer, he seems not to heed the bearing of

your reference, but immediately tells you that Mr. Hautboy,
too, regards Chaucer as a poet of the first order, and he is
delighted to find that two such judges, as you and Hautboy,
are at one.

What is the reason of all this subdued ecstasy, moving
about, hat in hand, with well-dressed hair, and attitudes of
unimpeachable correctness ? Some persons, conscious of sagacity, decide at once that Hinze knows what he is about in
flattering Tulpian, and has a carefully appraised end to serve,
though they may not see it. They are misled by the common mistake of supposing that men's behavior, whether habitual or occasional, is chiefly determined by a distinctly
conceived motive, a definite object to be gained or a definite
evil to be avoided. The truth is that, the primitive wants of
nature once tolerably satisfied, the majority of mankind, even
in a civilized life full of solicitations, are with difficulty
aroused to the distinct conception of an object toward which
they will direct their actions with careful adaptation ; and it
is yet rarer to find one who can persist in the systematic pursuit of such an end. Few lives are shaped, few characters
formed, by the contemplation of definite consequences seen
from a distance, and made the goal of continuous effort or the
beacon of a constantly avoided danger. Such control by foresight, such vivid picturing and practical logic, are the distinction of exceptionally strong natures ; but society is chiefly
made up of human beings whose daily acts are all performed
either in unreflecting obedience to custom and routine, or
from immediate promptings of thought or feeling to execute
an immediate purpose. They pay their poor-rates, give their
vote in affairs political or parochial, wear a certain amount
of starch, hinder boys from tormenting the helpless, and
spend money on tedious observances called pleasures, without mentally adjusting these practices to their own well-
understood interest, or to the general, ultimate welfare of
the human race ; and when they fall into ungraceful compliment, excessive smiling, or other luckless efforts of com-
plaisant behavior, these are but the tricks or habits gradually

formed under the successive promptings of a wish to be agreeable, stimulated day by day without any widening resources for gratifying the wish. It does not in the least follow that they are seeking by studied hypocrisy to get something for themselves. And so with Hinze's deferential bearing, complimentary parentheses, and worshipful tones, which seem to some like the overacting of a part in a comedy. He expects no appointment or other appreciable gain through Tulpian's favor; he has no doubleness toward Felicia; there is no sneering or backbiting obverse to his ecstatic admiration. He is very well off in the world, and cherishes no unsatisfied ambition that could feed design and direct flattery. As you perceive, he has had the education and other advantages of a gentleman, without being conscious of marked result, such as a decided preference for any particular ideas or functions; his mind is furnished as hotels are, with everything for occasional and transient use. But one cannot be an Englishman and gentleman in general; it is in the nature of things that one must have an individuality, though it may be of an often-repeated type. As Hinze in growing to maturity had grown into a particular form and expression of person, so he necessarily gathered a manner and frame of speech which made him additionally recognizable. His nature is not tuned to the pitch of a genuine direct admiration, only to an attitudinizing deference which does not fatigue itself with the formation of real judgments. All human achievement must be wrought down to this spoon-meat, this mixture of other persons' washy opinions and his own flux of reverence for what is third-hand, before Hinze can find a relish for it.

He has no more leading characteristic than the desire to stand well with those who are justly distinguished; he has no base admirations; and you may know by his entire presentation of himself, from the management of his hat to the angle at which he keeps his right foot, that he aspires to correctness. Desiring to behave becomingly, and also to make a figure in dialogue, he is only like the bad artist, whose picture is a failure. We may pity these ill-gifted strivers, but not pretend that their works are pleasant to behold. A man is bound to know something of his own weight and muscular dexterity, and the puny athlete is called foolish before he is seen to be thrown. Hinze has not the stuff in him to be at once agreeably conversational and sincere, and he has got himself up to be at all events agreeably conversational. Notwithstanding this deliberateness of intention in his talk, he is unconscious of falsity; for he has not enough of deep and lasting impression to find a contrast or diversity between his words and his thoughts. He is not fairly to be called a hypocrite; but I have already confessed to the more exasperation at his make-believe reverence, because it has no deep hunger to excuse it.

ONLY TEMPER.

WHAT is temper? Its primary meaning, the proportion and mode in which qualities are mingled, is much neglected in popular speech, yet even here the word often carries a reference to an habitual state or general tendency of the organism, in distinction from what are held to be specific virtues and vices. As people confess to bad memory without expecting to sink in mental reputation, so we hear a man declared to have a bad temper, and yet glorified as the possessor of every high quality. When he errs, or in any way commits himself, his temper is accused, not his character; and it is understood that, but for a brutal, bearish mood, he is kindness itself. If he kicks small animals, swears violently at a servant who mistakes orders, or is grossly rude to his wife, it is remarked apologetically that these things mean nothing — they are all temper.

Certainly there is a limit to this form of apology, and the forgery of a bill, or the ordering of goods without any prospect of paying for them, has never been set down to an unfortunate habit of sulkiness or of irascibility. But, on the whole, there is a peculiar exercise of indulgence toward the manifestations of bad temper, which tends to encourage them, so that we are in danger of having among us a number of virtuous persons who conduct themselves detestably, just as we have hysterical patients who, with sound organs, are apparently laboring under many sorts of organic disease. Let it be admitted, however, that a man may be "a good fellow" and yet have a bad temper, — so bad that we recognize his merits with reluctance, and are inclined to resent his occasionally amiable behavior as an unfair demand on our admiration.

Touchwood is that kind of good fellow. He is by turns insolent, quarrelsome, repulsively haughty to innocent people who approach him with respect, neglectful of his friends, angry in face of legitimate demands, procrastinating in the fulfilment of such demands, prompted to rude words and harsh looks by a moody disgust with his fellow-men in general — and yet, as everybody will assure you, the soul of honor, a steadfast friend, a defender of the oppressed, an affectionate-hearted creature. Pity that, after a certain experience of his moods, his intimacy becomes insupportable! A man who uses his balmorals to tread on your toes with much frequency, and an unmistakable emphasis, may prove a fast friend in adversity; but meanwhile your adversity has not arrived, and your toes are tender. The daily sneer or growl at your remarks is not to be made amends for by a possible eulogy, or defence of your understanding against depreciators who may not present themselves, and on an occasion which may never arise. I cannot submit to a chronic state of blue and green bruise as a form of insurance against an accident.

Touchwood's bad temper is of the contradicting, pugnacious sort. He is the honorable gentleman in opposition, whatever proposal or proposition may be broached ; and when others join him, he secretly damns their superfluous agreement, quickly discovering that his way of stating the case is not exactly theirs. An invitation, or any sign of expectation, throws him into an attitude of refusal. Ask his concurrence in a benevolent measure; he will not decline to give it, because he has a real sympathy with good aims, but he complies resentfully; though where he is let alone, he will do much more than any one would have thought of asking for. No man would shrink with greater sensitiveness from the imputation of not paying his debts; yet when a bill is sent in with any promptitude, he is inclined to make the tradesman wait for the money he is in such a hurry to get. One sees

that this antagonistic temper must be much relieved by finding a particular object, and that its worst moments must be
those where the mood is that of vague resistance, there being
nothing specific to oppose. Touchwood is never so little
engaging as when he comes down to breakfast with a cloud
on his brow, after parting from you the night before with an
affectionate effusiveness, at the end of a confidential conversation, which has assured you of mutual understanding. Impossible that you can have committed any offence! If mice
have disturbed him, that is not your fault; but, nevertheless,
your cheerful greeting had better not convey any reference to
the weather; else it will be met by a sneer which, taking you
unawares, may give you a crushing sense that you make a
poor figure with your cheerfulness, which was not asked for.
Some daring person perhaps introduces another topic, and
uses the delicate flattery of appealing to Touchwood for his
opinion, the topic being included in his favorite studies. An
indistinct muttering, with a look at the carving-knife, in reply,
teaches that daring person how ill he has chosen a market
for his deference. If Touchwood's behavior affects you very
closely, you had better break your leg in the course of the
day: his bad temper will then vanish at once; he will take
a painful journey on your behalf; he will sit up with you
night after night; he will do all the work of your department,
so as to save you from any loss in consequence of your accident; he will be even uniformly tender to you till you are
well on your legs again, when he will some fine morning insult you without provocation, and make you wish that his
generous goodness to you had not closed your lips against
retort.

It is not always necessary that a friend should break his
leg for Touchwood to feel compunction, and endeavor to make
amends for his bearishness or insolence. He becomes spon-
taneously conscious that he has misbehaved, and he is not
only ashamed of himself, but has the better prompting to try
and heal any wound he has inflicted. Unhappily, the habit
of being offensive "without meaning it" leads usually to a

way of making amends which the injured person cannot but regard as a being amiable without meaning it. The kindnesses, the complimentary indications or assurances, are apt to appear in the light of a penance adjusted to the foregoing lapses, and, by the very contrast they offer, call up a keener memory of the wrong they atone for. They are not a spontaneous prompting of good-will, but an elaborate compensation. And, in fact, Dion's atoning friendliness has a ring of artificiality. Because he formerly disguised his good feeling toward you, he now expresses more than he quite feels. It is in vain. Having made you extremely uncomfortable last week, he has absolutely diminished his power of making you happy to-day. He struggles against the result by excessive effort; but he has taught you to observe his fitfulness, rather than to be warmed by his episodic show of regard.

I suspect that many persons who have an uncertain, incalculable temper, flatter themselves that it enhances their fascination; but perhaps they are under the prior mistake of exaggerating the charm which they suppose to be thus strengthened; in any case, they will do well not to trust in the attractions of caprice and moodiness for a long continuance or for close intercourse. A pretty woman may fan the flame of distant adorers by harassing them; but if she lets one of them make her his wife, the point of view from which he will look at her poutings and tossings, and mysterious inability to be pleased, will be seriously altered. And if slavery to a pretty woman, which seems among the least conditional forms of abject service, will not bear too great a strain from her bad temper, even though her beauty remain the same, it is clear that a man whose claims lie in his high character, or high performances, had need impress us very constantly with his peculiar value and indispensableness, if he is to test our patience by an uncertainty of temper which leaves us absolutely without grounds for guessing how he will receive our persons or humbly advanced opinions, or what line he will take on any but the most momentous occasions.

For it is among the repulsive effects of this bad temper,

which is supposed to be compatible with shining virtues, that it is apt to determine a man's sudden adhesion to an opinion, whether on a personal or impersonal matter, without leaving him time to consider his grounds. The adhesion is sudden and momentary, but it either forms a precedent for his line of thought and action, or it is presently seen to have been inconsistent with his true mind. This determination of partisanship by temper has its worst effects in the career of the public man, who is always in danger of getting so enthralled by his own words that he looks into facts and questions, not to get rectifying knowledge, but to get evidence that will justify his actual attitude, which was assumed under an impulse dependent on something else than knowledge. There has been plenty of insistence on the evil of swearing by the words of a master, and having the judgment uniformly controlled by a "He said it;" but a much worse woe to befall a man is to have every judgment controlled by an "I said it" — to make a divinity of his own short-sightedness or passion-led aberration, and explain the world in its honor. There is hardly a more pitiable degradation than this, for a man of high gifts. Hence I cannot join with those who wish that Touchwood, being young enough to enter on public life, should get elected for Parliament, and use his excellent abilities to serve his country in that conspicuous manner. For hitherto, in the less momentous incidents of private life, his capricious temper has only produced the minor evil of inconsistency, and he is even greatly at ease in contradicting himself, provided he can contradict you, and disappoint any smiling expectation you may have shown that the impressions you are uttering are likely to meet with his sympathy, considering that the day before he himself gave you the example which your mind is following. He is at least free from those fetters of self-justification which are the curse of parliamentary speaking; and what I rather desire for him is that he should produce the great book which he is generally pronounced capable of writing, and put his best self imperturbably on record for the advantage of society; because I should then have steady ground for bearing with his diurnal incalculableness, and could fix my gratitude as by strong staple to that unvarying monumental service. Unhappily, Touchwood's great powers have been only so far manifested as to be believed in, not demonstrated. Everybody rates them highly, and thinks that whatever he chose to do would be done in a firstrate manner. Is it his love of disappointing complacent expectancy, which has gone so far as to keep up this lamentable negation, and made him resolve not to write the comprehensive work which he would have written if nobody had expected it of him ?

One can see that if Touchwood were to become a public man, and take to frequent speaking on platforms or from his seat in the House, it would hardly be possible for him to maintain much integrity of opinion, or to avoid courses of partisanship which a healthy public sentiment would stamp with discredit. Say that he were endowed with the purest honesty, it would inevitably be dragged captive by this mysterious, Protean, bad temper. There would be the fatal public necessity of justifying oratorical temper, which had got on its legs in its bitter mood and made insulting imputations, or of keeping up some decent show of consistency with opinions vented out of temper's contradictoriness. And words would have to be followed up by acts of adhesion.

Certainly, if a bad-tempered man can be admirably virtuous, he must be so under extreme difficulties. I doubt the possibility that a high order of character can coexist with a temper like Touchwood's. For it is of the nature of such temper to interrupt the formation of healthy mental habits, which depend on a growing harmony between perception, conviction, and impulse. There may be good feelings, good deeds, — for a human nature may pack endless varieties and blessed inconsistencies in its windings, — but it is essential to what is worthy to be called high character, that it may be safely calculated on, and that its qualities shall have taken the form of principles or laws, habitually, if not perfectly, obeyed.

If a man frequently passes unjust judgments, takes up false attitudes, intermits his acts of kindness with rude behavior or cruel words, and falls into the consequent vulgar error of supposing that he can make amends by labored agreeableness, I cannot consider such courses any the less ugly because they are ascribed to "temper." Especially I object to the assumption, that his having a fundamentally good disposition is either an apology or a compensation for his bad behavior. If his temper yesterday made him lash the horses, upset the curricle, and cause a breakage in my rib, I feel it no compensation that to-day he vows he will drive me anywhere, in the gentlest manner, any day, as long as he lives. Yesterday was what it was, — my rib is paining me; it is not a main object of my life to be driven by Touchwood, and I have no confidence in his life-long gentleness. The utmost form of placability I am capable of is to try and remember his better deeds already performed, and, mindful of my own offence, to bear him no malice. But I cannot accept his amends.

If the bad-tempered man wants to apologize, he had need to do it on a large public scale, — make some beneficent discovery, produce some stimulating work of genius, invent some powerful process, — prove himself such a good to contemporary multitudes and future generations as to make the discomfort he causes his friends and acquaintances a vanishing quality, a trifle even in their own estimate.

A POLITICAL MOLECULE.

THE most arrant denier must admit that a man often furthers larger ends than he is conscious of, and that while he is transacting his particular affairs with the narrow pertinacity of a respectable ant, he subserves an economy larger than any purpose of his own. Society is happily not dependent for the growth of fellowship on the small minority already endowed with comprehensive sympathy. Any molecule of the body politic, working toward his own interest in an orderly way, gets his understanding more or less penetrated with the fact that his interest is included in that of a large number. I have watched several political molecules being educated in this way, by the nature of things, into a faint feeling of fraternity. But at this moment I am thinking of Spike, an elector who voted on the side of Progress, though he was not inwardly attached to it under that name. For abstractions are deities having many specific names, local habitations, and forms of activity, and so get a multitude of devout servants, who care no more for them under their highest titles than the celebrated person who, putting with forcible brevity a view of human motives now much insisted on, asked what Posterity had done for him that he should care for Posterity? To many minds, even among the ancients (thought by some to have been invariably poetical), the goddess of wisdom was doubtless worshipped simply as the patroness of spinning and weaving. Now spinning and weaving, from a manufacturing, wholesale point of view, was the chief form under which Spike from early years had unconsciously been a devotee of Progress.

He was a political molecule of the most gentleman-like appearance, not less than six feet high, and showing the utmost nicety in the care of his person and equipment. His umbrella was especially remarkable for its neatness, though perhaps he swung it unduly in walking. His complexion was fresh, his eyes small, bright, and twinkling. He was seen to great advantage in a hat and great-coat — garments frequently fatal to the impressiveness of shorter figures ; but when he was uncovered in the drawing-room, it was impossible not to observe that his head shelved off too rapidly from the eyebrows toward the crown, and that his length of limb seemed to have used up his mind so as to cause an air of abstraction from conversational topics. He appeared, indeed, to be preoccupied with a sense of his exquisite cleanliness, clapped his hands together and rubbed them, frequently straightened his back, and even opened his mouth and closed it again with a slight snap, apparently for no other purpose than the confirmation to himself of his own powers in that line. These are innocent exercises, but they are not such as give weight to a man's personality. Sometimes Spike's mind, emerging from its preoccupation, burst forth in a remark delivered with smiling zest — as, that he did like to see gravel-walks well rolled, or that a lady should always wear the best jewelry, or that a bride was a most interesting object ; but finding these ideas received rather coldly, he would relapse into abstraction, draw up his back, wrinkle his brows longitudinally, and seem to regard society, even including gravel-walks, jewelry, and brides, as essentially a poor affair. Indeed, his habit of mind was desponding, and he took melancholy views as to the possible extent of human pleasure and the value of existence ; especially after he had made his fortune in the cotton manufacture, and had thus attained the chief object of his ambition — the object which had engaged his talent for order and persevering application — for his easy leisure caused him much *ennui*. He was abstemious, and had none of those temptations to sensual excess which fill up a man's time, first with indulgence, and then with the process

of getting well from its effects. He had not, indeed, exhausted the sources of knowledge, but here again his notions
of human pleasure were narrowed by his want of appetite;
for, though he seemed rather surprised at the consideration
that Alfred the Great was a Catholic, or that, apart from the
Ten Commandments, any conception of moral conduct had occurred to mankind, he was not stimulated to further inquiries
on these remote matters. Yet he aspired to what he regarded
as intellectual society, willingly entertained beneficed clergymen, and bought the books he heard spoken of, arranging
them carefully on the shelves of what he called his library,
and occasionally sitting alone in the same room with them.
But some minds seem well glaced by nature against the admission of knowledge, and Spike's was one of them. It was
not, however, entirely so with regard to politics. He had had
a strong opinion about the Reform Bill, and saw clearly that
the large trading-towns ought to send members. Portraits
of the Reform heroes hung framed and glazed in his library;
he prided himself on being a Liberal. In this last particular,
as well as in not giving benefactions, and not making loans
without interest, he showed unquestionable firmness. On the
Repeal of the Corn Laws, again, he was thoroughly convinced.
His mind was expansive toward foreign markets, and his
imagination could see that the people from whom we took
corn might be able to take the cotton goods which they had
hitherto dispensed with. On his conduct in these political
concerns, his wife, otherwise influential as a woman who belonged to a family with a title in it, and who had condescended in marrying him, could gain no hold; she had to
blush a little at what was called her husband's "radicalism,"
—an epithet which was a very unfair impeachment of Spike,
who never went to the root of anything. But he understood
his own trading affairs, and in this way became a genuine,
constant political element. If he had been born a little later
he could have been accepted as an eligible member of Parliament, and if he had belonged to a high family he might
have done for a member of the Government. Perhaps his

indifference to "views" would have passed for administrative judiciousness, and he would have been so generally silent that he must often have been silent in the right place. But this is empty speculation; there is no warrant for saying what Spike would have been and known, so as to have made a calculable political element, if he had not been educated by having to manage his trade. A small mind, trained to useful occupation for the satisfying of private need, becomes a representative of genuine class-needs. Spike objected to certain items of legislation, because they hampered his own trade, but his neighbor's trade was hampered by the same causes; and though he would have been simply selfish, in a question of light or water between himself and a fellow-townsman, his need for a change in legislation, being shared by all his neighbors in trade, ceased to be simply selfish, and raised him to a sense of common injury and common benefit. True, if the law could have been changed for the benefit of his particular business, leaving the cotton trade in general in a sorry condition while he prospered, Spike might not have thought that result intolerably unjust; but the nature of things did not allow of such a result being contemplated as possible; it allowed of an enlarged market for Spike, only through the enlargement of his neighbors' market, and the Possible is always the ultimate master of our efforts and desires. Spike was obliged to contemplate a general benefit, and thus became public-spirited in spite of himself. Or rather, the nature of things transmuted his active egoism into a demand for a public benefit.

Certainly, if Spike had been born a marquis he could not have had the same chance of being useful as a political element. But he might have had the same appearance, have been equally null in conversation, sceptical as to the reality of pleasure, and destitute of historical knowledge, — perhaps even dimly disliking Jesuitism as a quality in Catholic minds, or regarding Bacon as the inventor of physical science. The depths of middle-aged gentlemen's ignorance will never be known, for want of public examinations in this branch.

THE WATCH-DOG OF KNOWLEDGE.

MORDAX is an admirable man, ardent in intellectual work, public-spirited, affectionate, and able to find the right words in conveying ingenious ideas or elevated feeling. Pity that to all these graces he cannot add what would give them the utmost finish, — the occasional admission that he has been in the wrong, the occasional frank welcome of a new idea as something not before present to his mind! But no; Mordax's self-respect seems to be of that fiery quality which demands that none but the monarchs of thought shall have an advantage over him, and in the presence of contradiction, or the threat of having his notions corrected, he becomes astonishingly unscrupulous and cruel for so kindly and conscientious a man.

"You are fond of attributing those fine qualities to Mordax," said Acer, the other day, "but I have not much belief in virtues that are always requiring to be asserted, in spite of appearances against them. True fairness and good-will show themselves precisely where his are conspicuously absent — I mean in recognizing claims which the rest of the world are not likely to stand up for. It does not need much love of truth and justice in me to say that Aldebaran is a bright star, or Isaac Newton the greatest of discoverers; or much kindliness in me to want my notes to be heard above the rest in a chorus of hallelujahs to one already crowned. It is my way to apply tests. Does the man who has the ear of the public use his advantage tenderly toward poor fellows who may be hindered of their due if he treats their pretensions with scorn? That is my test of his justice and benevolence."

My answer was, that his system of moral tests might be as delusive as what ignorant people take to be tests of intellect and learning. If the scholar or savant cannot answer their haphazard questions on the shortest notice, their belief in his capacity is shaken. But the better-informed have given up the Johnsonian theory of mind as a pair of legs able to walk east or west according to choice. Intellect is no longer taken to be a ready-made dose of ability to attain eminence (or mediocrity) in all departments; it is even admitted that application in one line of study or practice has often a laming effect in other directions, and that an intellectual quality or special facility which is a furtherance in one medium of effort is a drag in another. We have convinced ourselves by this time that a man may be a sage in celestial physics, and a poor creature in the purchase of seed-corn, or even in theorizing about the affections; that he may be a mere fumbler in physiology, and yet show a keen insight into human motives; that he may seem the "poor Poll" of the company in conversation, and yet write with some humorous vigor. It is not true that a man's intellectual power is, like the strength of a timber beam, to be measured by its weakest point.

Why should we any more apply that fallacious standard of what is called consistency to a man's moral nature; and argue against the existence of fine impulses or habits of feeling in relation to his actions generally, because those better movements are absent in a class of cases which act peculiarly on an irritable form of his egoism? The mistake might be corrected by our taking notice that the ungenerous words or acts which seem to us the most utterly incompatible with good dispositions in the offender, are those which offend ourselves. All other persons are able to draw a milder conclusion. Laniger, who has a temper but no talent for repartee, having been run down in a fierce way by Mordax, is inwardly persuaded that the highly lauded man is a wolf at heart; he is much tried by perceiving that his own friends seem to think no worse of the reckless assailant than they did before; and Corvus, who has lately been flattered by some kindness from

Mordax, is unmindful enough of Laniger's feeling to dwell on this instance of good-nature with admiring gratitude. There is a fable that when the badger had been stung all over by bees, a bear consoled him by a rhapsodic account of how he himself had just breakfasted on their honey. The badger replied, peevishly, "The stings are in my flesh, and the sweetness is on your muzzle." The bear, it is said, was surprised at the badger's want of altruism.

But this difference of sensibility between Laniger and his friends only mirrors in a faint way the difference between his own point of view and that of the man who has injured him. If those neutral, perhaps even affectionate persons, form no lively conception of what Laniger suffers, how should Mordax have any such sympathetic imagination to check him in what he persuades himself is a scourging administered by the qualified man to the unqualified? Depend upon it, his conscience, though active enough in some relations, has never given him a twinge because of his polemical rudeness and even brutality. He would go from the room where he has been tiring himself through the watches of the night, in lifting and turning a sick friend, and straightway write a reply or rejoinder in which he mercilessly pilloried a Laniger who had supposed that he could tell the world something else or more than had been sanctioned by the eminent Mordax — and, what was worse, had sometimes really done so. Does this nullify the genuineness of motive which made him tender to his suffering friend? Not at all. It only proves that his arrogant egoism, set on fire, sends up smoke and flame where just before there had been the dews of fellowship and pity. He is angry, and equips himself accordingly — with a penknife to give the offender a *comprachico* countenance, a mirror to show him the effect, and a pair of nailed boots to give him his dismissal. All this to teach him who the Romans really were, and to purge Inquiry of incompetent intrusion, so rendering an important service to mankind.

When a man is in a rage, and wants to hurt another in consequence, he can always regard himself as the civil arm of a spiritual power, and all the more easily because there is real need to assert the righteous efficacy of indignation. I for my part feel with the Lanigers, and should object all the more to their or my being lacerated and dressed with salt, if the administrator of such torture alleged as a motive his care for truth and posterity, and got himself pictured with a halo in consequence. In transactions between fellow-men it is well to consider a little, in the first place, what is fair and kind toward the person immediately concerned, before we spit and roast him on behalf of the next century but one. Wide-reaching motives, blessed and glorious as they are, and of the highest sacramental virtue, have their dangers, like all else that touches the mixed life of the earth. They are arch-angels with awful brow and flaming sword, summoning and encouraging us to do the right and the divinely heroic, and we feel a beneficent tremor in their presence; but to learn what it is they thus summon us to do, we have to consider the mortals we are elbowing, who are of our own stature and our own appetites. I cannot feel sure how my voting will affect the condition of Central Asia in the coming ages, but I have good reason to believe that the future populations there will be none the worse off because I abstain from conjectural vilification of my opponents during the present parliamentary session, and I am very sure that I shall be less injurious to my contemporaries. On the whole, and in the vast majority of instances, the action by which we can do the best for future ages is of the sort which has a certain beneficence and grace for contemporaries. A sour father may reform prisons, but considered in his sourness he does harm. The deed of Judas has been attributed to far-reaching views, and the wish to hasten his Master's declaration of himself as the Messiah. Perhaps — I will not maintain the contrary — Judas repre-sented his motive in this way, and felt justified in his trai-torous kiss; but my belief that he deserved, metaphorically speaking, to be where Dante saw him, at the bottom of the Malebolge, would not be the less strong because he was not convinced that his action was detestable. I refuse to accept a man, who has the stomach for such treachery, as a hero impatient for the redemption of mankind, and for the beginning of a reign when the kisses shall be those of peace and righteousness.

All this is by the way, to show that my apology for Mordax was not found on his persuasion of superiority in his own motives, but on the compatibility of unfair, equivocal, and even cruel actions with a nature which, apart from special temptations, is kindly and generous; and also to enforce the need of checks, from a fellow-feeling with those whom our acts immediately (not distantly) concern. Will any one be so hardy as to maintain that an otherwise worthy man cannot be vain and arrogant? I think most of us have some interest in arguing the contrary. And it is of the nature of vanity and arrogance, if unchecked, to become cruel and self-justifying. There are fierce beasts within; chain them, chain them, and let them learn to cower before the creature with wider reason. This is what one wishes for Mordax — that his heart and brain should restrain the outleap of roar and talons.

As to his unwillingness to admit that an idea which he has not discovered is novel to him, one is surprised that quick intellect and shrewd observation do not early gather reasons for being ashamed of a mental trick which makes one among the comic parts of that various actor, Conceited Ignorance.

I have a sort of valet and factotum, an excellent, respectable servant, whose spelling is so unvitiated by non-phonetic superfluities that he writes *night* as *nit*. One day, looking over his accounts, I said to him jocosely: "You are in the latest fashion with your spelling, Pummel; most people spell 'night' with a *gh* between the *i* and the *t*, but the greatest scholars now spell it as you do." "So I suppose, sir," says Pummel; "I've seen it with a *gh*, but I've noways give in to that myself." You would never catch Pummel in an interjection of surprise. I have sometimes laid traps for his astonishment; but he has escaped them all, either by a respectful neutrality, as of one who would not appear to notice that his master had been taking too much wine, or else by that strong persuasion of his all-knowingness, which makes it simply impossible for him to feel himself newly informed.   If I tell him that the world is spinning round and along like a top, and that he is spinning with it, he says, "Yes, I 've heard a deal of that in my time, sir," and lifts the horizontal lines of his brow a little higher, balancing his head from side to side as if it were too painfully full.   Whether I tell him that they cook puppies in China, that there are ducks with fur coats in Australia, or that in some parts of the world it is the pink of politeness to put your tongue out on introduction to a respectable stranger, Pummel replies, "So I suppose, sir," with an air of resignation to hearing my poor version of well-known things, such as elders use in listening to lively boys lately presented ˙with an anecdote-book.   His utmost concession is that what you state is what he would have supplied if you had given him *carte blanche* instead of your needless instruction, and in this sense his favorite answer is, "I should say."

"Pummel," I observed, a little irritated at not getting my coffee, "if you were to carry your kettle and spirits of wine up a mountain of a morning, your water would boil there sooner."   "I should say, sir."   Or, "There are boiling springs in Iceland.   Better go to Iceland."   "That 's what I 've been thinking, sir."

I have taken to asking him hard questions, and, as I expected, he never admits his own inability to answer them, without representing it as common to the human race. "What is the cause of the tides, Pummel?"   "Well, sir, nobody rightly knows.   Many gives their opinion, but if I was to give mine, it 'ud be different."

But while he is never surprised himself, he is constantly imagining situations of surprise for others.   His own consciousness is that of one so thoroughly soaked in knowledge that further absorption is impossible; but his neighbors appear to him to be in the state of thirsty sponges, which it is a charity to besprinkle. His great interest in thinking of foreigners is that they must be surprised at what they see in England, and especially at the beef. He is often occupied with the surprise Adam must have felt at the sight of the assembled animals — "for he was not like us, sir, used from a b'y to Wombwell's shows." He is fond of discoursing to the lad who acts as shoeblack and general subaltern, and I have overheard him saying to that small upstart, with some severity, "Now don't you pretend to know, because the more you pretend the more I see your ignirance"— a lucidity on his part which has confirmed my impression that the thoroughly self-satisfied person is the only one fully to appreciate the charm of humility in others.

Your diffident, self-suspecting mortal is not very angry that others should feel more comfortable about themselves, provided they are not otherwise offensive : he is rather like the chilly person, glad to sit next a warmer neighbor; or the timid, glad to have a courageous fellow-traveller. It cheers him to observe the store of small comforts that his fellow-creatures may find in their self-complacency, just as one is pleased to see poor old souls soothed by the tobacco and snuff for which one has neither nose nor stomach one's self.

But your arrogant man will not tolerate a presumption which he sees to be ill-founded. The service he regards society as most in need of, is to put down the conceit which is so particularly rife around him that he is inclined to believe it the growing characteristic of the present age. In the schools of Magna Græcia, or in the sixth century of our era, or even under Kublai Khan, he finds a comparative freedom from that presumption by which his contemporaries are stirring his able gall. The way people will now flaunt notions which are not his, without appearing to mind that they are not his, strikes him as especially disgusting. It might seem surprising to us that one strongly convinced of his own value should prefer to exalt an age in which *he* did not flourish, if it were not for the reflection that the present age is the only one in which anybody has appeared to undervalue him.

A HALF-BREED.

AN early, deep-seated love to which we become faithless has its unfailing Nemesis, if only in that division of soul which narrows all newer joys by the intrusion of regret and the established presentiment of change. I refer not merely to the love of a person, but to the love of ideas, practical beliefs, and social habits. And faithlessness here means not a gradual conversion, dependent on enlarged knowledge, but a yielding to seductive circumstance; not a conviction that the original choice was a mistake, but a subjection to incidents that flatter a growing desire. In this sort of love it is the forsaker who has the melancholy lot; for an abandoned belief may be more effectively vengeful than Dido. The child of a wandering tribe, caught young and trained to polite life, if he feels a hereditary yearning, can run away to the old wilds and get his nature into tune. But there is no such recovery possible to the man who remembers what he once believed, without being convinced that he was in error; who feels within himself unsatisfied stirrings toward old beloved habits, and intimacies from which he has far receded, without conscious justification or unwavering sense of superior attractiveness in the new. This involuntary renegade has his character hopelessly jangled and out of tune. He is like an organ with its stops in the lawless condition of obtruding themselves without method, so that hearers are amazed by the most unexpected transitions — the trumpet breaking in on the flute, and the oboe confounding both.

Hence the lot of Mixtus affects me pathetically, notwithstanding that he spends his growing wealth with liberality and manifest enjoyment. To most observers he appears to be simply one of the fortunate and also sharp commercial men, who began with meaning to be rich, and have become what they meant to be — a man never taken to be well-born, but surprisingly better informed than the well-born usually are, and distinguished among ordinary commercial magnates by a personal kindness which prompts him not only to help the suffering in a material way through his wealth, but also by direct ministration of his own; yet with all this, diffusing, as it were, the odor of a man delightedly conscious of his wealth, as an equivalent for the other social distinctions of rank and intellect, which he can thus admire without envying. Hardly one among those superficial observers can suspect that he aims or has ever aimed at being a writer: still less can they imagine that his mind is often moved by strong currents of regret, and of the most unworldly sympathies, from the memories of a youthful time when his chosen associates were men and women whose only distinction was a religious, a philanthropic, or an intellectual enthusiasm; when the lady, on whose words his attention most hung, was a writer of minor religious literature; when he was a visitor and exhorter of the poor in the alleys of a great provincial town, and when he attended the lectures given especially to young men by Mr. Apollos, the eloquent Congregational preacher, who had studied in Germany, and had liberal advanced views, then far beyond the ordinary teaching of his sect. At that time Mixtus thought himself a young man of socially reforming ideas, of religious principles and religious yearnings. It was within his prospects also to be rich, but he looked forward to a use of his riches chiefly for reforming and religious purposes. His opinions were of a strongly democratic stamp; except that even then, belonging to the class of employers, he was opposed to all demands in the employed that would restrict the expansiveness of trade. He was the most democratic in relation to the unreasonable privileges of the aristocracy and landed interest, and he had also a religious sense of brotherhood with the poor. Altogether he was a sincerely benevolent young man, interested in ideas, and renouncing personal ease for the sake of study, religious communion, and good works. If you had known him then, you would have expected him to marry a highly serious and perhaps literary woman, sharing his benevolent and religious habits, and likely to encourage his studies — a woman who, along with himself, would play a distinguished part in one of the most enlightened religious circles of a great provincial capital.

How is it that Mixtus finds himself in a London mansion, and in society totally unlike that which made the ideal of his younger years ? And whom *did* he marry ?

Why, he married Scintilla, who fascinated him, as she had fascinated others, by her prettiness, her liveliness, and her music. It is a common enough case, that of a man being suddenly captivated by a woman nearly the opposite of his ideal ; or, if not wholly captivated, at least effectively captured, by a combination of circumstances, along with an unwarily manifested inclination which might otherwise have been transient. Mixtus was captivated and then captured on the worldly side of his disposition, which had been always growing and flourishing side by side with his philanthropic and religious tastes. He had ability in business, and he had early meant to be rich ; also, he was getting rich, and the taste for such success was naturally growing with the pleasure of rewarded exertion. It was during a business sojourn in London that he met Scintilla, who, though without fortune, associated with families of Greek merchants living in a style of splendor, and with artists patronized by such wealthy entertainers. Mixtus on this occasion became familiar with a world in which wealth seemed the key to a more brilliant sort of dominance than that of a religious patron in the provincial circles of X. Would it not be possible to unite the two kinds of sway ? A man bent on the most useful ends might, *with a fortune large enough*, make morality magnificent, and recommend religious principle by showing it in combination with the best kind of house and the most liberal of tables ; also with a wife whose graces, wit, and accomplishments gave a finish — sometimes lacking, even to establishments got up with that unhesitating worldliness to which high cost is a sufficient reason. Enough.

Mixtus married Scintilla. Now this lively lady knew nothing of Non-conformists, except that they were unfashionable; she did not distinguish one conventicle from another; and Mr. Apollos, with his enlightened interpretations, seemed to her as heavy a bore, if not quite so ridiculous, as Mr. Johns could have been, with his solemn twang, at the Baptist chapel in the lowest suburbs, or as a local preacher among the Methodists. In general, people who appeared seriously to believe in any sort of doctrine, whether religious, social, or philosophical, seemed rather absurd to Scintilla. Ten to one these theoretic people pronounced oddly, had some reason or other for saying that the most agreeable things were wrong, wore objectionable clothes, and wanted you to subscribe to something. They were probably ignorant of art and music, did not understand badinage, and, in fact, could talk of nothing amusing. In Scintilla's eyes the majority of persons were ridiculous, and deplorably wanting in that keen perception of what was good taste with which she herself was blessed by nature and education; but the people understood to be religious, or otherwise theoretic, were the most ridiculous of all, without being proportionately amusing and invitable.

Did Mixtus not discover this view of Scintilla's before their marriage? Or did he allow her to remain in ignorance of habits and opinions which had made half the occupation of his youth?

When a man is inclined to marry a particular woman, and has made any committal of himself, this woman's opinions, however different from his own, are readily regarded as part of her pretty ways, especially if they are merely negative; as, for example, that she does not insist on the Trinity, or on the rightfulness or expediency of Church rates, but simply regards her lover's troubling himself in disputation on these heads as stuff and nonsense. The man feels his own superior strength, and is sure that marriage will make no difference to him on the subjects about which he is in earnest. And to laugh at men's affairs is a woman's privilege, tending to enliven the domestic hearth. If Scintilla had no liking for the best sort of Non-conformity, she was without any troublesome bias toward Episcopacy, Anglicanism, and early sacraments, and was quite contented not to go to church.

As to Scintilla's acquaintance with her lover's tastes on these subjects, she was equally convinced on her side that a husband's queer ways, while he was a bachelor, would be easily laughed out of him when he had married an adroit woman. Mixtus, she felt, was an excellent creature, quite likable, who was getting rich; and Scintilla meant to have all the advantages of a rich man's wife. She was not in the least a wicked woman; she was simply a pretty animal of the ape kind, with an aptitude for certain accomplishments, which education had made the most of.

But we have seen what has been the result to poor Mixtus. He has become richer even than he dreamed of being, has a little palace in London, and entertains with splendor the half-aristocratic, professional, and artistic society which he is proud to think select. This society regards him as a clever fellow in his particular branch, seeing that he has become a considerable capitalist, and as a man desirable to have on the list of one's acquaintance. But from every other point of view Mixtus finds himself personally submerged : what he happens to think is not felt by his esteemed guests to be of any consequence; and what he used to think, with the ardor of conviction, he now hardly ever expresses. He is transplanted, and the sap within him has long been diverted into other than the old lines of vigorous growth. How could he speak to the artist Crespi, or to Sir Hong Kong Bantam, about the enlarged doctrine of Mr. Apollos? How could he mention to them his former efforts toward evangelizing the inhabitants of the X. alleys? And his references to his historical and geographical studies, toward a survey of possible markets for English products, are received with an air of ironical suspicion by many of his political friends, who take his pretension to give advice concerning the Amazon, the Euphrates, and the Niger, as equivalent to the currier's wide views on the applicability of leather. He can only make a figure through his genial hospitality. It is in vain that he buys the best pictures and statues of the best artists. Nobody will call him a judge in art. If his pictures and statues are well chosen, it is generally thought that Scintilla told him what to buy; and yet Scintilla, in other connections, is spoken of as having only a superficial and often questionable taste. Mixtus, it is decided, is a good fellow, not ignorant, no — really having a good deal of knowledge as well as sense, but not easy to classify otherwise than as a rich man. He has, consequently, become a little uncertain as to his own point of view; and in his most unreserved moments of friendly intercourse, even when speaking to listeners whom he thinks likely to sympathize with the earlier part of his career, he presents himself in all his various aspects, and feels himself in turn what he has been, what he is, and what others take him to be (for this last status is what we must all more or less accept). He will recover with some glow of enthusiasm the vision of his old associates, the particular limit he was once accustomed to trace of freedom in religious speculation, and his old ideal of a worthy life; but he will presently pass to the argument that money is the only means by which you can get what is best worth having in the world, and will arrive at the exclamation, "Give me money!" with the tone and gesture of a man who both feels and knows. Then if one of his audience, not having money, remarks that a man may have made up his mind to do without money, because he prefers something else, Mixtus is with him immediately, cordially concurring in the supreme value of mind and genius, which indeed make his own chief delight, in that he is able to entertain the admirable possessors of these attributes at his own table, though not himself reckoned among them. Yet he will proceed to observe there was a time when he sacrificed his sleep to study; and even now, amidst the press of business, he from time to time thinks of taking up the manuscripts which he hopes some day to complete, and is always increasing his collection of valuable works bearing on his favorite topics. And it is true that he has read much in certain directions, and can remember what he has read; he knows the history and theories of colonization, and the social condition of countries that do not at present consume a sufficiently large share of our products and manufactures. He continues his early habit of regarding the spread of Christianity as a great result of our commercial intercourse with black, brown, and yellow populations; but this is an idea not spoken of in the sort of fashionable society that Scintilla collects round her husband's table; and Mixtus now philosophically reflects that the cause must come before the effect, and that the thing to be directly striven for is the commercial intercourse — not excluding a little war, if that also should prove needful as a pioneer of Christianity. He has long been wont to feel bashful about his former religion, as if it were an old attachment, having consequences which he did not abandon but kept in decent privacy, his avowed objects and actual position being incompatible with their public acknowledgment.

There is the same kind of fluctuation in his aspect toward social questions and duties. He has not lost the kindness that used to make him a benefactor and succorer of the needy, and he is still liberal in helping forward the clever and industrious; but in his active superintendence of commercial undertakings he has contracted more and more of the bitterness which capitalists and employers often feel to be a reasonable mood toward obstructive proletaries. Hence many who have occasionally met him when trade questions were being discussed, conclude him to be indistinguishable from the ordinary run of moneyed and money-getting men. Indeed, hardly any of his acquaintances know what Mixtus really is, considered as a whole — nor does Mixtus himself know it.

DEBASING THE MORAL CURRENCY.

"IL ne faut pas mettre un ridicule où il n'y en a point : c'est se gâter le goût, c'est corrompre son jugement et celui des autres. Mais le ridicule qui est quelque part, il faut l'y voir, l'en tirer avec grâce et d'une manière qui plaise et qui instruise."

I am fond of quoting this passage from La Bruyère, because the subject is one where I like to show a Frenchman on my side, to save my sentiments from being set down to my peculiar dulness and deficient sense of the ludicrous ; and also that they may profit by that enhancement of ideas when presented in a foreign tongue, that glamour of unfamiliarity conferring a dignity on the foreign names of very common things, of which even a philosopher like Dugald Stewart confesses the influence. I remember hearing a fervid woman attempt to recite in English the narrative of a begging Frenchman, who described the violent death of his father in the July days. The narrative had impressed her, through the mists of her flushed anxiety to understand it, as something quite grandly pathetic ; but finding the facts turn out meagre, and her audience cold, she broke off, saying, "It sounded so much finer in French — *J'ai vu le sang de mon père* and so on — I wish I could repeat it in French." This was a pardonable illusion in an old-fashioned lady, who had not received the polyglot education of the present day ; but I observe that even now much nonsense and bad taste win admiring acceptance solely by virtue of the French language, and one may fairly desire that what seems just discrimination should profit by the fashionable prejudice in favor of La Bruyère's idiom. But

I wish he had added that the habit of dragging the ludicrous into topics where the chief interest is of a different or even opposite kind, is a sign not of endowment but of deficiency. The art of spoiling is within reach of the dullest faculty : the coarsest clown, with a hammer in his hand, might chip the nose off every statue and bust in the Vatican, and stand grinning at the effect of his work. Because wit is an exquisite product of high powers, we are not therefore forced to admit the sadly confused inference of the monotonous jester, that he is establishing his superiority over every less facetious person, and over every topic on which he is ignorant or insensible, by being uneasy until he has distorted it in the small cracked mirror which he carries about with him as a joking apparatus. Some high authority is needed to give many worthy and timid persons the freedom of muscular repose, under the growing demand on them to laugh when they have no other reason than the peril of being taken for dullards ; still more, to inspire them with the courage to say that they object to the theatrical spoiling, for themselves and their children, of all affecting themes, all the grander deeds and aims of men, by burlesque associations, adapted to the taste of rich fishmongers in the stalls and their assistants in the gallery. The English people in the present generation are falsely reputed to know Shakspeare (as by some innocent persons the Florentine mule-drivers are believed to have known the " Divina Commedia," not, perhaps, excluding all the subtle discourses in the *Purgatorio* and *Paradiso*) ; but there seems a clear prospect that in the coming generation he will be known to them through burlesques, and that his plays will find a new life as pantomimes. A bottle-nosed Lear will come on with a monstrous corpulence, from which he will frantically dance himself free during the midnight storm ; Rosalind and Celia will join in a grotesque ballet with shepherds and shepherdesses ; Ophelia, in fleshings and a voluminous brevity of grenadine, will dance through the mad scene, finishing with the famous " attitude of the scissors " in the arms of Laertes ; and all the speeches in

"Hamlet" will be so ingeniously parodied that the origi-
nals will be reduced to a mere *memoria technica* of the im-
prover's puns — premonitory signs of a hideous millennium,
in which the lion will have to lie down with the lascivious
monkeys, whom (if we may trust Pliny) his soul naturally
abhors.

I have been amazed to find that some artists, whose own
works have the ideal stamp, are quite insensible to the damaging tendency of the burlesquing spirit which ranges to and
fro, and up and down, on the earth, seeing no reason (except
a precarious censorship) why it should not appropriate every
sacred, heroic, and pathetic theme which serves to make up
the treasure of human admiration, hope, and love.　One
would have thought that their own half-despairing efforts to
invest in worthy outward shape the vague inward impressions
of sublimity, and the consciousness of an implicit ideal in the
commonest scenes, might have made them susceptible of
some disgust or alarm at a species of burlesque which is
likely to render their compositions no better than a dissolving view, where every noble form is seen melting into its
preposterous caricature.　It used to be imagined of the
unhappy mediæval Jews that they parodied Calvary by cru-
cifying dogs; if they had been guilty, they would at least
have had the excuse of the hatred and rage begotten by
persecution.　Are we on the way to a parody which shall
have no other excuse than the reckless search after fodder
for degraded appetites — after the pay to be earned by pas-
turing Circe's herd where they may defile every monument
of that growing life which should have kept them human?

The world seems to me well supplied with what is genuinely ridiculous; wit and humor may play as harmlessly or
beneficently round the changing facets of egoism, absurdity,
and vice, as the sunshine over the rippling sea or the dewy
meadows.　Why should we make our delicious sense of the
ludicrous — with its invigorating shocks of laughter, and its
irrepressible smiles, which are the outglow of an inward
radiation as gentle and cheering as the warmth of morning —

flourish like a brigand on the robbery of our mental wealth? or let it take its exercise as a madman might, if allowed a free nightly promenade, by drawing the populace with bon-fires which leave some venerable structure a blackened ruin, or send a scorching smoke across the portraits of the past, at which we once looked with a loving recognition of fellowship, and disfigure them into butts of mockery? — nay, worse, use it to degrade the healthy appetites and affections of our nature, as they are seen to be degraded in insane patients, whose system, all out of joint, finds matter for screaming laughter in mere topsy-turvy, makes every passion preposter-ous or obscene, and turns the hard-won order of life into a second chaos, hideous enough to make one wail that the first was ever thrilled with light?

This is what I call debasing the moral currency: lowering the value of every inspiring fact and tradition, so that it will command less and less of the spiritual products, the generous motives, which sustain the charm and elevation of our social existence — the something besides bread by which man saves his soul alive. The bread-winner of the family may demand more and more coppery shillings or assignats or greenbacks for his day's work, and so get the needful quantum of food; but let that moral currency be emptied of its value, let a greedy buffoonery debase all historic beauty, majesty, and pathos, and the more you heap up the desecrated symbols, the greater will be the lack of the ennobling emotions which subdue the tyranny of suffering, and make ambition one with social virtue.

And yet, it seems, parents will put into the hands of their children ridiculous parodies (perhaps with more ridiculous illustrations) of the poems which stirred their own ten-derness or filial piety, and carry them to make their first acquaintance with great men, great works, or solemn crises, through the medium of some miscellaneous burlesque, which, with its idiotic puns and farcical attitudes, will remain among their primary associations, and reduce them, throughout their time of studious preparation for life, to the moral imbecility of an inward giggle at what might have stimulated their high emulation, or fed the fountains of compassion, trust, and constancy. One wonders where these parents have deposited that stock of morally educating stimuli which is to be independent of poetic tradition, and to subsist, in spite of the finest images being degraded, and the finest works cf genius being poisoned as with some befooling drug.

Will fine wit, will exquisite humor, prosper the more through this turning of all things indiscriminately into food for a gluttonous laughter, an idle craving, without sense of flavors? On the contrary. That delightful power which La Bruyère points to — "le ridicule qui est quelque part, il faut l'y voir, l'en tirer avec grâce et d'une manière qui plaise et qui instruise" — depends on a discrimination only compatible with the varied sensibilities which give sympathetic insight, and with the justice of perception which is another name for grave knowledge. Such a result is no more to be expected from faculties on the strain to find some small hook by which they may attach the lowest incongruity to the most momentous subject, than it is to be expected of a sharper, watching for gulls in a great political assemblage, that he will notice the blundering logic of partisan speakers, or season his observation with the salt of historical parallels. But after all our psychological teaching, and in the midst of our zeal for education, we are still, most of us, at the stage of believing that mental powers and habits have somehow, not perhaps in the general statement but in any particular case, a kind of spiritual glaze against conditions which we are continually applying to them. We soak our children in habits of contempt and exultant gibing, and yet are confident that, as Clarissa one day said to me, "We can always teach them to be reverent in the right place, you know." And doubtless if she were to take her boys to see a burlesque Socrates, with swollen legs, dying in the utterance of cockney puns, and were to hang up a sketch of this comic scene among their bedroom prints, she would think this preparation not at all to the prejudice of their emotions on hearing their tutor read that narrative of the "Apology," which has been consecrated by the reverent gratitude of ages.   This is the impoverishment that threatens our posterity : a new Famine, a meagre fiend, with lewd grin and clumsy hoof, is breathing a moral mildew over the harvest of our human sentiments.   These are the most delicate elements of our too easily perishable civilization.   And here again I like to quote a French testimony. Sainte-Beuve, referring to a time of insurrectionary disturbance, says : " Rien de plus prompt à baisser que la civilisation dans les crises comme celle-ci ; on perd en trois semaines le résultat de plusieurs siècles.   La civilisation, la *vie*, est une chose apprise et inventée, qu'on le sache bien : ' *Inventas aut qui vitam excoluere per artes.*'   Les hommes après quelques années de paix oublient trope cette vérité : ils arrivent à croire que la *culture* est chose innée, qu'elle est la même chose que la *nature*.   La sauvagerie est toujours là à deux pas, et, dès qu'on lâche pied, elle recommence."   We have been severely enough taught (if we were willing to learn) that our civilization, considered as a splendid material fabric, is helplessly in peril without the spiritual police of sentiments or ideal feelings.   And it is this invisible police which we had need, as a community, strive to maintain in efficient force. How if a dangerous " Swing " were sometimes disguised in a versatile entertainer, devoted to the amusement of mixed audiences ?   And I confess that sometimes when I see a certain style of a young lady, who checks our tender admiration with rouge and henna and all the blazonry of an extravagant expenditure, with slang and bold *brusquerie* intended to signify her emancipated view of things, and the cynical mockery which she mistakes for penetration, I am sorely tempted to hiss out " *Petroleuse !* "   It is a small matter to have our palaces set aflame, compared with the misery of having our sense of a noble womanhood, which is the inspiration of a purifying shame, the promise of life-penetrating affection, stained and blotted out by images of repulsiveness.   These things come not of higher education but of dull ignorance, fostered into pertness by the greedy vulgarity which reverses Peter's vision·

ary lesson, and learns to call all things common and unclean.
It comes of debasing the moral currency.

The Tirynthians, according to an ancient story reported
by Athenæus, becoming conscious that their trick of laughter
at everything and nothing was making them unfit for the conduct of serious affairs, appealed to the Delphic oracle for
some means of cure. The god prescribed a peculiar form of
sacrifice, which would be effective if they could carry it
through without laughing. They did their best; but the
flimsy joke of a boy upset their unaccustomed gravity, and in
this way the oracle taught them that even the gods could not
prescribe a quick cure for a long vitiation, or give power and
dignity to a people who, in a crisis of the public well-being,
were at the mercy of a poor jest.

THE WASP CREDITED WITH THE
HONEY–COMB.

NO man, I imagine, would object more strongly than Euphorion to communistic principles in relation to material property, but with regard to property in ideas he entertains such principles willingly, and is disposed to treat the distinction between Mine and Thine in original authorship as egoistic, narrowing, and low. I have known him, indeed, insist, at some expense of erudition, on the prior right of an ancient, a mediæval, or an eighteenth-century writer to be credited with a view or statement lately advanced with some show of originality ; and this championship seems to imply a nicety of conscience toward the dead. He is evidently unwilling that his neighbors should get more credit than is due to them, and in this way he appears to recognize a certain proprietorship even in spiritual production. But perhaps it is no real inconsistency that, with regard to many instances of modern origination, it is his habit to talk with a Gallic largeness and refer to the universe : he expatiates on the diffusive nature of intellectual products, free and all-embracing as the liberal air ; on the infinitesimal smallness of individual origination compared with the massive inheritance of thought on which every new generation enters ; on that growing preparation for every epoch through which certain ideas or modes of view are said to be in the air, and, still more metaphorically speaking, to be inevitably absorbed, so that every one may be excused for not knowing how he got them. Above all, he insists on the proper subordination of the irritable self, the mere vehicle of an idea or combination which, being produced by the sum total of the human race, must belong to that multiple entity, from the accomplished lecturer or popularizer who transmits it, to the remotest generation of Fuegians or Hottentots, however indifferent these may be to the superiority of their right above that of the eminently perishable dyspeptic author.

One may admit that such considerations carry a profound truth, to be even religiously contemplated, and yet object all the more to the mode in which Euphorion seems to apply them. I protest against the use of these majestic conceptions to do the dirty work of unscrupulosity, and justify the non-payment of conscious debts, which cannot be defined or enforced by the law; especially since it is observable that the large views as to intellectual property, which can apparently reconcile an able person to the use of lately borrowed ideas as if they were his own, when this spoliation is favored by the public darkness, never hinder him from joining in the zealous tribute of recognition and applause to those warriors of truth whose triumphal arches are seen in the public ways, those conquerors whose battles and "annexations" even the carpenters and bricklayers know by name. Surely the acknowledgment of a mental debt which will not be immediately detected, and may never be asserted, is a case to which the traditional susceptibility to "debts of honor" would be suitably transferred. There is no massive public opinion that can be expected to tell on these relations of thinkers and investigators, relations to be thoroughly understood and felt only by those who are interested in the life of ideas and acquainted with their history. To lay false claim to an invention or discovery which has an immediate market value; to vamp up a professedly new book of reference by stealing from the pages of one already produced at the cost of much labor and material; to copy somebody else's poem and send the manuscript to a magazine, or hand it about among friends as an original "effusion;" to deliver an elegant extract from a known writer as a piece of improvised eloquence — these are the limits within which the dishonest pretence of originality is likely to get hissed or hooted, and bring more or less shame on the culprit. It is not necessary to understand the merit of a performance, or even to spell with any comfortable confidence, in order to perceive at once that such pretences are not respectable. But the difference between these vulgar frauds — these devices of ridiculous jays, whose ill-secured plumes are seen falling off them as they run — and the quiet appropriation of other people's philosophic or scientific ideas, can hardly be held to lie in their moral quality, unless we take impunity as our criterion. The pitiable jays had no presumption in their favor, and foolishly fronted an alert incredulity; but Euphorion, the accomplished theorist, has an audience who expect much of him, and take it as the most natural thing in the world that every unusual view which he presents anonymously should be due solely to his ingenuity. His borrowings are no incongruous feathers, awkwardly stuck on; they have an appropriateness which makes them seem an answer to anticipation, like the return phrases of a melody. Certainly one cannot help the ignorant conclusions of polite society; and there are, perhaps, fashionable persons who, if a speaker has occasion to explain what the occiput is, will consider that he has lately discovered that curiously named portion of the animal frame. One cannot give a genealogical introduction to every long-stored item of fact or conjecture that may happen to be a revelation for the large class of persons who are understood to judge soundly on a small basis of knowledge; but Euphorion would be very sorry to have it supposed that he is unacquainted with the history of ideas, and sometimes carries even into minutiæ the evidence of his exact registration of names in connection with quotable phrases or suggestions. I can therefore only explain the apparent infirmity of his memory in cases of larger "conveyance" by supposing that he is accustomed, by the very association of largeness, to range them at once under those grand laws of the universe in the light of which Mine and Thine disappear and are resolved into Everybody's or Nobody's; and one man's particular obligations to another melt untraceably into the obligations of the earth to the solar system in general.

Euphorion himself, if a particular omission of acknowledgment were brought home to him, would probably take a narrower ground of explanation. It was a lapse of memory; or it did not occur to him as necessary in this case to mention a name, the source being well known; or (since this seems usually to act as a strong reason for mention) he rather abstained from adducing the name because it might injure the excellent matter advanced, just as an obscure trade-mark casts discredit on a good commodity, and even on the retailer who has furnished himself from a quarter not likely to be esteemed firstrate. No doubt this last is a genuine and frequent reason for the non-acknowledgment of indebtedness to what one may call impersonal as well as personal sources: even an American editor of school classics, whose own English could not pass for more than a syntactical shoddy of the cheapest sort, felt it unfavorable to his reputation for sound learning that he should be obliged to the " Penny Cyclopædia," and disguised his references to it under contractions in which *Us. Knowl.* took the place of the low word *Penny.* Works of this convenient stamp, easily obtained and well nourished with matter, are felt to be like rich but unfashionable relations, who are visited and received in privacy, and whose capital is used or inherited without any ostentatious insistence on their names and places of abode. As to memory, it is known that this frail faculty naturally lets drop the facts which are less flattering to our self-love — when it does not retain them carefully as subjects not to be approached, marshy spots with a warning flag over them. But it is always interesting to bring forward eminent names, such as Patricius or Scaliger, Euler or Lagrange, Bopp or Humboldt. To know exactly what has been drawn from them is erudition, and heightens our own influence, which seems advantageous to mankind; whereas to cite an author whose ideas may pass as higher currency under our own signature, can have no object except the contradictory one of throwing the illumination over his figure, when it is important to be seen one's self. All these reasons must weigh considerably with those speculative persons who have to ask themselves whether or not Universal Utilitarianism requires that in the particular instance before them they should injure a man who has been of service to them, and rob a fellow-workman of the credit which is due to him.

After all, however, it must be admitted that hardly any accusation is more difficult to prove, and more liable to be false, than that of a plagiarism which is the conscious theft of ideas and deliberate reproduction of them as original. The arguments on the side of acquittal are obvious and strong — the inevitable coincidences of contemporary thinking, and our continual experience of finding notions turning up in our minds without any label on them to tell us whence they came; so that if we are in the habit of expecting much from our own capacity we accept them at once as a new inspiration. Then, in relation to the elder authors, there is the difficulty first of learning and then of remembering exactly what has been wrought into the backward tapestry of the world's history, together with the fact that ideas acquired long ago reappear as the sequence of an awakened interest or a line of inquiry which is really new in us; whence it is conceivable that if we were ancients some of us might be offering grateful hecatombs by mistake, and proving our honesty in a ruinously expensive manner. On the other hand, the evidence on which plagiarism is concluded is often of a kind which, though much trusted in questions of erudition and historical criticism, is apt to lead us injuriously astray in our daily judgments, especially of the resentful, condemnatory sort. How Pythagoras came by his ideas, whether St. Paul was acquainted with all the Greek poets, what Tacitus must have known by hearsay and systematically ignored, are points on which a false persuasion of knowledge is less damaging to justice and charity than an erroneous confidence, supported by reasoning fundamentally similar, of my neighbor's blameworthy behavior in a case where I am personally concerned.

No premises require closer scrutiny than those which lead to the constantly echoed conclusion, "He must have known," or "He must have read." I marvel that this facility of belief on the side of knowledge can subsist under the daily demonstration that the easiest of all things to the human mind is *not* to know and *not* to read. To praise, to blame, to shout, grin, or hiss, where others shout, grin, or hiss — these are native tendencies; but to know and to read are artificial, hard accomplishments, concerning which the only safe supposition is, that as little of them has been done as the case admits. An author, keenly conscious of having written, can hardly help imagining his condition of lively interest to be shared by others ; just as we are all apt to suppose that the chill or heat we are conscious of must be general, or even to think that our sons and daughters, our pet schemes, and our quarrelling correspondence, are themes to which intelligent persons will listen long without weariness. But if the ardent author happen to be alive to practical teaching, he will soon learn to divide the larger part of the enlightened public into those who have not read him, and think it necessary to tell him so when they meet him in polite society, and those who have equally abstained from reading him, but wish to conceal this negation, and speak of his "incomparable works" with that trust in testimony which always has its cheering side.

Hence it is worse than foolish to entertain silent suspicions of plagiarism, still more to give them voice, when they are founded on a construction of probabilities which a little more attention to every-day occurrences, as a guide in reasoning, would show us to be really worthless, considered as proof. The length to which one man's memory can go in letting drop associations that are vital to another can hardly find a limit. It is not to be supposed that a person desirous to make an agreeable impression on you would deliberately choose to insist to you, with some rhetorical sharpness, on an argument which you were the first to elaborate in public ; yet any who listens may overhear such instances of obliviousness. You naturally remember your peculiar connection with your acquaintance's judicious views; but why should *he?* Your fatherhood, which is an intense feeling to you, is only an additional fact of meagre interest for him to remember; and a sense of obligation to the particular living fellow-struggler who has helped us in our thinking, is not yet a form of memory the want of which is felt to be disgraceful or derogatory, unless it is taken to be a want of polite instruction, or causes the missing of a cockade on a day of celebration. In our suspicions of plagiarism we must recognize, as the first weighty probability, that what we, who feel injured, remember best is precisely what is least likely to enter lastingly into the memory of our neighbors. But it is fair to maintain that the neighbor who borrows your property, loses it for awhile, and when it turns up again forgets your connection with it and counts it his own, shows himself so much the feebler in grasp and rectitude of mind. Some absent persons cannot remember the state of wear in their own hats and umbrellas, and have no mental check to tell them that they have carried home a fellow-visitor's more recent purchase. They may be excellent householders, far removed from the suspicion of low devices, but one wishes them a more correct perception, and a more wary sense that a neighbor's umbrella may be newer than their own.

True, some persons are so constituted that the very excellence of an idea seems to them a convincing reason that it must be, if not solely, yet especially theirs. It fits in so beautifully with their general wisdom, it lies implicitly in so many of their manifested opinions, that, if they have not yet expressed it (because of preoccupation), it is clearly a part of their indigenous produce, and is proved by their immediate eloquent promulgation of it to belong more naturally and appropriately to them than to the person who seemed first to have alighted on it, and who sinks in their all-originating consciousness to that low kind of entity, a second cause. This is not lunacy, or pretence, but a genuine state of mind very effective in practice, and often carrying the public with it, so that the poor Columbus is found to be a very faulty adventurer, and the continent is named after Amerigo. Lighter examples of this instinctive appropriation are constantly met with among brilliant talkers. Aquila is too agreeable and amusing for any one, who is not himself bent on display, to be angry at his conversational rapine — his habit of darting down on every morsel of booty that other birds may hold in their beaks, with an innocent air, as if it were all intended for his use, and honestly counted on by him as a tribute in kind. Hardly any man, I imagine, can have had less trouble in gathering a showy stock of information than Aquila. On close inquiry you would probably find that he had not read one epoch-making book of modern times, for he has a career which obliges him to much correspondence and other official work, and he is too fond of being in company to spend his leisure moments in study; but to his quick eye, ear, and tongue, a few predatory excursions in conversation, where there are instructed persons, gradually furnish surprisingly clever modes of statement and allusion on the dominant topic. When he first adopts a subject he necessarily falls into mistakes, and it is interesting to watch his gradual progress into fuller information and better nourished irony, without his ever needing to admit that he has made a blunder or to appear conscious of correction. Suppose, for example, he had incautiously founded some ingenious remarks on a hasty reckoning that nine thirteens made a hundred and two, and the insignificant Bantam, hitherto silent, seemed to spoil the flow of ideas by stating that the product could not be taken as less than a hundred and seventeen. Aquila would glide on in the most graceful manner, from a repetition of his previous remark to the continuation — "All this is on the supposition that a hundred and two were all that could be got out of nine thirteens, but as all the world knows that nine thirteens will yield," etc. — proceeding straightway into a new train of ingenious consequences, and causing Bantam to be regarded by all present as one of those slow persons who take irony for ignorance, and who would warn the weasel to keep awake. How should a small-eyed, feebly crowing mortal like him be quicker in arithmetic than the keen-faced, forcible Aquila, in whom universal knowledge is easily credible? Looked into closely, the conclusion, from a man's profile, voice, and fluency, to his certainty in multiplication beyond the twelves, seems to show a confused notion of the way in which very common things are connected; but it is on such false correlations that men found half their inferences about each other, and high places of trust may sometimes be held on no better foundation.

It is a commonplace that words, writings, measures, and performances in general, have qualities assigned them, not by a direct judgment on the performances themselves, but by a presumption of what they are likely to be, considering who is the performer. We all notice in our neighbors this reference to names as guides in criticism, and all furnish illustrations of it in our own practice; for check ourselves as we will, the first impression from any sort of work must depend on a previous attitude of mind, and this will constantly be determined by the influences of a name. But that our prior confidence or want of confidence in given names is made up of judgments just as hollow as the consequent praise or blame they are taken to warrant, is less commonly perceived, though there is a conspicuous indication of it in the surprise or disappointment often manifested in the disclosure of an authorship about which everybody has been making wrong guesses. No doubt if it had been discovered who wrote the "Vestiges," many an ingenious structure of probabilities would have been spoiled, and some disgust might have been felt for a real author who made comparatively so shabby an appearance of likelihood. It is this foolish trust in prepossessions, founded on spurious evidence, which makes a medium of encouragement for those who, happening to have the ear of the public, give other people's ideas the advantage of appearing under their own well-received name; while any remonstrance from the real producer becomes an unwelcome disturbance of complacency with each person who has paid complimentary tributes in the wrong place.

Hardly any kind of false reasoning is more ludicrous than this on the probabilities of origination. It would be amusing to catechise the guessers as to their exact reasons for thinking their guess "likely;" why Hoopoe of John's has fixed on Toucan of Magdalen; why Shrike attributes its peculiar style to Buzzard, who has not hitherto been known as a writer; why the fair Columbia thinks it must belong to the Reverend Merula; and why they are all alike disturbed in their previous judgment of its value by finding that it really came from Skunk, whom they had either not thought of at all, or thought of as belonging to a species excluded by the nature of the case. Clearly they were all wrong in their notion of the specific conditions. which lay u⁻ xpectedly in the small Skunk, and in him alone — in spite of his education nobody knows where, in spite of somebody's knowing his uncles and cousins, and in spite of nobody's knowing that he was cleverer than they thought him.

Such guesses remind one of a fabulist's imaginary council of animals assembled to consider what sort of creature had constructed a honey-comb, found and much tasted by Bruin and other epicures. The speakers all started from the probability that the maker was a bird, because this was the quarter from which a wondrous nest might be expected; for the animals at that time, knowing little of their own history, would have rejected as inconceivable the notion that the nest could be made by a fish; and as to the insects, they were not willingly received in society and their ways were little known. Several complimentary presumptions were expressed that the honey-comb was due to one or the other admired and popular bird, and there was much fluttering on the part of the Nightingale and Swallow, neither of whom gave a positive denial, their confusion perhaps extending to their sense of identity; but the Owl hissed at this folly, arguing from his particular knowledge that the animal which produced honey must be the Musk-rat, the wondrous nature of whose secretions required no proof; and, in the powerful logical procedure of the Owl, from musk to honey was but a step. Some disturbance arose hereupon, for the Musk-rat began to make himself obtrusive, believing in the Owl's opinion of his powers, and feeling that he could have produced the honey if he had thought of it, until an experimental Butcher-bird proposed to anatomize him as a help to decision. The hubbub increased, the opponents of the Musk-rat inquiring who his ancestors were, until a diversion was created by an able discourse of the Macaw on structures generally, which he classified so as to include the honey-comb, entering into so much admirable exposition that there was a prevalent sense of the honey-comb having probably been produced by one who understood it so well. But Bruin, who had probably eaten too much to listen with edification, grumbled, in his low kind of language, that " Fine words butter no parsnips ; " by which he meant to say that there was no new honey forthcoming.

Perhaps the audience generally was beginning to tire, when the Fox entered with his snout dreadfully swollen, and reported that the beneficent originator in question was the Wasp, which he had found much smeared with undoubted honey, having applied his nose to it; whence, indeed, the able insect, perhaps justifiably irritated at what might seem a sign of scepticism, had stung him with some severity, an infliction Reynard could hardly regret, since the swelling of a snout normally so delicate would corroborate his statement, and satisfy the assembly that he had really found the honey-creating genius.

The Fox's admitted acuteness, combined with the visible swelling, were taken as undeniable evidence, and the revelation undoubtedly met a general desire for information on a point of interest. Nevertheless, there was a murmur the reverse of delighted, and the feelings of some eminent animals were too strong for them : the Orang-outang's jaw dropped so as seriously to impair the vigor of his expression, the edifying Pelican screamed and flapped her wings, the

Owl hissed again, the Macaw became loudly incoherent, and the Gibbon gave his hysterical laugh; while the Hyena, after indulging in a more splenetic guffaw, agitated the question whether it would not be better to hush up the whole affair, instead of giving public recognition to an insect whose produce, it was now plain, had been much over-estimated. But this narrow-spirited motion was negatived by the sweet-toothed majority. A complimentary deputation to the Wasp was resolved on, and there was a confident hope that this diplomatic measure would tell on the production of honey.

"SO YOUNG!"

G ANYMEDE was once a girlishly handsome, precocious youth. That one cannot, for any considerable number of years, go on being youthful, girlishly handsome, and precocious, seems, on consideration, to be a statement as worthy of credit as the famous syllogistic conclusion, "Socrates was mortal." But many circumstances have conspired to keep up in Ganymede the illusion that he is surprisingly young. He was the last born of his family, and from his earliest memory was accustomed to be commended as such to the care of his elder brothers and sisters; he heard his mother speak of him as her youngest darling with a loving pathos in her tone, which naturally suffused his own view of himself, and gave him the habitual consciousness of being at once very young and very interesting. Then, the disclosure of his tender years was a constant matter of astonishment to strangers who had had proof of his precocious talents; and the astonishment extended to what is called the world at large, when he produced "A Comparative Estimate of European Nations" before he was well out of his teens. All comers, on a first interview, told him that he was marvellously young, and some repeated the statement each time they saw him; all critics who wrote about him called attention to the same ground for wonder; his deficiencies and excesses were alike to be accounted for by the flattering fact of his youth, and his youth was the golden background which set off his many-hued endowments. Here was already enough to establish a strong association between his sense of identity and his sense of being unusually young. But after this he devised and

founded an ingenious organization for consolidating the literary interests of all the four continents (subsequently including Australasia and Polynesia), he himself presiding in the
central office, which thus became a new theatre for the constantly repeated situation of an astonished stranger in the
presence of a boldly scheming administrator found to be remarkably young. If we imagine with due charity the effect
on Ganymede, we shall think it greatly to his credit that he
continued to feel the necessity of being something more than
young, and did not sink by rapid degrees into a parallel of
that melancholy object, a superannuated youthful phenomenon. Happily he had enough of valid, active faculty to save
him from that tragic fate. He had not exhausted his fountain of eloquent opinion in his "Comparative Estimate," so
as to feel himself like some other juvenile celebrities, the sad
survivor of his own manifest destiny, or like one who has
risen too early in the morning, and finds all the solid day
turned into a fatigued afternoon. He has continued to be
productive both of schemes and writings, being perhaps
helped by the fact that his "Comparative Estimate" did not
greatly affect the currents of European thought, and left him
with the stimulating hope that he had not done his best, but
might yet produce what would make his youth more surprising than ever.

I saw something of him through his Antinoüs period, the
time of rich chestnut locks, parted not by a visible white line,
but by a shadowed furrow from which they fell in massive
ripples to right and left. In these slim days he looked the
younger for being rather below the middle size; and though
at last one perceived him contracting an indefinable air of
self-consciousness, a slight exaggeration of the facial movements, the attitudes, the little tricks, and the romance in
shirt collars, which must be expected from one who, in spite
of his knowledge, was so exceedingly young, it was impossible to say that he was making any great mistake about himself. He was only undergoing one form of a common moral
disease; being strongly mirrored for himself in the remark

of others, he was getting to see his real characteristics as a dramatic part, a type to which his doings were always in correspondence. Owing to my absence on travel, and to other causes, I had lost sight of him for several years; but such a separation, between two who have not missed each other, seems in this busy century only a pleasant reason, when they happen to meet again in some old accustomed haunt, for the one who has stayed at home to be more communicative about himself than he can well be to those who have all along been in his neighborhood. He had married in the interval, and as if to keep up his surprising youthfulness in all relations, he had taken a wife considerably older than himself. It would probably have seemed to him a disturbing inversion of the natural order that any one very near to him should have been younger than he, except his own children, who, however young, would not necessarily hinder the normal surprise at the youthfulness of their father. And if my glance had revealed my impression on first seeing him again, he might have received a rather disagreeable shock, which was far from my intention. My mind, having retained a very exact image of his former appearance, took note of unmistakable changes, such as a painter would certainly not have made by way of flattering his subject. He had lost his slimness, and that curved solidity, which might have adorned a taller man, was a rather sarcastic threat to his short figure. The English branch of the Teutonic race does not produce many fat youths, and I have even heard an American lady say, that she was much "disappointed" at the moderate number and size of our fat men, considering their reputation in the United States; hence a stranger would now have been apt to remark that Ganymede was unusually plump for a distinguished writer, rather than unusually young. But how was he to know this? Many long-standing prepossessions are as hard to be corrected as a long-standing mispronunciation, against which the direct experience of eye and ear is often powerless. And I could perceive that Ganymede's inwrought sense of his surprising youthfulness had been stronger than the superficial reckoning of his years and the merely optical phenomena of the looking-glass. He now held a post under government, and not only saw, like most subordinate functionaries, how ill everything was managed, but also what were the changes that a high constructive ability would dictate; and in mentioning to me his own speeches, and other efforts toward propagating reformatory views in his department, he concluded by changing his tone to a sentimental head-voice and saying: —

"But I am so young, people object to any prominence on my part; I can only get myself heard anonymously, and when some attention has been drawn the name is sure to creep out. The writer is known to be young, and things are none the forwarder."

"Well," said I, "youth seems the only drawback that is sure to diminish. You and I have seven years less of it than when we last met."

"Ah," returned Ganymede, as lightly as possible, at the same time casting an observant glance over me, as if he were marking the effect of seven years on a person who had probably begun life with an old look, and even as an infant had given his countenance to that significant doctrine, the transmigration of ancient souls into modern bodies.

I left him on that occasion without any melancholy forecast that his illusion would be suddenly or painfully broken up. I saw that he was well victualled and defended against a ten years' siege from ruthless facts; and in the course of time observation convinced me that his resistance received considerable aid from without. Each of his written productions, as it came out, was still commented on as the work of a very young man. One critic, finding that he wanted solidity, charitably referred to his youth as an excuse. Another, dazzled by his brilliancy, seemed to regard his youth as so wondrous that all other authors appeared decrepit by comparison, and their style such as might be looked for from gentlemen of the old school. Able pens (according to a familiar metaphor) appeared to shake their heads good-humoredly, implying that Ganymede's crudities were pardonable in one so exceedingly young. Such unanimity amidst diversity, which a distant posterity might take for evidence that on the point of age at least there could have been no mistake, was not really more difficult to account for than the prevalence of cotton in our fabrics. Ganymede had been first introduced into the writing world as remarkably young, and it was no exceptional consequence that the first deposit of information about him held its ground against facts which, however open to observation, were not necessarily thought of. It is not so easy, with our rates and taxes and need for economy in all directions, to cast away an epithet or remark that turns up cheaply, and to go in expensive search after more genuine substitutes. There is high Homeric precedent for keeping fast hold of an epithet under all changes of circumstance, and so the precocious author of the "Comparative Estimate" heard the echoes repeating "Young Ganymede," when an illiterate beholder at a railway station would have given him forty years at least. Besides, important elders, sachems of the clubs and public meetings, had a genuine opinion of him as young enough to be checked for speech on subjects which they had spoken mistakenly about when he was in his cradle; and then, the midway parting of his crisp hair, not common among English committee-men, formed a presumption against the ripeness of his judgment which nothing but a speedy baldness could have removed.

It is but fair to mention all these outward confirmations of Ganymede's illusion, which shows no signs of leaving him. It is true that he no longer hears expressions of surprise at his youthfulness, on a first introduction to an admiring reader; but this sort of external evidence has become an unnecessary crutch to his habitual inward persuasion. His manners, his costume, his suppositions of the impression he makes on others, have all their former correspondence with the dramatic part of the young genius. As to the incongruity of his contour, and other little accidents of physique, he is probably no more aware that they will affect others as incon-

gruities, than Armida is conscious how much her rouge provokes our notice of her wrinkles, and causes us to mention
sarcastically that motherly age which we should otherwise
regard with affectionate reverence.

But let us be just enough to admit that there may be old
young coxcombs as well as old-young coquettes.

HOW WE COME TO GIVE OURSELVES FALSE
TESTIMONIALS, AND BELIEVE IN THEM.

IT is my way, when I observe any instance of folly, any queer habit, any absurd illusion, straightway to look for something of the same type in myself, feeling sure that, amidst all differences, there will be a certain correspondence; just as there is more or less correspondence in the natural history even of continents widely apart, and of islands in opposite zones. No doubt men's minds differ in what we may call their climate, or share of solar energy, and a feeling or tendency which is comparable to a panther in one may have no more imposing aspect than that of a weasel in another: some are like a tropical habitat, in which the very ferns cast a mighty shadow, and the grasses are a dry ocean in which a hunter may be submerged; others like the chilly latitudes in which your forest-tree, fit elsewhere to prop a mine, is a pretty miniature suitable for fancy potting. The eccentric man might be typified by the Australian fauna, refuting half our judicious assumptions of what nature allows. Still, whether fate commanded us to thatch our persons among the Eskimos or to choose the latest thing in tattooing among the Polynesian isles, our precious guide, Comparison, would teach us in the first place by likeness, and our clew to further knowledge would be resemblance to what we already know. Hence, having a keen interest in the natural history of my inward self, I pursue this plan I have mentioned, of using my observation as a clew or lantern by which I detect small herbage or lurking life; or I take my neighbor, in his least becoming tricks or efforts, as an opportunity for luminous deduction concerning the figure the human genus makes in the specimen which I myself furnish.

Introspection which starts with the purpose of finding out one's own absurdities is not likely to be very mischievous, yet of course it is not free from dangers, any more than breathing is, or the other functions that keep us alive and active. To judge of others by one's self is, in its most innocent meaning, the briefest expression for our only method of knowing mankind; yet, we perceive, it has come to mean in many cases either the vulgar mistake which reduces every man's value to the very low figure at which the valuer himself happens to stand, or else the amiable illusion of the higher nature misled by a too generous construction of the lower. One cannot give a recipe for wise judgment; it resembles appropriate muscular action, which is attained by the myriad lessons in nicety of balance and of aim that only practice can give. The danger of the inverse procedure, judging of self by what one observes in others, if it is carried on with much impartiality and keenness of discernment, is that it has a laming effect, enfeebling the energies of indignation and scorn, which are the proper scourges of wrongdoing and meanness, and which should continually feed the wholesome restraining power of public opinion. I respect the horsewhip when applied to the back of cruelty, and think that he who applies it is a more perfect human being because his outleap of indignation is not checked by a too curious reflection on the nature of guilt — a more perfect human being because he more completely incorporates the best social life of the race, which can never be constituted by ideas that nullify action. This is the essence of Dante's sentiment (it is painful to think that he applies it very cruelly) —

" E cortesia fù, lui esser villano — "[1]

and it is undeniable that a too intense consciousness of one's kinship with all frailties and vices undermines the active heroism which battles against wrong.

[1] Inferno, xxxii. 150.

But certainly nature has taken care that this danger should not at present be very threatening. One could not fairly describe the generality of one's neighbors as too lucidly aware of manifesting in their own persons the weaknesses which they observe in the rest of her Majesty's subjects; on the contrary, a hasty conclusion as to schemes of Providence, might lead to the supposition that one man was intended to correct another by being most intolerant of the ugly quality or trick which he himself possesses. Doubtless philosophers will be able to explain how it must necessarily be so, but pending the full extension of the *à priori* method, which will show that only blockheads could expect anything to be otherwise, it does seem surprising that Heloisa should be disgusted at Laura's attempts to disguise her age — attempts which she recognizes so thoroughly because they enter into her own practice; that Semper, who often responds at public dinners and proposes resolutions on platforms, though he has a trying gestation of every speech and a bad time for himself and others at every delivery, should yet remark pitilessly on the folly of precisely the same course of action in Ubique; that Aliquis, who lets no attack on himself pass unnoticed, and for every handful of gravel against his windows sends a stone in reply, should deplore the ill-advised retorts of Quispiam, who does not perceive that to show one's self angry with an adversary is to gratify him. To be unaware of our own little tricks of manner or our own mental blemishes and excesses is a comprehensible unconsciousness; the puzzling fact is that people should apparently take no account of their deliberate actions, and should expect them to be equally ignored by others. It is an inversion of the accepted order: *there* it is the phrases that are official, and the conduct or privately manifested sentiment that is taken to be real; *here* it seems that the practice is taken to be official and entirely nullified by the verbal representation which contradicts it. The thief making a vow to Heaven of full restitution and whispering some reservations, expecting to cheat Omniscience by an "aside," is hardly more ludicrous than the many ladies and gentlemen who have more belief, and expect others to have it, in their own statement about their habitual doings than in the contradictory fact which is patent in the daylight. One reason of the absurdity is that we are led by a tradition about ourselves, so that long after a man has practically departed from a rule or principle, he continues innocently to state it as a true description of his practice — just as he has a long tradition that he is not an old gentleman, and is startled when he is seventy at overhearing himself called by an epithet which he has only applied to others.

"A person with your tendency of constitution should take as little sugar as possible," said Pilulus to Bovis, somewhere in the darker decades of this century. "It has made a great difference to Avis since he took my advice in that matter; he used to consume half a pound a day."

"God bless me!" cries Bovis. "I take very little sugar myself."

"Twenty-six large lumps every day of your life, Mr. Bovis," says his wife.

"No such thing!" exclaims Bovis.

"You drop them into your tea, coffee, and whiskey yourself, my dear, and I count them."

"Nonsense!" laughs Bovis, turning to Pilulus, that they may exchange a glance of mutual amusement at a woman's inaccuracy.

But she happened to be right. Bovis had never said inwardly that he would take a large allowance of sugar, and he had the tradition about himself that he was a man of the most moderate habits; hence, with this conviction, he was naturally disgusted at the saccharine excesses of Avis.

I have sometimes thought that this facility of men in believing that they are still what they once meant to be — this undisturbed appropriation of a traditional character which is often but a melancholy relic of early resolutions, like the worn and soiled testimonial to soberness and honesty carried in the pocket of a tippler whom the need of a dram has driven into peculation — may sometimes diminish the turpitude of what seems a flat, barefaced falsehood. It is notorious that a man may go on uttering false assertions about his own acts till he at last believes in them. Is it not possible that sometimes, in the very first utterance, there may be a shape of creed-reciting belief, a reproduction of a traditional self which is clung to against all evidence? There is no knowing all the disguises of the lying serpent.

When we come to examine in detail what is the sane mind in sane body, the final test of completeness seems to be a security of distinction between what we have professed and what we have done, what we have aimed at and what we have achieved, what we have invented and what we have witnessed or had evidenced to us, what we think and feel in the present and what we thought and felt in the past.

I know that there is a common prejudice which regards the habitual confusion of *now* and *then*, of *it was* and *it is*, of *it seemed so* and *I should like it to be so*, as a mark of high imaginative endowment, while the power of precise statement and description is rated lower, as the attitude of an every-day prosaic mind. High imagination is often assigned or claimed as if it were a ready activity in fabricating extravagances such as are presented by fevered dreams, or as if its possessors were in that state of inability to give credible testimony which would warrant their exclusion from the class of acceptable witnesses in a court of justice; so that a creative genius might fairly be subjected to the disability which some laws have stamped on dicers, slaves, and other classes whose position was held perverting to their sense of social responsibility.

This endowment of mental confusion is often boasted of by persons whose imaginativeness would not otherwise be known, unless it were by the slow process of detecting that their descriptions and narratives were not to be trusted. Callista is always ready to testify of herself that she is an imaginative person; and sometimes adds, in illustration, that if she had taken a walk and seen an old heap of stones on her way, the account she would give on returning would include many pleasing particulars of her own invention, transforming the simple heap into an interesting castellated ruin. This creative freedom is all very well in the right place; but before I can grant it to be a sign of unusual mental power, I must inquire whether, on being requested to give a precise description of what she saw, she would be able to cast aside her arbitrary combinations and recover the objects she really perceived, so as to make them recognizable by another person who passed the same way. Otherwise her glorifying imagination is not an addition to the fundamental power of strong, discerning perception, but a cheaper substitute. And in fact, I find, on listening to Callista's conversation, that she has a very lax conception even of common objects, and an equally lax memory of events. It seems of no consequence to her whether she shall say that a stone is overgrown with moss or with lichen; that a building is of sandstone or of granite; that Meliboeus once forgot to put on his cravat or that he always appears without it; that everybody says so, or that one stock-broker's wife said so yesterday; that Philemon praised Euphemia up to the skies, or that he denied knowing any particular evil of her. She is one of those respectable witnesses who would testify to the exact moment of an apparition, because any desirable moment will be as exact as another to her remembrance; or who would be the most worthy to witness the action of spirits on slates and tables, because the action of limbs would not probably arrest her attention. She would describe the surprising phenomena exhibited by the powerful Medium, with the same freedom that she vaunted in relation to the old heap of stones. Her supposed imaginativeness is simply a very usual lack of discriminating perception, accompanied with a less usual activity of misrepresentation, which, if it had been a little more intense, or had been stimulated by circumstance, might have made her a profuse writer, unchecked by the troublesome need of veracity.

These characteristics are the very opposite of such as yield a fine imagination, which is always based on a keen vision, a keen consciousness of what *is*, and carries the store of definite knowledge as material for the construction of its inward visions. Witness Dante, who is at once the most precise and homely in his reproduction of actual objects, and the most soaringly at large in his imaginative combinations. On a much lower level we distinguish the hyperbole, and rapid development in descriptions of persons and events, which are lit up by humorous intention in the speaker — we distinguish this charming play of intelligence, which resembles musical improvisation on a given motive, where the farthest sweep of curve is looped into relevancy by an instinctive method, from the florid inaccuracy or helpless exaggeration, which is really something commoner than the correct simplicity often depreciated as prosaic.

Even if high imagination were to be identified with illusion, there would be the same sort of difference between the imperial wealth of illusion which is informed by industrious observation, and the trumpery stage-property illusion which depends on the ill-defined impressions gathered by capricious inclination, as there is between a good and a bad picture of the Last Judgment. In both these the subject is a combination never actually witnessed, and in the good picture the general combination may be of surpassing boldness; but on examination it is seen that the separate elements have been closely studied from real objects. And even where we find the charm of ideal elevation with wrong drawing and fantastic color, the charm is dependent on the selective sensibility of the painter to certain real delicacies of form which confer the expression he longed to render; for apart from this basis of an effect perceived in common, there could be no conveyance of æsthetic meaning by the painter to the beholder. In this sense it is as true to say of Fra Angelico's Coronation of the Virgin, that it has a strain of reality, as to say so of a portrait by Rembrandt, which also has its strain of ideal elevation to Rembrandt's virile selective sensibility.

To correct such self-flatterers as Callista, it is worth repeating that powerful imagination is not false outward vision, but intense inward representation, and a creative energy constantly fed by susceptibility to the veriest minutiæ of experience, which it reproduces and constructs in fresh and fresh wholes, — not the habitual confusion of provable fact with the fictions of fancy and transient inclination, but a breadth of ideal association which informs every material object, every incidental fact, with far-reaching memories and stored residues of passion, bringing into new light the less obvious relations of human existence. The illusion to which it is liable is not that of habitually taking duck-ponds for lilied pools, but of being more or less transiently and in varying degrees so absorbed in ideal vision as to lose the consciousness of surrounding objects or occurrences; and when that rapt condition is past, the sane genius discriminates clearly between what has been given in this parenthetic state of excitement, and what he has known, and may count on, in the ordinary world of experience. Dante seems to have expressed these conditions perfectly in that passage of the *Purgatorio* where, after a triple vision which has made him forget his surroundings, he says: —

> " Quando l'anima mia tonò di fuori
> Alle cose che son fuor di lei vere,
> Io riconobbi i miei non falsi errori."
>   CANTO XV.

He distinguishes the ideal truth of his entranced vision from the series of external facts to which his consciousness had returned. Isaiah gives us the date of his vision in the Temple, "the year that King Uzziah died;" and if afterward the mighty-winged seraphim were present with him as he trod the street, he doubtless knew them for images of memory, and did not cry, "Look!" to the passers-by.

Certainly the seer, whether prophet, philosopher, scientific discoverer, or poet, may happen to be rather mad; his powers may have been used up, like Don Quixote's, in their visionary or theoretic constructions, so that the reports of common-sense fail to affect him, or the continuous strain of excitement may have robbed his mind of its elasticity. It is hard for our frail mortality to carry the burden of greatness with steady gait and full alacrity of perception. But he is the strongest seer who can support the stress of creative energy, and yet keep that sanity of expectation which consists in distinguishing, as Dante does, between the *cose che son vere* outside the individual mind, and the *non falsi errori* which are the revelations of true imaginative power.

THE TOO READY WRITER.

ONE who talks too much, hindering the rest of the company from taking their turn, and apparently seeing no reason why they should not rather desire to know his opinion or experience in relation to all subjects, or at least to renounce the discussion of any topic where he can make no figure, has never been praised for this industrious monopoly of work which others would willingly have shared in. However various and brilliant his talk may be, we suspect him of impoverishing us by excluding the contributions of other minds, which attract our curiosity the more because he has shut them up in silence. Besides, we get tired of a "manner" in conversation as in painting, when one theme after another is treated with the same lines and touches. I begin with a liking for an estimable master, but by the time he has stretched his interpretation of the world unbrokenly along a palatial gallery, I have had what the cautious Scotch mind would call "enough" of him. There is monotony and narrowness already to spare in my own identity; what comes to me from without should be larger and more impartial than the judgment of any single interpreter. On this ground even a modest person, without power or will to shine in the conversation, may easily find the predominating talker a nuisance; while those who are full of matter on special topics are continually detecting miserably thin places in the web of that information which he will not desist from imparting. Nobody that I know of ever proposed a testimonial to a man for thus volunteering the whole expense of the conversation.

Why is there a different standard of judgment with regard to a writer who plays much the same part in literature as the excessive talker plays in what is traditionally called conversation? The busy Adrastus, whose professional engagements might seem more than enough for the nervous energy of one man, and who yet finds time to print essays on the chief current subjects, from the tri-lingual inscriptions, or the idea of the infinite among the prehistoric Lapps, to the Colorado beetle and the grape disease in the south of France, is generally praised, if not admired, for the breadth of his mental range and his gigantic powers of work. Poor Theron, who has some original ideas on a subject to which he has given years of research and meditation, has been waiting anxiously from month to month to see whether his condensed exposition will find a place in the next advertised programme, but sees it, on the contrary, regularly excluded, and twice the space he asked for filled with the copious brew of Adrastus, whose name carries custom like a celebrated trade-mark. Why should the eager haste to tell what he thinks on the shortest notice, as if his opinion were a needed preliminary to discussion, get a man the reputation of being a conceited bore in conversation, when nobody blames the same tendency if it shows itself in print? The excessive talker can only be in one gathering at a time, and there is the comfort of thinking that everywhere else other fellow-citizens who have something to say may get a chance of delivering themselves; but the exorbitant writer can occupy space and spread over it the more or less agreeable flavor of his mind in four "mediums" at once, and on subjects taken from the four winds. Such restless and versatile occupants of literary space and time should have lived earlier, when the world wanted summaries of all extant knowledge, and this knowledge being small, there was the more room for commentary and conjecture. They might have played the part of an Isidor of Seville or a Vincent of Beauvais brilliantly, and the willingness to write everything themselves would have been strictly in place. In the present day, the busy retailer of other people's knowledge, which he has spoiled in the handling, the restless guesser and commentator, the importunate hawker of undesirable superfluities, the everlasting word-compeller, who rises early in the morning to praise what the world has already glorified, or makes himself haggard at night in writing out his dissent from what nobody ever believed, is not simply "gratis, anhelans, multa agendo nihil agens;" he is an obstruction. Like an incompetent architect, with too much interest at his back, he obtrudes his ill-considered work where place ought to have been left to better men.

Is it out of the question that we should entertain some scruple about mixing our own flavor, as of the too cheap and insistent nutmeg, with that of every great writer and every great subject — especially when our flavor is all we have to give, the matter or knowledge having been already given by somebody else ? What if we were only like the Spanish wineskins which impress the innocent stranger with the notion that the Spanish grape has naturally a taste of leather. One could wish that even the greatest minds should leave some themes unhandled, or at least leave us no more than a paragraph or two on them, to show how well they did in not being more lengthy.

Such entertainment of scruple can hardly be expected from the young; but happily their readiness to mirror the universe anew for the rest of mankind is not encouraged by easy publicity. In the vivacious Pepin I have often seen the image of my early youth, when it seemed to me astonishing that the philosophers had left so many difficulties unsolved, and that so many great themes had raised no great poet to treat them. I had an elated sense that I should find my brain full of theoretic clews when I looked for them, and that wherever a poet had not done what I expected, it was for want of my insight. Not knowing what had been said about the play of Romeo and Juliet, I felt myself capable of writing something original on its blemishes and beauties. In relation to all subjects I had a joyous consciousness of that ability which is prior to knowledge, and of only needing to apply myself in order to master any task — to conciliate philosophers whose systems were at present but dimly known to me, to estimate foreign poets whom I had not yet read, to show up mistakes in a historical monograph that roused my interest in an epoch which I had been hitherto ignorant of — when I should once have had time to verify my views of probability by looking into an encyclopædia. So Pepin; save only that he is industrious while I was idle. Like the astronomer in Rasselas, I swayed the universe in my consciousness, without making any difference outside me; whereas Pepin, while feeling himself powerful with the stars in their courses, really raises some dust here below. He is no longer in his spring-tide; but having been always busy, he has been obliged to use his first impressions as if they were deliberate opinions, and to range himself on the corresponding side in ignorance of much that he commits himself to; so that he retains some characteristics of a comparatively tender age, and among them a certain surprise that there have not been more persons equal to himself. Perhaps it is unfortunate for him that he early gained a hearing, or at least a place in print, and was thus encouraged in acquiring a fixed habit of writing, to the exclusion of any other bread-winning pursuit. He is already to be classed as a "general writer," corresponding to the comprehensive wants of the "general reader," and with this industry on his hands it is not enough for him to keep up the ingenuous self-reliance of youth: he finds himself under an obligation to be skilled in various methods of seeming to know; and having habitually expressed himself before he was convinced, his interest in all subjects is chiefly to ascertain that he has not made a mistake, and to feel his infallibility confirmed. That impulse to decide, that vague sense of being able to achieve the unattempted, that dream of aerial unlimited movement at will without feet or wings, which were once but the joyous mounting of young sap, are already taking shape as unalterable woody fibre; the impulse has hardened into "style," and into a pattern of peremptory sentences; the sense of ability in the presence of other men's failures is turning into the official arrogance of one who habitually issues directions which he has never himself been called on to execute; the dreamy buoyancy of the stripling has taken on a fatal sort of reality in written pretensions which carry consequences. He is on the way to become like the loud-buzzing, bouncing Bombus, who combines conceited illusions enough to supply several patients in a lunatic asylum, with the freedom to show himself at large in various forms of print. If one who takes himself for the telegraphic centre of all American wires is to be confined as unfit to transact affairs, what shall we say to the man who believes himself in possession of the unexpressed motives and designs dwelling in the breasts of all sovereigns and all politicians? And I grieve to think that poor Pepin, though less political, may by and by manifest a persuasion hardly more sane, for he is beginning to explain people's writings by what he does not know about them. Yet he was once at the comparatively innocent stage, which I have confessed to be that of my own early astonishment at my powerful originality; and copying the just humility of the old Puritan, I may say, "But for the grace of discouragement, this coxcombry might have been mine."

Pepin made for himself a necessity of writing (and getting printed) before he had considered whether he had the knowledge or belief that would furnish eligible matter. At first, perhaps, the necessity galled him a little, but it is now as easily borne, nay, is as irrepressible a habit as the outpouring of inconsiderate talk. He is gradually being condemned to have no genuine impressions, no direct consciousness of enjoyment, or the reverse, from the quality of what is before him: his perceptions are continually arranging themselves in forms suitable to a printed judgment; and hence they will often turn out to be as much to the purpose if they are written without any direct contemplation of the object, and are guided by a few external conditions which serve to classify it for him. In this way he is irrevocably losing the faculty of accurate mental vision; having bound himself to express judgments which will satisfy some other demands than that of veracity,

he has blunted his perceptions by continual preoccupation.
We cannot command veracity at will; the power of seeing
and reporting truly is a form of health that has to be delicately guarded, and as an ancient Rabbi has solemnly said,
"The penalty of untruth is untruth." But Pepin is only a
mild example of the fact that incessant writing with a view
to printing carries internal consequences which have often
the nature of disease. And however unpractical it may be
held to consider whether we have anything to print which it
is good for the world to read, or which has not been better
said before, it will perhaps be allowed to be worth considering
what effect the printing may have on ourselves. Clearly
there is a sort of writing which helps to keep the writer in a
ridiculously contented ignorance, — raising in him continually
the sense of having delivered himself effectively, so that the
acquirement of more thorough knowledge seems as superfluous as the purchase of costume for a past occasion. He
has invested his vanity (perhaps his hope of income) in his
own shallownesses and mistakes, and must desire their prosperity. Like the professional prophet, he learns to be glad
of the harm that keeps up his credit, and to be sorry for the
good that contradicts him. It is hard enough for any of us,
amidst the changing winds of fortune and the hurly-burly of
events, to keep quite clear of a gladness which is another's
calamity; but one may choose not to enter on a course which
will turn such gladness into a fixed habit of mind, committing ourselves to be continually pleased that others should
appear to be wrong, in order that we may have the air of
being right.

In some cases, perhaps, it might be urged that Pepin has
remained the more self-contented because he has *not* written
everything he believed himself capable of. He once asked
me to read a sort of programme of the species of romance
which he should think it worth while to write — a species
which he contrasted in strong terms with the productions of
illustrious but overrated authors in this branch. Pepin's
romance was to present the splendors of the Roman Empire

at the culmination of its grandeur, when decadence was spiritually but not visibly imminent; it was to show the workings of human passion in the most pregnant and exalted of human circumstances, the designs of statesmen, the interfusion of philosophies, the rural relaxation and converse of immortal poets, the majestic triumphs of warriors, the mingling of a quaint and sublime in religious ceremony, the gorgeous delirium of gladiatorial shows, and under all the secretly working leaven of Christianity. Such a romance would not call the attention of society to the dialect of stable-boys, the low habits of rustics, the vulgarity of small schoolmasters, the manners of men in livery, or to any other form of uneducated talk and sentiments; its characters would have virtues and vices alike on the grand scale, and would express themselves in an English representing the discourse of the most powerful minds, in the best Latin, or possibly Greek, when there occurred a scene with a Greek philosopher on a visit to Rome, or resident there as a teacher. In this way Pepin would do in fiction what had never been done before; something not at all like " Rienzi " or "Notre Dame de Paris," or any other attempt of that kind, but something at once more penetrating and more magnificent, more passionate and more philosophical, more panoramic yet more select; something that would present a conception of a gigantic period; in short, something truly Roman and world-historical.

When Pepin gave me this programme to read he was much younger than at present. Some slight success in another vein diverted him from the production of panoramic and select romance; and the experience of not having tried to carry out his programme has naturally made him more biting and sarcastic on the failures of those who have actually written romances without apparently having had a glimpse of a conception equal to his. Indeed, I am often comparing his rather touchingly inflated *naïveté*, as of a small young person walking on tiptoe while he is talking of elevated things, at the time when he felt himself the author of that unwritten romance, with his present epigrammatic curtness and affectation of power kept strictly in reserve. His paragraphs now seem to have a bitter smile in them, from the consciousness of a mind too penetrating to accept any other man's ideas, and too equally competent in all directions to seclude his power in any one form of creation, but rather fitted to hang over them all as a lamp of guidance to the stumblers below. You perceive how proud he is of not being indebted to any writer; even with the dead he is on the creditor's side, for he is doing them the service of letting the world know what they meant better than those poor pre-Pepinians themselves had any means of doing; and he treats the mighty shades very cavalierly.

Is this fellow-citizen of ours, considered simply in the light of a baptized Christian and tax-paying Englishman, really as madly conceited, as empty of reverential feeling, as unveracious and careless of justice, as full of catch-penny devices and stagey attitudinizing, as on examination his writing shows itself to be ? By no means. He has arrived at the present pass in "the literary calling" through the self-imposed obligation to give himself a manner which would convey the impression of superior knowledge and ability. He is much worthier and more admirable than his written productions, because the moral aspects exhibited in his writing are felt to be ridiculous or disgraceful in the personal relations of life. In blaming Pepin's writing, we are accusing the public conscience, which is so lax and ill-formed on the momentous bearings of authorship, that it sanctions the total absence of scruple in undertaking and prosecuting what should be the best warranted of vocations.

Hence I still accept friendly relations with Pepin, for he has much private amiability ; and though he probably thinks of me as a man of slender talents, without rapidity of *coup d'œil*, and with no compensatory penetration, he meets me very cordially, and would not, I am sure, willingly pain me in conversation by crudely declaring his low estimate of my capacity. Yet I have often known him to insult my betters, and contribute (perhaps unreflectingly) to encourage injurious conceptions of them ; but that is done in the course of his professional writing, and the public conscience still leaves such writing nearly on a level of the Merry-Andrew's dress, which permits an impudent deportment and extraordinary gambols to one who, in his ordinary clothing, shows himself the decent father of a family.

DISEASES OF SMALL AUTHORSHIP.

PARTICULAR callings, it is known, encourage particular diseases. There is a painter's colic; the Sheffield grinder falls a victim to the inhalation of steel-dust; clergymen so often have a kind of sore throat that this otherwise secular ailment gets named after them. And perhaps, if we were to inquire, we should find a similar relation between certain moral ailments and these various occupations, though here in the case of clergymen there would be specific differences; the poor curate, equally with the rector, is liable to clergyman's sore throat, but he would probably be found free from the chronic moral ailments encouraged by the possession of glebe and those higher chances of preferment which follow on having a good position already. On the other hand, the poor curate might have severe attacks of calculating expectancy concerning parishioners' turkeys, cheeses, and fat geese, or of uneasy rivalry for the donations of clerical charities.

Authors are so miscellaneous a class that their personified diseases, physical and moral, might include the whole procession of human disorders, led by dyspepsia and ending in madness — the awful dumb-show of a world-historic tragedy. Take a large enough area of human life, and all comedy melts into tragedy, like the Fool's part of the side of Lear. The chief scenes get filled with erring heroes, guileful usurpers, persecuted discoverers, dying deliverers: everywhere the protagonist has a part pregnant with doom. The comedy sinks to an accessory, and if there are loud laughs they seem a convulsive transition from sobs; or if the comedy is touched with a gentle lovingness, the panoramic scene is one where

> " Sadness is a kind of mirth,
> So mingled as if mirth did make us sad
> And sadness merry." [1]

But I did not set out on the wide survey that would carry me into tragedy, and, in fact, had nothing more serious in my mind than certain small chronic ailments that come of small authorship. I was thinking principally of Vorticella, who flourished in my youth, not only as a portly lady walking in silk attire, but also as the authoress of a book entitled "The Channel Islands, with Notes and an Appendix." I would by no means make it a reproach to her that she wrote no more than one book ; on the contrary, her stopping there seems to me a laudable example. What one would have wished, after experience, was that she had refrained from producing even that single volume, and thus from giving herself-importance a troublesome kind of double incorporation which became oppressive to her acquaintances, and set up in herself one of those slight chronic forms of disease to which I have just referred. She lived in the considerable provincial town of Pumpiter, which had its own newspaper press, with the usual divisions of political partisanship and the usual varieties of literary criticism — the florid and allusive, the *staccato* and peremptory, the clairvoyant and prophetic, the safe and pattern-phrased, or what one might call "the many-a-long-day style."

Vorticella, being the wife of an important townsman, had naturally the satisfaction of seeing "The Channel Islands " reviewed by all the organs of Pumpiter opinion, and their articles or paragraphs held as naturally the opening pages in the elegantly bound album prepared by her for the reception of "critical opinions." This ornamental volume lay on a special table in her drawing-room, close to the still more gorgeously bound work of which it was the significant

---

[1] The Two Noble Kinsmen.

effect, and every guest was allowed the privilege of reading
what had been said of the authoress and her work in the
" Pumpiter Gazette and Literary Watchman," the " Pumpshire
Post," the " Church Clock," the " Independent Monitor," and
the lively but judicious publication known as the " Medley
Pie ; " to be followed up, if he chose, by the instructive perusal
of the strikingly confirmatory judgments, sometimes concurrent in the very phrases, of journals from the most distant
countries, as the " Latchgate Argus," the " Penllwy Universe,"
the "Cockaleekie Advertiser," the " Goodwin Sands Opinion,"
and the " Land's End Times."

I had friends in Pumpiter, and occasionally paid a long
visit there.   When I called on Vorticella, who had a cousin-
ship with my hosts, she had to excuse herself because a
message claimed her attention for eight or ten minutes ; and
handing me the album of critical opinions, said, with a certain
emphasis which, considering my youth, was highly complimentary, that she would really like me to read what I should
find there.   This seemed a permissive politeness which I
could not feel to be an oppression ; and I ran my eyes over the
dozen pages, each with a strip or islet of newspaper in the
centre, with that freedom of mind (in my case meaning freedom to forget) which would be a perilous way of preparing
for examination.   This *ad libitum* perusal had its interest for
me.   The private truth being that I had not read "The
Channel Islands," I was amazed at the variety of matter
which the volume must contain, to have impressed these
different judges with the writer's surpassing capacity to
handle almost all branches of inquiry and all forms of presentation.   In Jersey she had shown herself a historian, in
Guernsey a poetess, in Alderney a political economist, and in
Sark a humorist.   There were sketches of character scattered
through the pages which might put our " fictionists " to the
blush ; the style was eloquent and racy, studded with gems
of felicitous remark ; and the moral spirit throughout was so
superior that, said one, " the recording angel " (who is not
supposed to take account of literature as such) " would

assuredly set down the work as a deed of religion." The force
of this eulogy on the part of several reviewers was much
heightened by the incidental evidence of their fastidious and
severe taste, which seemed to suffer considerably from the
imperfections of our chief writers, even the dead and canonized : one afflicted them with the smell of oil ; another lacked
erudition, and attempted (though vainly) to dazzle them with
trivial conceits ; one wanted to be more philosophical than
nature had made him ; another, in attempting to be comic,
produced the melancholy effect of a half-starved Merry-Andrew ; while one and all, from the author of the " Areopagi-
tica " downward, had faults of style which must have made an
able hand in the " Latchgate Argus " shake the many-glanced
head belonging thereto with a smile of compassionate dis-
approval. Not so the authoress of " The Channel Islands ; "
Vorticella and Shakspeare were allowed to be faultless.   I
gathered that no blemishes were observable in the work of
this accomplished writer, and the repeated information that
she was " second to none " seemed after this superfluous.   Her
thick octavo — notes, appendix, and all — was unflagging from
beginning to end ; and the " Land's End Times," using a rather
dangerous rhetorical figure, recommended you not to take up
the volume unless you had leisure to finish it at a sitting.   It
had given one writer more pleasure than he had had for
many a long day — a sentence which had a melancholy resonance, suggesting a life of studious languor such as all
previous achievements of the human mind failed to stimulate
into enjoyment.   I think the collection of critical opinions
wound up with this sentence, and I had turned back to look
at the lithographed sketch of the authoress which fronted
the first page of the album, when the fair original re-entered,
and I laid down the volume on its appropriate table.

"Well, what do you think of them ? " said Vorticella, with
an emphasis which had some significance unperceived by me.
" I know you are a great student.   Give me *your* opinion of
these opinions."

"They must be very gratifying to you," I answered, with

a little confusion; for I perceived that I might easily mistake my footing, and I began to have a presentiment of an examination for which I was by no means crammed.

"On the whole — yes," said Vorticella, in a tone of concession. "A few of the notices are written with some pains, but not one of them has really grappled with the chief idea in the appendix. I don't know whether you have studied political economy, but you saw what I said on page 398 about the Jersey fisheries?"

I bowed — I confess it — with the mean hope that this movement in the nape of my neck would be taken as sufficient proof that I had read, marked, and learned. I do not forgive myself for this pantomimic falsehood; but I was young and morally timorous, and Vorticella's personality had an effect on me something like that of a powerful mesmerizer, when he directs all his ten fingers toward your eyes, as unpleasantly visible ducts for the invisible stream. I felt a great power of contempt in her if I did not come up to her expectations.

"Well," she resumed, "you observe that not one of them has taken up that argument; but I hope I convinced you about the drag-nets?"

Here was a judgment on me. Orientally speaking, I had lifted up my foot on the steep descent of falsity, and was compelled to set it down on a lower level. "I should think you must be right," said I, inwardly resolving that on the next topic I would tell the truth.

"I *know* that I am right," said Vorticella. "The fact is that no critic in this town is fit to meddle with such subjects unless it be Volvox, and he, with all his command of language, is very superficial. It is Volvox who writes in the 'Monitor.' I hope you noticed how he contradicts himself?"

My resolution, helped by the equivalence of dangers, stoutly prevailed, and I said "No."

"No! I am surprised. He is the only one who finds fault with me. He is a Dissenter, you know. The 'Monitor' is the Dissenters' organ, but my husband has been so useful to them in municipal affairs that they would not venture to run my book down; they feel obliged to tell the truth about me. Still, Volvox betrays himself. After praising me for my penetration and accuracy, he presently says I have allowed myself to be imposed upon, and have let my active imagination run away with me. That is like his Dissenting impertinence. Active my imagination may be, but I have it under control. Little Vibrio, who writes the playful notice in the 'Medley Pie,' has a clever hit at Volvox in that passage about the steeple-chase of imagination, where the loser wants to make it appear that the winner was only run away with. But if you did not notice Volvox's self-contradiction you would not see the point," added Vorticella, with rather a chilling intonation. "Or perhaps you did not read the 'Medley Pie' notice? That is a pity. Do take up the book again. Vibrio is a poor little tippling creature; but, as Mr. Carlyle would say, he has an eye, and he is always lively."

I did take up the book again, and read as demanded.

"It is very ingenious," said I, really appreciating the difficulty of being lively in this connection; it seemed even more wonderful than that a Vibrio should have an eye.

"You are probably surprised to see no notices from the London press," said Vorticella. "I have one, — a very remarkable one, — but I reserve it until the others have spoken, and then I shall introduce it to wind up. I shall have them reprinted, of course, and inserted in future copies. This from the 'Candelabrum' is only eight lines in length, but full of venom. It calls my style dull and pompous. I think that will tell its own tale, placed after the other *critiques*."

"People's impressions are so different," said I. "Some persons find 'Don Quixote' dull."

"Yes," said Vorticella, in emphatic chest-tones, "dulness is a matter of opinion; but pompous! That I never was and never could be. Perhaps he means that my matter is too important for his taste; and I have no objection to *that*. I did not intend to be trivial. I should just like to read you that passage about the drag-nets, because I could make it clearer to you."

A second (less ornamental) copy was at her elbow and was already opened, when to my great relief another guest was announced, and I was able to take my leave without seeming to run away from "The Channel Islands," though not with out being compelled to carry with me the loan of "the marked copy," which I was to find advantageous in a reperusal of the appendix, and was only requested to return before my departure from Pumpiter. Looking into the volume now with some curiosity, I found it a very ordinary combination of the commonplace and ambitious — one of those books which one might imagine to have been written under the old Grub Street coercion of hunger and thirst, if they were not known beforehand to be the gratuitous productions of ladies and gentlemen, whose circumstances might be called altogether easy, but for an uneasy vanity that happened to have been directed toward authorship. Its importance was that of a polypus, tumor, fungus, or other erratic outgrowth, noxious and disfiguring in its effect on the individual organism which nourishes it. Poor Vorticella might not have been more wearisome on a visit than the majority of her neighbors, but for this disease of magnified self-importance belonging to small authorship. I understand that the chronic complaint of "The Channel Islands" never left her. As the years went on, and the publication tended to vanish in the distance for her neighbors' memory, she was still bent on dragging it to the foreground ; and her chief interest in new acquaintances was the possibility of lending them her book, entering into all details concerning it, and requesting them to read her album of "critical opinions." This really made her more tiresome than Gregarina, whose distinction was that she had had cholera, and who did not feel herself in her true position with strangers until they knew it.

My experience with Vorticella led me for a time into the false supposition that this sort of fungous disfiguration, which makes Self disagreeably larger, was most common to the female sex ; but I presently found that here too the male could assert his superiority and show a more vigorous boredom. I have known a man with a single pamphlet containing an assurance that somebody else was wrong, together with a few approved quotations, produce a more powerful effect of shuddering at his approach than ever Vorticella did with her varied octavo volume, including notes and appendix. Males of more than one nation recur to my memory who produced from their pocket on the slightest encouragement a small pink or buff duodecimo pamphlet, wrapped in silver paper, as a present held ready for an intelligent reader. "A mode of propagandism," you remark in excuse; "they wished to spread some useful corrective doctrine." Not necessarily; the indoctrination aimed at was perhaps to convince you of their own talents by the sample of an "Ode on Shakspeare's Birthday," or a translation from Horace.

Vorticella may pair off with Monas, who had also written his one book, — "Here and There; or, a Trip from Truro to Transylvania, " — and not only carried it in his portmanteau when he went on visits, but took the earliest opportunity of depositing it in the drawing-room, and afterward would enter to look for it, as if under pressure of a need for reference, begging the lady of the house to tell him whether she had seen "a small volume bound in red." One hostess at last ordered it to be carried into his bedroom to save his time; but it presently reappeared in his hands, and was again left, with inserted slips of paper, on the drawing-room table.

Depend upon it, vanity is human — native alike to men and women; only in the male it is of denser texture, less volatile, so that it less immediately informs you of its presence, but is more massive and capable of knocking you down if you come into collision with it; while in woman vanity lays by its small revenges as in a needle-case always at hand. The difference is in muscle and finger-tips, in traditional habits and mental perspective, rather than in the original appetite of vanity. It is an approved method now to explain ourselves by a reference to the races as little like us as possible; which leads me to observe that in Fiji the men use the most elaborate hairdressing, and that wherever tattooing is in vogue the male expects to carry off the prize of admiration for pattern and workmanship. Arguing analogically, and looking for this tendency of the Fijian or Hawaian male in the eminent European, we must suppose that it exhibits itself under the forms of civilized apparel; and it would be a great mistake to estimate passionate effort by the effect it produces on our perception or understanding. It is conceivable that a man may have concentrated no less will and expectation on his wristbands, gaiters, and the shape of his hat-brim, or an appearance which impresses you as that of the modern "swell," than the Ojibbeway on an ornamentation which seems to us much more elaborate. In what concerns the search for admiration, at least, it is not true that the effect is equal to the cause and resembles it. The cause of a flat curl on the masculine forehead, such as might be seen when George the Fourth was king, must have been widely different in quality and intensity from the impression made by that small scroll of hair on the organ of the beholder. Merely to maintain an attitude and gait which I notice in certain club men, and especially an inflation of the chest accompanying very small remarks, there goes, I am convinced, an expenditure of psychical energy little appreciated by the multitude — a mental vision of Self and deeply impressed beholders, which is quite without antitype in what we call the effect produced by that hidden process.

No! there is no need to admit that women would carry away the prize of vanity in a competition where differences of custom were fairly considered. A man cannot show his vanity in a tight skirt which forces him to walk sideways down the staircase; but let the match be between the respective vanities of largest beard and tightest skirt, and here too the battle would be to the strong.

MORAL SWINDLERS.

IT is a familiar example of irony in the degradation of words that "what a man is worth" has come to mean how much money he possesses; but there seems a deeper and more melancholy irony in the shrunken meaning that popular or polite speech assigns to "morality" and "morals." The poor part these words are made to play recalls the fate of those pagan divinities who, after being understood to rule the powers of the air and the destinies of men, came down to the level of insignificant demons, or were even made a farcical show for the amusement of the multitude.

Talking to Melissa in a time of commercial trouble, I found her disposed to speak pathetically of the disgrace which had fallen on Sir Gavial Mantrap, because of his conduct in relation to the Eocene Mines, and to other companies ingeniously devised by him for the punishment of ignorance in people of small means: a disgrace by which the poor titled gentleman was actually reduced to live in comparative obscurity on his wife's settlement of one or two hundred thousand in the consols.

"Surely your pity is misapplied," said I, rather dubiously; for I like the comfort of trusting that a correct moral judgment is the strong point in woman (seeing that she has a majority of about a million in our island), and I imagined that Melissa might have some unexpressed grounds for her opinion. "I should have thought you would rather be sorry for Mantrap's victims—the widows, spinsters, and hard-working fathers, whom his unscrupulous haste to make himself rich has cheated of all their savings, while he is eating well, lying softly, and, after impudently justifying himself before the public, is perhaps joining in the General Confession with a sense that he is an acceptable object in the sight of God, though decent men refuse to meet him."

"Oh, all that about the Companies, I know, was most unfortunate. In commerce people are led to do so many things, and he might not know exactly how everything would turn out. But Sir Gavial made a good use of his money, and he is a thoroughly *moral* man."

"What do you mean by a thoroughly moral man?" said I.

"Oh, I suppose every one means the same by that," said Melissa, with a slight air of rebuke. "Sir Gavial is an excellent family man — quite blameless there; and so charitable round his place at Tip-top. Very different from Mr. Barabbas, whose life, my husband tells me, is most objectionable, with actresses and that sort of thing. I think a man's morals should make a difference to us. I'm not sorry for Mr. Barabbas, but I *am* sorry for Sir Gavial Mantrap."

I will not repeat my answer to Melissa, for I fear it was offensively brusque, my opinion being that Sir Gavial was the more pernicious scoundrel of the two, since his name for virtue served as an effective part of a swindling apparatus; and perhaps I hinted that to call such a man "moral" showed rather a silly notion of human affairs. In fact, I had an angry wish to be instructive, and Melissa, as will sometimes happen, noticed my anger without appropriating my instruction; for I have since heard that she speaks of me as rather violent-tempered, and not over-strict in my views of morality.

I wish that this narrow use of words which are wanted in their full meaning were confined to women like Melissa. Seeing that "morality" and "morals," under their *alias* of Ethics, are the subject of voluminous discussion, and their true basis a pressing matter of dispute — seeing that the most famous book ever written on Ethics, and forming a chief study in our colleges, allies ethical with political science, or that which treats of the constitution and prosperity of states, one might expect that educated men would find reason to avoid a per-

version of language which lends itself to no wider view of
life than that of village gossips.   Yet I find even respectable
historians of our own and of foreign countries, after showing
that a king was treacherous, rapacious, and ready to sanction
gross breaches in the administration of justice, end by praising him for his pure moral character; by which one must suppose them to mean that he was not lewd nor debauched, not
the European twin of the typical Indian potentate whom
Macaulay describes as passing his life in chewing bang and
fondling dancing-girls.   And since we are sometimes told of
such maleficent kings that they were religious, we arrive at
the curious result, that the most serious wide-reaching duties
of man lie quite outside both morality and religion — the
one of these consisting in not keeping mistresses (and perhaps not drinking too much), and the other in certain ritual
and spiritual transactions with God, which can be carried on
equally well side by side with the basest conduct toward
men.   With such a classification as this it is no wonder, considering the strong reaction of language on thought, that
many minds, dizzy with indigestion of recent science and
philosophy, are far to seek for the grounds of social duty,
and without entertaining any private intention of committing
a perjury which would ruin an innocent man, or seeking gain
by supplying bad preserved meats to our navy, feel themselves speculatively obliged to inquire why they should not
do so, and are inclined to measure their intellectual subtlety
by their dissatisfaction with all answers to this "Why?"   It
is of little use to theorize in ethics while our habitual phraseology stamps the larger part of our social duties as something
that lies aloof from the deepest needs and affections of our
nature.   The informal definitions of popular language are the
only medium through which theory really affects the mass of
minds, even among the nominally educated; and when a man
whose business hours, the solid part of every day, are spent
in an unscrupulous course of public or private action which
has every calculable chance of causing wide-spread injury
and misery, can be called moral because he comes home to

dine with his wife and children and cherishes the happiness
of his own hearth, the augury is not good for the use of high
ethical and theological disputation.

Not for one moment would one willingly lose sight of the
truth that the relation of the sexes and the primary ties of
kinship are the deepest roots of human well-being, but to
make them by themselves the equivalent of morality is ver-
bally to cut off the channels of feeling through which they
are the feeders of that well-being. They are the original
fountains of a sensibility to the claims of others, which is the
bond of societies; but being necessarily in the first instance
a private good, there is always the danger that individual selfishness will see in them only the best part of its own gain;
just as knowledge, navigation, commerce, and all the conditions which are of a nature to awaken men's consciousness of
their mutual dependence and to make the world one great
society, are the occasions of selfish, unfair action, of war and
oppression, so long as the public conscience or chief force of
feeling and opinion is not uniform and strong enough in its
insistence on what is demanded by the general welfare. And
among the influences that must retard a right public judgment, the degradation of words which involve praise and
blame will be reckoned worth protesting against by every
mature observer. To rob words of half their meaning, while
they retain their dignity as qualifications, is like allowing to
men who have lost half their faculties the same high and
perilous command which they won in their time of vigor, or
like selling food and seeds after fraudulently abstracting their
best virtues; in each case what ought to be beneficently
strong is fatally enfeebled, if not empoisoned. Until we
have altered our dictionaries and have found some other word
than "morality" to stand in popular use for the duties of man
to man, let us refuse to accept as moral the contractor who
enriches himself by using large machinery to make paste-
board soles pass as leather for the feet of unhappy conscripts
fighting at miserable odds against invaders; let us rather
call him a miscreant, though he were the tenderest, most

faithful of husbands, and contend that his own experience of home happiness makes his reckless infliction of suffering on others all the more atrocious. Let us refuse to accept as moral any political leader who should allow his conduct in relation to great issues to be determined by egoistic passion, and boldly say that he would be less immoral, even though he were as lax in his personal habits as Sir Robert Walpole, if at the same time his sense of the public welfare were supreme in his mind, quelling all pettier impulses beneath a magnanimous impartiality. And though we were to find among that class of journalists who live by recklessly reporting injurious rumors, insinuating the blackest motives in opponents, descanting at large and with an air of infallibility on dreams which they both find and interpret, and stimulating bad feeling between nations by abusive writing which is as empty of real conviction as the rage of a pantomime-king, and would be ludicrous if its effects did not make it appear diabolical — though we were to find among these a man who was benignancy itself in his own circle, a healer of private differences, a soother in private calamities, let us pronounce him nevertheless flagrantly immoral, a root of hideous cancer in the commonwealth, turning the channels of instruction into feeders of social and political disease.

In opposite ways one sees bad effects likely to be encouraged by this narrow use of the word "morals," shutting out from its meaning half those actions of a man's life which tell momentously on the well-being of his fellow-citizens, and on the preparation of a future for the children growing up around him. Thoroughness of workmanship, care in the execution of every task undertaken, as if it were the acceptance of a trust which it would be a breach of faith not to discharge well, is a form of duty so momentous that if it were to die out from the feeling and practice of a people, all reforms of institutions would be helpless to create national prosperity and national happiness. Do we desire to see public spirit penetrating all classes of the community and affecting every man's conduct, so that he shall make neither the saving of

his soul nor any other private saving an excuse for indifference to the general welfare? Well and good. But the
sort of public spirit that scamps its bread-winning work,
whether with the trowel, the pen, or the overseeing brain,
that it may hurry to scenes of political or social agitation,
would be as baleful a gift to our people as any malignant
demon could devise. One best part of educational training
is that which comes through special knowledge and manipula-
tive or other skill, — with its usual accompaniment of delight,
in relation to work which is the daily bread-winning occupation, — which is a man's contribution to the effective wealth
of society in return for what he takes as his own share. But
this duty of doing one's proper work well, and taking care
that every product of one's labor shall be genuinely what
it pretends to be, is not only left out of morals in popular
speech; it is very little insisted on by public teachers, at
least in the only effective way — by tracing the continuous
effects of ill-done work. Some of them seem to be still
hopeful that it will follow as a necessary consequence from
week-day services, ecclesiastical decoration, and improved
hymn-books; others apparently trust to descanting on self-
culture in general, or to raising a general sense of faulty
circumstances; and meanwhile lax, makeshift work, from the
high conspicuous kind to the average and obscure, is allowed
to pass unstamped with the disgrace of immorality, though
there is not a member of society who is not daily suffering
from it materially and spiritually, and though it is the fatal
cause that must degrade our national rank and our commerce,
in spite of all open markets and discovery of available coal-
seams.

I suppose one may take the popular misuse of the words
"morality" and "morals" as some excuse for certain absurdities which are occasional fashions in speech and writing — certain old lay-figures, as ugly as the queerest Asiatic idol, which
at different periods get propped into loftiness, and attired in
magnificent Venetian drapery, so that whether they have a
human face or not is of little consequence One is the no-

tión that there is a radical, irreconcilable opposition between intellect and morality. I do not mean the simple statement of fact, which everybody knows, that remarkably able men have had very faulty morals, and have outraged public feeling even at its ordinary standard; but the supposition that the ablest intellect, the highest genius, will see through morality as a sort of twaddle for bibs and tuckers, a doctrine of dulness, a mere incident in human stupidity. We begin to understand the acceptance of this foolishness by considering that we live in a society where we may hear a treacherous monarch, or a malignant and lying politician, or a man who uses either official or literary power as an instrument of his private partiality or hatred, or a manufacturer who devises the falsification of wares, or a trader who deals in virtueless seed-grains, praised or compassionated because of his excellent morals. Clearly, if morality meant no more than such decencies as are practised by these poisonous members of society, it would be possible to say, without suspicion of light-headedness, that morality lay aloof from the grand stream of human affairs, as a small channel fed by the stream and not missed from it. While this form of nonsense is conveyed in the popular use of words, there must be plenty of well-dressed ignorance at leisure to run through a box of books, which will feel itself initiated in the freemasonry of intellect by a view of life which might take for a Shakspearian motto,

> "Fair is foul and foul is fair,
> Hover through the fog and filthy air,"

and will find itself easily provided with striking conversation by the rule of reversing all the judgments on good and evil which have come to be the calendar and clock-work of society. But let our habitual talk give morals their full meaning as the conduct which, in every human relation, would follow from the fullest knowledge and the fullest sympathy,— a meaning perpetually corrected and enriched by a more thorough appreciation of dependence in things, and a finer sensibility to both physical and spiritual fact, — and this ridiculous ascription of superlative power to minds which have no effective awe-inspiring vision of the human lot, no response of understanding to the connection between duty and the material processes by which the world is kept habitable for cultivated man, will be tacitly discredited without any need to cite the immortal names that all are obliged to take as the measure of intellectual rank and highly charged genius.

Suppose a Frenchman — I mean no disrespect to the great French nation, for all nations are afflicted with their peculiar parasitic growths, which are lazy, hungry forms, usually characterized by a disproportionate swallowing apparatus — suppose a Parisian who should shuffle down the Boulevard with a soul ignorant of the gravest cases and the deepest tenderness of manhood, and a frame more or less fevered by debauchery, mentally polishing into utmost refinement of phrase and rhythm verses which were an enlargement on that Shakspearian motto, and worthy of the most expensive title to be furnished by the venders of such antithetic ware as " Les Marguerites de l'Enfer," or "Les delices de Beelzebuth." This supposed personage might probably enough regard his negation of those moral sensibilities which make half the warp and woof of human history — his indifference to the hard thinking and hard handiwork of life, to which he owed even his own gauzy mental garments, with their spangles of poor paradox — as the royalty of genius, for we are used to witness such self-crowning in many forms of mental alienation; but he would not, I think, be taken, even by his own generation, as a living proof that there can exist such a combination as that of moral stupidity and trivial emphasis of personal indulgence, with the large yet finely discriminating vision which marks the intellectual masters of our kind. Doubtless there are many sorts of transfiguration, and a man who has come to be worthy of all gratitude and reverence may have had his swinish period, wallowing in ugly places; but suppose it had been handed down to us that Sophocles or Virgil had at one time made himself scandalous in this way; the works which have consecrated their memory for our admiration and gratitude are not a glorifying of swinishness, but an artistic incorporation of the highest sentiment known to their age.

All these may seem to be wide reasons for objecting to Melissa's pity for Sir Gavial Mantrap, on the ground of his good morals; but their connection will not be obscure to any one who has taken pains to observe the links uniting the scattered signs of our social development.

"MELROSE," RICHMOND, SURREY, WHERE GEORGE ELIOT LIVED.

SHADOWS OF THE COMING RACE.

MY friend Trost, who is no optimist as to the state of
the universe hitherto, but is confident that at some
future period, within the duration of the solar system, ours
will be the best of all possible worlds, — a hope which I
always honor as a sign of beneficent qualities, — my friend
Trost always tries to keep up my spirits, under the sight of
the extremely unpleasant and disfiguring work by which
many of our fellow-creatures have to get their bread, with
the assurance that "all this will soon be done by machinery."
But he sometimes neutralizes the consolation by extending it
over so large an area of human labor, and insisting so im-
pressively on the quantity of energy which will thus be set
free for loftier purposes, that I am tempted to desire an occasional famine of invention in the coming ages, lest the
humbler kinds of work should be entirely nullified while
there are still left some men and women who are not fit for
the highest.

Especially, when one considers the perfunctory way in
which some of the most exalted tasks are already executed
by those who are understood to be educated for them, there
rises a fearful vision of the human race evolving machinery
which will by and by throw itself fatally out of work. When,
in the Bank of England, I see a wondrously delicate machine
for testing sovereigns, a shrewd implacable little steel Rhad-
amanthus that, once the coins are delivered up to it, lifts and
balances each in turn for the fraction of an instant, finds it
wanting or sufficient, and dismisses it to right or left with
rigorous justice; when I am told of micrometers and thermo-

piles and tasimeters, which deal physically with the invisible, the impalpable, and the unimaginable; of cunning wires and wheels and pointing needles which will register your and my quickness so as to exclude flattering opinion; of a machine for drawing the right conclusion, which will doubtless by-and-by be improved into an automaton for finding true premises; of a microphone which detects the cadence of a fly's foot on the ceiling, and may be expected presently to discriminate the noises of our various follies as they soliloquize or converse in our brains, — my mind seeming too small for these things, I get a little out of it, like an unfortunate savage too suddenly brought face to face with civilization, and I exclaim:

"Am I already in the shadow of the Coming Race? and will the creatures who are to transcend and finally supersede us be steely organisms, giving out the effluvia of the laboratory, and performing, with infallible exactness, more than everything that we have performed, with a slovenly approximativeness, and self-defeating inaccuracy?"

"But," says Trost, treating me with cautious mildness on hearing me vent this raving notion, "you forget that these wonder-workers are the slaves of our race, need our tendance and regulation, obey the mandates of our consciousness, and are only deaf and dumb bringers of reports which we decipher and make use of. They are simply extensions of the human organism, so to speak, limbs immeasurably more powerful, ever more subtle finger-tips, ever more mastery over the invisibly great and the invisibly small. Each new machine needs a new appliance of human skill to construct it, new devices to feed it with material, and often keener-edged faculties to note its registrations or performances. How, then, can machines supersede us? They depend upon us. When we cease, they cease."

"I am not so sure of that," said I, getting back into my mind, and becoming rather wilful in consequence. "If, as I have heard you contend, machines as they are more and more perfected will require less and less of tendance, how do I know that they may not be ultimately made to carry, or may not in themselves evolve, conditions of self-supply, self-repair, and reproduction, and not only do all the mighty and subtle work possible on this planet better than we could do it, but with the immense advantage of banishing from the earth's atmosphere screaming consciousnesses which, in our comparatively clumsy race, make an intolerable noise and fuss to each other about every petty ant-like performance, looking on at all work only as it were to spring a rattle here or blow a trumpet there, with a ridiculous sense of being effective ? I for my part cannot see any reason why a sufficiently penetrating thinker, who can see his way through a thousand years or so, should not conceive a parliament of machines, in which the manners were excellent and the motions infallible in logic; one honorable instrument, a remote descendant of the Voltaic family, might discharge a powerful current (entirely without animosity) on an honorable instrument opposite, of more upstart origin, but belonging to the ancient edge-tool race, which we already at Sheffield see paring thick iron as if it were mellow cheese — by this unerringly directed discharge operating on movements corresponding to what we call Estimates, and by necessary mechanical consequence on movements corresponding to what we call the Funds, which, with a vain analogy, we sometimes speak of as 'sensitive.' For every machine would be perfectly educated, that is to say, would have the suitable molecular adjustments, which would act not the less infallibly for being free from the fussy accompaniment of that consciousness to which our prejudice gives a supreme governing rank, when in truth it is an idle parasite on the grand sequence of things."

"Nothing of the sort !" returned Trost, getting angry, and judging it kind to treat me with some severity; "what you have heard me say is, that our race will and must act as a nervous centre to the utmost development of mechanical processes : the subtly refined powers of machines will react in producing more subtly refined thinking processes, which will occupy the minds set free from grosser labor. Say, for example, that all the scavengers' work in London were done, so far as human attention is concerned, by the occasional pressure of a brass button (as in the ringing of an electric bell), you will then have a multitude of brains set free for the exquisite enjoyment of dealing with the exact sequences and high speculations supplied and prompted by the delicate machines which yield a response to the fixed stars, and give readings of the spiral vortices fundamentally concerned in the production of epic poems or great judicial harangues. So far from mankind being thrown out of work, according to your notion," concluded Trost, with a peculiar nasal note of scorn, "if it were not for your incurable dilettanteism in science as in all other things — if you had once understood the action of any delicate machine — you would perceive that the sequences it carries throughout the realm of phenomena would require many generations, perhaps eons of understandings considerably stronger than yours, to exhaust the store of work it lays open."

"Precisely," said I, with a meekness which I felt was praiseworthy; "it is the feebleness of my capacity, bringing me nearer than you to the human average, that perhaps enables me to imagine certain results better than you can. Doubtless the very fishes of your rivers, gullible as they look, and slow as they are to be rightly convinced in another order of facts, form fewer false expectations about each other than we should form about them if we were in a position of somewhat fuller intercourse with their species; for even as it is, we have continually to be surprised that they do not rise to our carefully selected bait. Take me then as a sort of reflective and experienced carp, but do not estimate the justice of my ideas by my facial expression."

"Pooh!" says Trost. (We are on very intimate terms.)

"Naturally," I persisted, "it is less easy to you than to me to imagine our race transcended and superseded, since the more energy a being is possessed of, the harder it must be for him to conceive his own death. But I, from the point of view of a reflective carp, can easily imagine myself and my congeners dispensed with in the frame of things, and giving way not only to a superior but a vastly different kind of entity. What I would ask you is, to show me why, since each new invention casts a new light along the pathway of discovery, and each new combination or structure brings into play more conditions than its inventor foresaw, there should not at length be a machine of such high mechanical powers that it would find and assimilate the material to supply its own waste, and then, by a further evolution of internal molecular movements, reproduce itself by some process of fission or budding. This last stage having been reached, either by man's contrivance or as an unforeseen result, one sees that the process of natural selection must drive men altogether out of the field; for they will long before then have begun to sink into the miserable condition of those unhappy characters in fable, who having demons or djinns at their beck, and being obliged to supply them with work, found too much of everything done in too short a time. What demons so potent as molecular movements, none the less tremendously potent for not carrying the futile cargo of a consciousness screeching irrelevantly, like a fowl tied head downmost to the saddle of a swift horseman ? Under such uncomfortable circumstances, our race will have diminished with the diminishing call on their energies; and by the time that the self-repairing and reproducing machines arise, all but a few of the rare inventors, calculators, and speculators will have become pale, pulpy, and cretinous from fatty or other degeneration, and behold around them a scanty hydrocephalous offspring. As to the breed of the ingenious and intellectual, their nervous systems will at last have been overwrought in following the molecular revelations of the immensely more powerful unconscious race, and they will naturally, as the less energetic combinations of movement, subside like the flame of a candle in the sunlight. Thus the feebler race, whose corporeal adjustments happened to be accompanied with a maniacal consciousness which imagined itself moving its mover, will have vanished, as all less adapted existences do before the fittest — i. e., the existence composed of the most persistent groups of movements and the most capable of incorporating new groups in harmonious relation. Who, if our consciousness is, as I have been given to understand, a mere stumbling of our organisms on their way to unconscious perfection, — who shall say that those fittest existences will not be found along the track of what we call inorganic combinations, which will carry on the most elaborate processes as mutely and painlessly as we are now told that the minerals are metamorphosing themselves continually in the dark laboratory of the earth's crust? Thus this planet may be filled with beings who will be blind and deaf as the inmost rock, yet will execute changes as delicate and complicated as those of human language, and all the intricate web of what we call its effects, without sensitive impression, without sensitive impulse; there may be, let us say, mute orations, mute rhapsodies, mute discussions, and no consciousness there even to enjoy the silence."

"Absurd!" grumbled Trost.

"The supposition is logical," said I. "It is well argued from the premises."

"Whose premises?" cried Trost, turning on me with some fierceness. "You don't mean to call them mine, I hope?"

"Heaven forbid. They seem to be flying about in the air with other germs, and have found a sort of nidus among my melancholy fancies. Nobody really holds them. They bear the same relation to real belief, as walking on the head for a show does to running away from an explosion or walking fast to catch the train."

THE MODERN HEP! HEP! HEP!

TO discern likeness amidst diversity, it is well known, does not require so fine a mental edge as the discerning of diversity amidst general sameness. The primary rough classification depends on the prominent resemblances of things : the progress is toward finer and finer discrimination according to minute differences.

Yet even at this stage of European culture, one's attention is continually drawn to the prevalence of that grosser mental sloth which makes people dull to the most ordinary prompting of comparison, the bringing things together because of their likeness. The same motives, the same ideas, the same practices, are alternately admired and abhorred, lauded and denounced, according to their association with superficial differences, historical or actually social. Even learned writers, treating of great subjects, often show an attitude of mind not greatly superior in its logic to that of the frivolous fine lady who is indignant at the frivolity of her maid.

To take only the subject of the Jews : it would be difficult to find a form of bad reasoning about them which has not been heard in conversation or been admitted to the dignity of print ; but the neglect of resemblances is a common property of dulness which unites all the various points of view — the prejudiced, the puerile, the spiteful, and the abysmally ignorant.

That the preservation of national memories is an element and a means of national greatness ; that their revival is a sign of reviving nationality ; that every heroic defender, every patriotic restorer, has been inspired by such memories and has

made them his watchword ; that even such a corporate existence as that of a Roman legion or an English regiment has
been made valorous by memorial standards, — these are the
glorious commonplaces of historic teaching at our public
schools and universities, being happily ingrained in Greek
and Latin classics. They have also been impressed on the
world by conspicuous modern instances. That there is a free
modern Greece is due — through all infiltration of other than
Greek blood — to the presence of ancient Greece in the
consciousness of European men ; and every speaker would
feel his point safe if he were to praise Byron's devotion to a
cause made glorious by ideal identification with the past ;
hardly so, if he were to insist that the Greeks were not to be
helped further because their history shows that they were
anciently unsurpassed in treachery and lying, and that many
modern Greeks are highly disreputable characters, while
others are disposed to grasp too large a share of our commerce. The same with Italy ; the pathos of his country's
lot pierced the youthful soul of Mazzini, because, like Dante's,
his blood was fraught with the kinship of Italian greatness,
his imagination filled with a majestic past that wrought itself into a majestic future. Half a century ago, what was
Italy ? An idling-place of dilettanteism or of itinerant
motiveless wealth, a territory parcelled out for papal sustenance, dynastic convenience, and the profit of an alien
Government. What were the Italians ? No people, no voice
in European counsels, no massive power in European affairs .
a race thought of in English and French society as chiefly
adapted to the operatic stage, or to secure as models for
painters ; disposed to smile gratefully at the reception of
half-pence ; and by the more historical remembered to be
rather polite than truthful — in all probability, a combination
of Machiavelli, Rubini, and Masaniello. Thanks chiefly to the
divine gift of a memory which inspires the moments with a
past, a present, and a future, and gives the sense of corporate
existence that raises man above the otherwise more respectable
and innocent brute, all that, or most of it, is changed.

Again, one of our living historians finds just sympathy in his vigorous insistence on our true ancestry, on our being the strongly marked heritors, in language and genius, of those old English seamen, who, beholding a rich country with a most convenient seaboard, came, doubtless with a sense of divine warrant, and settled themselves on this or the other side of fertilizing streams, gradually conquering more and more of the pleasant land from the natives who knew nothing of Odin, and finally making unusually clean work in ridding themselves of those prior occupants. " Let us," he virtually says — " let us know who were our forefathers, who it was that won the soil for us, and brought the good seed of those institutions through which we should not arrogantly but gratefully feel ourselves distinguished among the nations as possessors of long-inherited freedom ; let us not keep up an ignorant kind of naming which disguises our true affinities of blood and language, but let us see thoroughly what sort of notions and traditions our forefathers had, and what sort of song inspired them. Let the poetic fragments which breathe forth their fierce bravery in battle, and their trust in fierce gods who helped them, be treasured with affectionate rever-ence. These seafaring, invading, self-asserting men were the English of old time, and were our fathers, who did rough work by which we are profiting. They had virtues which incorporated themselves in wholesome usages, to which we trace our own political blessings. Let us know and acknowl-edge our common relationship to them, and be thankful that, over and above the affections and duties which spring from our manhood, we have the closer and more constantly guiding duties which belong to us as Englishmen."

To this view of our nationality most persons, who have feeling and understanding enough to be conscious of the connection between the patriotic affection and every other affection which lifts us above emigrating rats and free-loving baboons, will be disposed to say Amen. True, we are not indebted to those ancestors for our religion ; we are rather proud of having got that illumination from elsewhere. The men who planted our nation were not Christians, though they began their work centuries after Christ, and they had a decided objection to Christianity when it was first proposed to them; they were not monotheists, and their religion was the reverse of spiritual. But since we have been fortunate enough to keep the island home they won for us, and have been on the whole a prosperous people, rather continuing the plan of invading and spoiling other lands than being forced to beg for shelter in them, nobody has reproached us because our fathers, thirteen hundred years ago, worshipped Odin, massacred Britons, and were with difficulty persuaded to accept Christianity, knowing nothing of Hebrew history and the reasons why Christ should be received as the Saviour of mankind. The Red Indians, not liking us when we settled among them, might have been willing to fling such facts in our faces, but they were too ignorant; and, besides, their opinions did not signify, because we were able, if we liked, to exterminate them. The Hindoos also have doubtless had their rancors against us, and still entertain enough ill-will to make unfavorable remarks on our character, especially as to our historic rapacity and arrogant notions of our own superiority. They perhaps do not admire the usual English profile, and they are not converted to our way of feeding; but though we are a small number of an alien race, profiting by the territory and produce of these prejudiced people, they are unable to turn us out; at least, when they tried, we showed them their mistake. We do not call ourselves a dispersed and a punished people; we are a colonizing people, and it is we who have punished others.

Still, the historian guides us rightly in urging us to dwell on the virtues of our ancestors with emulation, and to cherish our sense of a common descent as a bond of obligation. The eminence, the nobleness of a people, depends on its capability of being stirred by memories, and for striving for what we call spiritual ends — ends which consist not in an immediate material possession, but in the satisfaction of a great feeling that animates the collective body as with one soul. A people having the seed of worthiness in it must feel an answering thrill when it is adjured by the deaths of its heroes who died to preserve its national existence; when it is reminded of its small beginnings and gradual growth through past labors and struggles, such as are still demanded of it in order that the freedom and well-being thus inherited may be transmitted unimpaired to children and children's children; when an appeal against the permission of injustice is made to great precedents in its history, and to the better genius breathing in its institutions. It is this living force of sentiment in common which makes a national consciousness. Nations so moved will resist conquest with the very breasts of their women, will pay their millions and their blood to abolish slavery, will share privation in famine and all calamity, will produce poets to sing "some great story of a man," and thinkers whose theories will bear the test of action. An individual man, to be harmoniously great, must belong to a nation of this order, if not in actual existence yet existing in the past — in memory, as a departed, invisible, beloved ideal, once a reality, and perhaps to be restored. A common humanity is not yet enough to feed the rich blood of various activity which makes a complete man. The time is not come for cosmopolitanism to be highly virtuous, any more than of communism to suffice for social energy. I am not bound to feel for a Chinaman as I feel for my fellow-countryman : I am bound not to demoralize him with opium, not to compel him to my will by destroying or plundering the fruits of his labor, on the alleged ground that he is not cosmopolitan enough, and not to insult him for his want of my tailoring and religion when he appears as a peaceable visitor on the London pavement. It is admirable in a Briton with a good purpose to learn Chinese; but it would not be a proof of fine intellect in him to taste Chinese poetry in the original more than he tastes the poetry of his own tongue. Affection, intelligence, duty, radiate from a centre, and nature has decided that for us English folk that centre can be neither China nor Peru. Most of us feel this unreflectingly, for the affectation of undervaluing everything native, and being too fine for one's own country, belongs only to a few minds of no dangerous leverage. What is wanting is that we should recognize a corresponding attachment to nationality as legitimate in every other people, and understand that its absence is a privation of the greatest good.

For, to repeat, not only the nobleness of a nation depends on the presence of this national consciousness, but also the nobleness of each individual citizen. Our dignity and rectitude are proportioned to our sense of relationship with something great, admirable, pregnant with high possibilities, worthy of sacrifice, a continual inspiration to self-repression and discipline by the presentation of aims larger and more attractive to our generous part than the securing of personal ease or prosperity. And a people possessing this good should surely feel not only a ready sympathy with the effort of those who, having lost the good, strive to regain it, but a profound pity for any degradation resulting from its loss, — nay, something more than pity when happier nationalities have made victims of the unfortunate whose memories, nevertheless, are the very fountain to which the persecutors trace their most vaunted blessings.

These notions are familiar; few will deny them in the abstract, and many are found loudly asserting them in relation to this or the other particular case. But here as elsewhere, in the ardent application of ideas, there is a notable lack of simple comparison or sensibility to resemblance. The European world has long been used to consider the Jews as altogether exceptional, and it has followed naturally enough that they have been excepted from the rules of justice and mercy, which are based on human likeness. But to consider a people whose ideas have determined the religion of half the world, and that the more cultivated half, and who made the most eminent struggle against the power of Rome, as a purely exceptional race, is a demoralizing offence against rational knowledge, a stultifying inconsistency in historical interpretation. Every nation of forcible character, *i. e.*, of strongly

marked characteristics, is so far exceptional. The distinctive
note of each bird-species is in this sense exceptional, but the
necessary ground of such distinction is a deeper likeness.
The superlative peculiarity in the Jews admitted, our affinity
with them is only the more apparent when the elements of
their peculiarity are discerned.

From whatever point of view the writings of the Old Testament may be regarded, the picture they present of a national
development is of high interest and speciality; nor can their
historic momentousness be much affected by any varieties of
theory as to the relation they bear to the New Testament
or to the rise and constitution of Christianity. Whether
we accept the canonical Hebrew books as a revelation, or
simply as a part of an ancient literature, makes no difference
to the fact that we find there the strongly characterized por-
traiture of a people educated from an earlier or later period
to a sense of separateness unique in its intensity — a people
taught by many concurrent influences to identify faithfulness
to its national traditions with the highest social and religious
blessings. Our too scanty sources of Jewish history, from
the return under Ezra to the beginning of the desperate resistance against Rome, show us the heroic and triumphant
struggle of the Maccabees, which rescued the religion and
independence of the nation from the corrupting sway of the
Syrian Greeks, adding to the glorious sum of its memorials,
and stimulating continuous efforts of a more peaceful sort to
maintain and develop that national life which the heroes had
fought and died for, by internal measures of legal administration and public teaching. Thenceforth the virtuous elements
of the Jewish life were engaged, as they had been with varying aspects during the long and changeful prophetic period
and the restoration under Ezra, on the side of preserving the
specific national character against a demoralizing fusion with
that of foreigners whose religion and ritual were idolatrous
and often obscene. There was always a Foreign party reviling
the National party as narrow, and sometimes manifesting
their own breadth in extensive views of advancement or profit

to themselves by flattery of a foreign power. Such internal conflict naturally tightened the bands of conservatism, which needed to be strong if it were to rescue the sacred Ark, the vital spirit of a small nation — "the smallest of the nations" — whose territory lay on the highway between three continents; and when the dread and hatred of foreign sway had condensed itself into dread and hatred of the Romans, many Conservatives became Zealots, whose chief mark was that they advocated resistance to the death against the submergence of their nationality. Much might be said on this point toward distinguishing the desperate struggle against a conquest which is regarded as degradation and corruption, from rash, hopeless insurrection against an established native government; and for my part (if that were of any consequence) I share the spirit of the Zealots. I take the spectacle of the Jewish people defying the Roman edict, and preferring death by starvation or the sword to the introduction of Caligula's deified statue into the temple, as a sublime type of steadfastness. But all that need be noticed here is the continuity of that national education (by outward and inward circumstance) which created in the Jews a feeling of race, a sense of corporate existence, unique in its intensity.

But not, before the dispersion, unique in essential qualities. There is more likeness than contrast between the way we English got our island and the way the Israelites got Canaan. We have not been noted for forming a low estimate of ourselves in comparison with foreigners, or for admitting that our institutions are equalled by those of any other people under the sun. Many of us have thought that our sea-wall is a specially divine arrangement to make and keep us a nation of sea-kings after the manner of our forefathers, secure against invasion, and able to invade other lands when we need them, though they may lie on the other side of the ocean. Again, it has been held that we have a peculiar destiny as a Protestant people, not only able to bruise the head of an idolatrous Christianity in the midst of us, but fitted, as possessors of the most truth and the most tonnage, to carry our purer religion over the world and convert mankind to our way of thinking. The Puritans, asserting their liberty to restrain tyrants, found the Hebrew history closely symbolical of their feelings and purpose; and it can hardly be correct to cast the blame of their less laudable doings on the writings they invoked, since their opponents made use of the same writings for different ends, finding there a strong warrant for the divine right of kings and the denunciation of those who, like Korah, Dathan, and Abiram, took on themselves the office of the priesthood, which belonged of right solely to Aaron and his sons, or, in other words, to men ordained by the English bishops. We must rather refer the passionate use of the Hebrew writings to affinities of disposition between our own race and the Jewish. Is it true that the arrogance of a Jew was so immeasurably beyond that of a Calvinist? And the just sympathy and admiration which we give to the ancestors who resisted the oppressive acts of our native kings, and by resisting rescued or won for us the best part of our civil and religious liberties — is it justly to be withheld from those brave and steadfast men of Jewish race who fought and died, or strove by wise administration to resist, the oppression and corrupting influences of foreign tyrants, and by resisting, rescued the nationality which was the very hearth of our own religion? At any rate, seeing that the Jews were more specifically than any other nation educated into a sense of their supreme moral value, the chief matter of surprise is that any other nation is found to rival them in this form of self-confidence.

More exceptional — less like the course of our own history —has been their dispersion and their subsistence as a separate people through ages in which, for the most part, they were regarded and treated very much as beasts hunted for the sake of their skins, or of a valuable secretion peculiar to their species. The Jews showed a talent for accumulating what was an object of more immediate desire to Christians than animal oils or well-furred skins, and their cupidity and avarice were found at once particularly hateful and particularly useful: hateful when seen as a reason for punishing them by mulcting or robbery; useful when this retributive process could be successfully carried forward. Kings and emperors naturally were more alive to the usefulness of subjects who could gather and yield money; but edicts issued to protect "the King's Jews" equally with the King's game from being harassed and hunted by the commonalty, were only slight mitigations to the deplorable lot of a race held to be under the divine curse, and had little force after the Crusades began. As the slaveholders in the United States counted the curse on Ham a justification of negro slavery, so the curse on the Jews was counted a justification for hindering them from pursuing agriculture and handicrafts; for marking them out as execrable figures by a peculiar dress; for torturing them to make them part with their gains, or for more gratuitously spitting at them and pelting them; for taking it as certain that they killed and ate babies, poisoned the wells, and took pains to spread the plague; for putting it to them whether they would be baptized or burned, and not failing to burn and massacre them when they were obstinate; but also for suspecting them of disliking the baptism when they had got it, and then burning them in punishment of their insincerity; finally, for hounding them by tens on tens of thousands from the homes where they had found shelter for centuries, and inflicting on them the horrors of a new exile and a new dispersion. All this to avenge the Saviour of mankind, or else to compel these stiff-necked people to acknowledge a Master whose servants showed such beneficent effects of his teaching.

With a people so treated, one of two issues was possible: either from being of feebler nature than their persecutors, and caring more for ease than for the sentiments and ideas which constituted their distinctive character, they would everywhere give way to pressure and get rapidly merged in the populations around them; or being endowed with uncommon tenacity, physical and mental, feeling peculiarly the ties of inheritance both in blood and faith, remembering national glories, trusting in their recovery, abhorring apostasy, able to bear all things and hope all things with the conscious- ness of being steadfast to spiritual obligations, the kernel of their number would harden into an inflexibility more and more insured by motive and habit. They would cherish all differences that marked them off from their hated oppressors, all memories that consoled them with a sense of virtual though unrecognized superiority ; and the separateness which was made their badge of ignominy would be their inward pride, their source of fortifying defiance. Doubtless such a people would get confirmed in vices. An oppressive govern- ment and a persecuting religion, while breeding vices in those who hold power, are well known to breed answering vices in those who are powerless and suffering. What more direct plan than the course presented by European history could have been pursued in order to give the Jews a spirit of bitter isolation, and scorn for the wolfish hypocrisy that made victims of them, of triumph in prospering at the expense of the blunderers who stoned them away from the open paths of industry ; or, on the other hand, to encourage in the less defiant a lying conformity, a pretence of conversion for the sake of the social advantages attached to baptism, an out- ward renunciation of their hereditary ties, with the lack of real love toward the society and creed which exacted this galling tribute ; or again, in the most unhappy specimens of the race, to rear transcendent examples of odious vice, reckless instruments of rich men with bad propensities, unscrupulous grinders of alien people who wanted to grind *them ?*

No wonder the Jews have their vices ; no wonder if it were proved (which it has not hitherto appeared to be) that some of them have a bad pre-eminence in evil, an unrivalled superfluity of naughtiness. It would be more plausible to make a wonder of the virtues which have prospered among them under the shadow of oppression. But instead of dwell- ing on these, or treating as admitted what any hardy or ignorant person may deny, let us found simply on the loud

assertions of the hostile. The Jews, it is said, resisted the
expansion of their own religion into Christianity; they were
in the habit of spitting on the cross; they have held the name
of Christ to be *Anathema*. Who taught them that? The
men who made Christianity a curse to them; the men who
made the name of Christ a symbol for the spirit of vengeance,
and, what was worse, made the execution of the vengeance a
pretext for satisfying their own savageness, greed, and envy;
the men who sanctioned with the name of Christ a barbaric
and blundering copy of Pagan fatalism, in taking the words
" His blood be upon us and on our children " as a divinely
appointed verbal warrant for wreaking cruelty, from generation to generation, on the people from whose sacred writings
Christ drew his teaching. Strange retrogression in the professors of an expanded religion, boasting an illumination
beyond the spiritual doctrine of Hebrew prophets! For
Hebrew prophets proclaimed a God who demanded mercy
rather than sacrifices. The Christians also believed that God
delighted not in the blood of rams and of bulls, but they
apparently conceived him as requiring for his satisfaction the
sighs and groans, the blood and roasted flesh, of men whose
forefathers had misunderstood the metaphorical character of
prophecies which spoke of spiritual pre-eminence under the
figure of a material kingdom. Was this the method by
which Christ desired his title to the Messiahship to be commended to the nation in which he was born? Many of his
sayings bear the stamp of that patriotism which places
fellow-countrymen in the inner circle of affection and duty.
And did the words " Father, forgive them, they know not
what they do," refer only to the centurion and his band, a
tacit exception being made of every Hebrew there present
from the mercy of the Father and the compassion of the
Son, — nay, more, of every Hebrew yet to come, who remained unconverted after hearing of his claim to the Messiahship, not from his own lips or those of his native apostles,
but from the lips of alien men, whom cross, creed, and baptism had left cruel, rapacious, and debauched? It is more

reverent to Christ to believe that he must have approved the
Jewish martyrs who deliberately chose to be burned or
massacred rather than be guilty of a blaspheming lie, more
than he approved the rabble of Crusaders who robbed and
murdered them in his name.

But these remonstrances seem to have no direct application to personages who take up the attitude of philosophic
thinkers and discriminating critics, professedly accepting
Christianity from a rational point of view, as a vehicle of the
highest religious and moral truth, and condemning the Jews
on the ground that they are obstinate adherents of an outworn creed, maintain themselves in moral alienation from the
peoples with whom they share citizenship, and are destitute
of real interest in the welfare of the community and state
with which they are thus identified.   These anti-Judaic
advocates usually belong to a party which has felt itself
glorified in winning for Jews, as well as Dissenters and
Catholics, the full privileges of citizenship, laying open to
them every path to distinction.   At one time the voice of
this party urged that differences of creed were made dangerous only by the denial of citizenship, that you must make
a man a citizen before he could feel like one.   At present,
apparently, this confidence has been succeeded by a sense of
mistake; there is a regret that no limiting clauses were insisted on, such as would have hindered the Jews from coming
too far and in too large proportion along those opened
pathways; and the Roumanians are thought to have shown
an enviable wisdom in giving them as little chance as possible.
But then the reflection occurring that some of the most
objectionable Jews are baptized Christians, it is obvious that
such clauses would have been insufficient, and the doctrine
that you can turn a Jew into a good Christian is emphatically
retracted.   But, clearly, these liberal gentlemen, too late
enlightened by disagreeable events, must yield the palm of
wise foresight to those who argued against them long ago;
and it is a striking spectacle to witness minds so panting for
advancement in some directions that they are ready to force

it on an unwilling society, in this instance despairingly recurring to mediæval types of thinking — insisting that the Jews are made viciously cosmopolitan by holding the world's money-bag; that for them all national interests are resolved into the algebra of loans ; that they have suffered an inward degradation stamping them as morally inferior, and — "serve them right," since they rejected Christianity. All which is mirrored in an analogy, namely, that of the Irish, also a servile race, who have rejected Protestantism, though it has been repeatedly urged on them by fire and sword and penal laws, and whose place in the moral scale may be judged by our advertisements, where the clause, "No Irish need apply," parallels the sentence which for many polite persons sums up the question of Judaism, "I never *did* like the Jews."

It is certainly worth considering whether an expatriated, denationalized race, used for ages to live among antipathetic populations, must not inevitably lack some conditions of nobleness. If they drop that separateness which is made their reproach, they may be in danger of lapsing into a cosmopolitan indifference equivalent to cynicism, and of missing that inward identification with the nationality immediately around them which might make some amends for their inherited privation. No dispassionate observer can deny this danger. Why, our own countrymen who take to living abroad, without purpose or function to keep up their sense of fellowship in the affairs of their own land, are rarely good specimens of moral healthiness ; still, the consciousness of having a native country, the birthplace of common memories and habits of mind, existing like a parental hearth quitted but beloved ; the dignity of being included in a people which has a part in the comity of nations and the growing federation of the world ; that sense of special belonging which is the root of human virtues, both public and private, — all these spiritual links may preserve migratory Englishmen from the worst consequences of their voluntary dispersion. Unquestionably the Jews, having been more than any other race exposed to the adverse moral influences of alienism, must, both in individuals and in groups, have suffered some corresponding moral degradation; but in fact they have escaped with less of abjectness, and less of hard hostility toward the nations whose hand has been against them, than could have happened in the case of a people who had neither their adhesion to a separate religion founded on historic memories, nor their characteristic family affectionateness. Tortured, flogged, spit upon, the *corpus vile* on which rage or wantonness vented themselves with impunity, their name flung at them as an opprobrium by superstition, hatred, and contempt, they have remained proud of their origin. Does any one call this an evil pride ? Perhaps he belongs to that order of man who, while he has a democratic dislike to dukes and earls, wants to make believe that his father was an idle gentleman, when in fact he was an honorable artisan, or who would feel flattered to be taken for other than an English. man. It is possible to be too arrogant about our blood or our calling, but that arrogance is virtue compared with such mean pretence. The pride which identifies us with a great historic body is a humanizing, elevating habit of mind, inspiring sacrifices of individual comfort, gain, or other selfish ambition, for the sake of that ideal whole; and no man swayed by such a sentiment can become completely abject. That a Jew of Smyrna, where a whip is carried by passengers ready to flog off the too officious specimens of his race, can still be proud to say "I am a Jew," is surely a fact to awaken admiration in a mind capable of understanding what we may call the ideal forces in human history. And again, a varied, impartial observation of the Jews in different countries tends to the impression that they have a predominant kindliness which must have been deeply ingrained in the constitution of their race to have outlasted the ages of persecution and oppression. The concentration of their joys in domestic life has kept up in them the capacity of tenderness; the pity for the fatherless and the widow, the care for the women and the little ones, blent intimately with their religion, is a well of mercy that cannot long or widely be pent up by exclusive-ness. And the kindliness of the Jew overflows the line of division between him and the Gentile. On the whole, one of the most remarkable phenomena in the history of this scattered people, made for ages "a scorn and a hissing," is, that after being subjected to this process, which might have been ex-pected to be in every sense deteriorating and vitiating, they have come out of it (in any estimate which allows for numer-ical proportion) rivalling the nations of all European coun-tries in healthiness and beauty of physique, in practical ability, in scientific and artistic aptitude, and in some forms of ethical value. A significant indication of their natural rank is seen in the fact that at this moment the leader of the Liberal party in Germany is a Jew, the leader of the Repub-lican party in France is a Jew, and the head of the Conserva-tive ministry in England is a Jew.

And here it is that we find the ground for the obvious jealousy which is now stimulating the revived expression of old antipathies. "The Jews," it is felt, "have a dangerous tendency to get the uppermost places, not only in commerce but in political life. Their monetary hold on governments is tending to perpetuate in leading Jews a spirit of universal alienism (euphemistically called cosmopolitanism), even where the West has given them a full share in civil and political rights. A people with Oriental sunlight in their blood, yet capable of being everywhere acclimatized, they have a force and toughness which enables them to carry off the best prizes; and their wealth is likely to put half the seats in Parliament at their disposal."

There is truth in these views of Jewish social and political relations ; but it is rather too late for Liberal pleaders to urge them in a merely vituperative sense. Do they propose, as a remedy for the impending danger of our healthier national influences getting overridden by Jewish predominance, that we should repeal our emancipatory laws ? Not all the Ger-manic immigrants who have been settling among us for gen-erations, and are still pouring in to settle, are Jews, but thoroughly Teutonic and more or less Christian craftsmen, mechanicians, or skilled and erudite functionaries; and the Semitic Christians who swarm among us are dangerously like their unconverted brethren in complexion, persistence, and wealth. Then there are the Greeks, who, by the help of Phœnician blood or otherwise, are objectionably strong in the city. Some judges think that the Scotch are more numerous and prosperous here in the South than is quite for the good of us Southerners; and the early inconvenience felt under the Stuarts, of being quartered upon by a hungry, hard-working people, with a distinctive accent and form of religion, and higher cheek-bones than English taste requires, has not yet been quite neutralized. As for the Irish, it is felt in high quarters that we have always been too lenient toward them; at least if they had been harried a little more, there might not have been so many of them on the English press, of which they divide the power with the Scotch, thus driving many Englishmen to honest and ineloquent labor.

So far shall we be carried if we go in search of devices to hinder people of other blood than our own from getting the advantage of dwelling among us.

Let it be admitted that it is a calamity to the English, as to any other great historic people, to undergo a premature fusion with immigrants of alien blood, — that its distinctive national characteristics should be in danger of obliteration by the predominating quality of foreign settlers. I not only admit this; I am ready to unite in groaning over the threatened danger. To one who loves his native language, who would delight to keep our rich and harmonious English undefiled by foreign accent, and those foreign tinctures of verbal meaning which tend to confuse all writing and discourse, it is an affliction as harassing as the climate, that on our stage, in our studies, at our public and private gatherings, in our offices, warehouses, and workshops, we must expect to hear our beloved English, with its words clipped, its vowels stretched and twisted, its phrases of acquiescence and politeness, of cordiality, dissidence, or argument, delivered always in the wrong tones, like ill-rendered melodies, marred beyond recognition, — that there should be a general ambition to speak every language except our mother English, which persons "of style" are not ashamed of corrupting with slang, false foreign equivalents, and a pronunciation that crushes out all color from the vowels and jams them between jostling consonants. An ancient Greek might not like to be resuscitated for the sake of hearing Homer read in our universities; still he would at least find more instructive marvels in other developments to be witnessed at those institutions; but a modern Englishman is invited from his after-dinner repose to hear Shakspeare delivered under circumstances which offer no other novelty than some novelty of false intonation, some new distribution of strong emphasis on prepositions, some new misconception of a familiar idiom. Well, it is our inertness that is in fault, our carelessness of excellence, our willing ignorance of the treasures that lie in our national heritage, while we are agape after what is foreign, though it may be only a vile imitation of what is native.

This marring of our speech, however, is a minor evil compared with what must follow from the predominance of wealth-acquiring immigrants, whose appreciation of our political and social life must often be as approximative or fatally erroneous as their delivery of our language. But take the worst issues, what can we do to hinder them? Are we to adopt the exclusiveness for which we have punished the Chinese? Are we to tear the glorious flag of hospitality which has made our freedom the world-wide blessing of the oppressed? It is not agreeable to find foreign accents and stumbling locutions passing from the piquant exception to the general rule of discourse. But to urge on that account that we should spike away the peaceful foreigner, would be a view of international relations not in the long run favorable to the interests of our fellow-countrymen; for we are at least equal to the races we call obtrusive in the disposition to settle wherever money is to be made and cheaply idle living to be found. In meeting the national evils which are brought upon us by the onward course of the world, there is often no more immediate hope or resource than that of striving after fuller national excellence, which must consist in the moulding of more excellent individual natives. The tendency of things is toward the quicker or slower fusion of races. It is impossible to arrest this tendency : all we can do is to moderate its course, so as to hinder it from degrading the moral status of societies by a too rapid effacement of those national traditions and customs which are the language of the national genius, the deep suckers of healthy sentiment. Such moderating and guidance of inevitable movement is worthy of all effort. And it is in this sense that the modern insistence on the idea of nationalities has value. That any people, at once distinct and coherent enough to form a state, should be held in subjection by an alien antipathetic government, has been becoming more and more a ground of sympathetic indignation; and, in virtue of this, at least one great state has been added to European councils. Nobody now complains of the result in this case, though far-sighted persons see the need to limit analogy by discrimination. We have to consider who are the stifled people and who the stiflers, before we can be sure of our ground. The only point in this connection on which Englishmen are agreed is, that England itself shall not be subject to foreign rule. The fiery resolve to resist invasion, though with an improvised array of pitchforks, is felt to be virtuous, and to be worthy of a historic people. Why ? Because there is a national life in our veins. Because there is something specifically English which we feel to be supremely worth striving for, worth dying for, rather than living to renounce it. Because we too have our share — perhaps a principal share — in that spirit of separateness which has not yet done its work in the education of mankind, which has created the varying genius of nations, and, like the Muses, is the offspring of memory.

Here, as everywhere else, the human task seems to be the discerning and adjustment of opposite claims. But the end can hardly be achieved by urging contradictory reproaches, and, instead of laboring after discernment as a preliminary to intervention, letting our zeal burst forth according to a capricious selection, first determined accidentally, and afterward justified by personal predilection. Not only John Gilpin and his wife, or Edwin and Angelina, seem to be of opinion that their preference or dislike of Russians, Servians, or Greeks, consequent, perhaps, on hotel adventures, has something to do with the merits of the Eastern Question; even in a higher range of intellect and enthusiasm we find a distribution of sympathy or pity for sufferers of different blood or votaries of different religions, strangely unaccountable on any other ground than a fortuitous direction of study or trivial circumstances of travel. With some even admirable persons one is never quite sure of any particular being included under a general term. A provincial physician, it is said, once ordering a lady patient not to eat salad, was asked pleadingly by the affectionate husband whether she might eat lettuce, or cresses, or radishes. The physician had too rashly believed in the comprehensiveness of the word "salad," just as we, if not enlightened by experience, might believe in the all-embracing breadth of "sympathy with the injured and oppressed." What mind can exhaust the grounds of exception which lie in each particular case? There is understood to be a peculiar odor from the negro body, and we know that some persons, too rationalistic to feel bound by the curse on Ham, used to hint very strongly that this odor determined the question on the side of negro slavery.

And this is the usual level of thinking in polite society concerning the Jews. Apart from theological purposes, it seems to be held surprising that anybody should take an interest in the history of a people whose literature has furnished all our devotional language; and if any reference is made to their past or future destinies, some hearer is sure to state, as a relevant fact which may assist our judgment, that she, for her part, is not fond of them, having known a Mr. Jacobson who was very unpleasant, or that he, for his part, thinks meanly of them as a race, though, on inquiry, you find that he is so little acquainted with their characteristics that he is astonished to learn how many persons whom he has blindly admired and applauded are Jews to the backbone. Again, men who consider themselves in the very van of modern advancement, knowing history and the latest philosophies of history, indicate their contemptuous surprise that any one should entertain the destiny of the Jews as a worthy subject, by referring to Moloch, and their own agreement with the theory that the religion of Jehovah was merely a transformed Moloch-worship, while in the same breath they are glorifying "civilization" as a transformed tribal existence of which some lineaments are traceable in grim marriage customs of the native Australians. Are these erudite persons prepared to insist that the name "Father" should no longer have any sanctity for us, because in their view of likelihood our Aryan ancestors were mere improvers on a state of things in which nobody knew his own father?

For less theoretic men, ambitious to be regarded as practical politicians, the value of the Hebrew race has been measured by their unfavorable opinion of a prime minister who is a Jew by lineage. But it is possible to form a very ugly opinion as to the scrupulousness of Walpole or of Chatham; and in any case I think Englishmen would refuse to accept the character and doings of those eighteenth-century statesmen as the standard of value for the English people and the part they have to play in the fortunes of mankind.

If we are to consider the future of the Jews at all, it seems reasonable to take, as a preliminary question, Are they destined to complete fusion with the peoples among whom they are dispersed, losing every remnant of a distinctive consciousness as Jews? or, Are there in the breadth and intensity with which the feeling of separateness, or what we may call the organized memory of a national consciousness, actually exists in the world-wide Jewish communities — the seven millions scattered from the east to west? and again, Are there, in the political relations of the world, the conditions present or approaching for the restoration of a Jewish State planted on the old ground as a centre of national feeling, a source of dignifying protection, a special channel for special energies, which may contribute some added form of national genius, and an added voice in the councils of the world?

They are among us everywhere; it is useless to say we are not fond of them. Perhaps we are not fond of proletaries and their tendency to form Unions, but the world is not therefore to be rid of them. If we wish to free ourselves from the inconveniences that we have to complain of, whether in proletaries or in Jews, our best course is to encourage all means of improving these neighbors who elbow us in a thickening crowd, and of sending their incommodious energies into beneficent channels. Why are we so eager for the dignity of certain populations of whom, perhaps, we have never seen a single specimen, and of whose history, legend, or literature we have been contentedly ignorant for ages, while we sneer at the notion of a renovated national dignity for the Jews, whose ways of thinking and whose very verbal forms are on our lips in every prayer which we end with an Amen? Some of us consider this question dismissed when they have said the wealthiest Jews have no desire to forsake their European palaces and go to live in Jerusalem. But in a return from exile, in the restoration of a people, the question is not whether certain rich men will choose to remain behind, but whether there will be found worthy men who will choose to lead the return. Plenty of prosperous Jews remained in Babylon when Ezra marshalled his band of forty thousand and began a new glorious epoch in the history of his race, making the preparation for that epoch in the history of the world which has been held glorious enough to be dated from forevermore. The hinge of possibility is simply the existence of an adequate community of feeling, as well as widespread need, in the Jewish race, and the hope that among its finer specimens there may arise some men of instruction and ardent public spirit, some new Ezras, modern Maccabees, who will know how to use all favoring outward conditions, how to triumph by heroic example over the indifference of their

fellows and the scorn of their foes, and will steadfastly set
their faces toward making their people once more one among
the nations.

Formerly, Evangelical Orthodoxy was prone to dwell on
the fulfilment of prophecy in the "restoration of the Jews."
Such interpretation of the prophets is less in vogue now.
The dominant mode is to insist on a Christianity that dis-
owns its origin, that is not a substantial growth, having a
genealogy, but is a vaporous reflex of modern notions. The
Christ of Matthew had the heart of a Jew : "Go ye first to
the lost sheep of the house of Israel." The Apostle of the
Gentiles had the heart of a Jew : "For I could wish that myself were accursed from Christ for my brethren, my kinsmen
according to the flesh : who are Israelites ; to whom per-
taineth the adoption, and the glory, and the covenants, and
the giving of the law, and the service of God, and the prom
ises ; whose are the fathers, and of whom, as concerning the
flesh, Christ came." Modern apostles, extolling Christianity,
are found using a different tone ; they prefer the mediæval
cry translated into modern phrase. But the mediæval cry,
too, was in substance very ancient — more ancient than the
days of Augustus. Pagans in successive ages said, "These
people are unlike us, and refuse to be made like us ; let us
punish them." The Jews were steadfast in their separateness,
and through that separateness Christianity was born. A modern book on Liberty has maintained that from the freedom of
individual men to persist in idiosyncrasies the world may be
enriched. Why should we not apply this argument to the
idiosyncrasy of a nation, and pause in our haste to hoot it
down ? There is still a great function for the steadfastness
of the Jew : not that he should shut out the utmost illumination which knowledge can throw on his national history, but
that he should cherish the store of inheritance which that history has left him. Every Jew should be conscious that he is
one of a multitude possessing common objects of piety, in the
immortal achievements and immortal sorrows of ancestors
who have transmitted to them a physical and mental type

strong enough, eminent enough in faculties, pregnant enough
with peculiar promise, to constitute a new beneficent individuality among the nations, and, by confuting the traditions of
scorn, nobly avenge the wrongs done to their fathers.

There is a sense in which the worthy child of a nation that
has brought forth illustrious prophets, high and unique
among the poets of the world, is bound by their visions.

Is bound ?

Yes, for the effective bond of human action is feeling; and
the worthy child of a people owning the triple name of Hebrew, Israelite, and Jew, feels his kinship with the glories
and the sorrows, the degradation and the possible renovation,
of his national family.

Will any one teach the nullification of this feeling, and
call his doctrine a philosophy ? He will teach a blinding
superstition, the superstition that a theory of human well-
being can be constructed in disregard of the influences which
have made us human.

THE LIFTED VEIL.

Give me no light, great Heaven, but such as turns
To energy of human fellowship ;
No powers beyond the growing heritage
That makes completer manhood.

THE LIFTED VEIL.

CHAPTER I.

THE time of my end approaches. I have lately been subject to attacks of *angina pectoris;* and in the ordinary course of things, my physician tells me, I may fairly hope that my life will not be protracted many months. Unless, then, I am cursed with an exceptional physical constitution, as I am cursed with an exceptional mental character, I shall not much longer groan under the wearisome burthen of this earthly existence. If it were to be otherwise — if I were to live on to the age most men desire and provide for — I should for once have known whether the miseries of delusive expectation can outweigh the miseries of true prevision. For I foresee when I shall die, and everything that will happen in my last moments.

Just a month from this day, on the 20th of September, 1850, I shall be sitting in this chair, in this study, at ten o'clock at night, longing to die, weary of incessant insight and foresight, without delusions and without hope. Just as I am watching a tongue of blue flame rising in the fire, and my lamp is burning low, the horrible contraction will begin at my chest. I shall only have time to reach the bell, and pull it violently, before the sense of suffocation will come. No one will answer my bell. I know why. My two servants are lovers, and will have quarrelled. My housekeeper will have rushed out of the house in a fury, two hours before, hoping that Perry will believe she has gone to drown herself. Perry is alarmed at last, and is gone out after her. The little scullery-maid is asleep on a bench : she never answers the bell ; it does not wake her.

The sense of suffocation increases: my lamp goes out with a horrible stench: I make a great effort, and snatch at the bell again. I long for life, and there is no help. I thirsted for the unknown: the thirst is gone. O God, let me stay with the known, and be weary of it: I am content. Agony of pain and suffocation — and all the while the earth, the fields, the pebbly brook at the bottom of the rookery, the fresh scent after the rain, the light of the morning through my chamber-window, the warmth of the hearth after the frosty air — will darkness close over them forever?

Darkness — darkness — no pain — nothing but darkness: but I am passing on and on through the darkness: my thought stays in the darkness, but always with a sense of moving onward. . . .

Before that time comes, I wish to use my last hours of ease and strength in telling the strange story of my experience. I have never fully unbosomed myself to any human being; I have never been encouraged to trust much in the sympathy of my fellow-men. But we have all a chance of meeting with some pity, some tenderness, some charity, when we are dead: it is the living only who cannot be forgiven — the living only from whom men's indulgence and reverence are held off, like the rain by the hard east wind. While the heart beats, bruise it — it is your only opportunity; while the eye can still turn towards you with moist timid entreaty, freeze it with an icy unanswering gaze; while the ear, that delicate messenger to the inmost sanctuary of the soul, can still take in the tones of kindness, put it off with hard civility, or sneering compliment, or envious affectation of indifference; while the creative brain can still throb with the sense of injustice, with the yearning for brotherly recognition — make haste — oppress it with your ill-considered judgments, your trivial comparisons, your care-less misrepresentations. The heart will by-and-by be still — *ubi sæva indignatio ulterius cor lacerare nequit ;* [1] the eye will cease to entreat; the ear will be deaf; the brain will have ceased from all wants as well as from all work. Then your charitable speeches may find vent; then you may remember

---

[1] Inscription on Swift's tombstone.

and pity the toil and the struggle and the failure; then you may give due honor to the work achieved; then you may find extenuation for errors, and may consent to bury them.

That is a trivial schoolboy text; why do I dwell on it? It has little reference to me, for I shall leave no works behind me for men to honor. I have no near relatives who will make up, by weeping over my grave, for the wounds they inflicted on me when I was among them. It is only the story of my life that will perhaps win a little more sympathy from strangers when I am dead, than I ever believed it would obtain from my friends while I was living.

My childhood perhaps seems happier to me than it really was, by contrast with all the after-years. For then the curtain of the future was as impenetrable to me as to other children: I had all their delight in the present hour, their sweet indefinite hopes for the morrow; and I had a tender mother: even now, after the dreary lapse of long years, a slight trace of sensation accompanies the remembrance of her caress as she held me on her knee — her arms round my little body, her cheek pressed on mine. I had a complaint of the eyes that made me blind for a little while, and she kept me on her knee from morning till night. That unequalled love soon vanished out of my life, and even to my childish consciousness it was as if that life had become more chill. I rode my little white pony with the groom by my side as before, but there were no loving eyes looking at me as I mounted, no glad arms opened to me when I came back. Perhaps I missed my mother's love more than most children of seven or eight would have done, to whom the other pleasures of life remained as before; for I was certainly a very sensitive child. I remember still the mingled trepidation and delicious excitement with which I was affected by the tramping of the horses on the pavement in the echoing stables, by the loud resonance of the grooms' voices, by the booming bark of the dogs as my father's carriage thundered under the archway of the courtyard, by the din of the gong as it gave notice of luncheon and dinner. The measured tramp of soldiery which I sometimes heard — for my father's house lay near a county town where there

were large barracks — made me sob and tremble; and yet
when they were gone past, I longed for them to come back
again.

I fancy my father thought me an odd child, and had little
fondness for me; though he was very careful in fulfilling what
he regarded as a parent's duties. But he was already past the
middle of life, and I was not his only son. My mother had
been his second wife, and he was five-and-forty when he married her. He was a firm, unbending, intensely orderly man,
in root and stem a banker, but with a flourishing graft of the
active landholder, aspiring to county influence: one of those
people who are always like themselves from day to day, who
are uninfluenced by the weather, and neither know melancholy
nor high spirits. I held him in great awe, and appeared more
timid and sensitive in his presence than at other times; a circumstance which, perhaps, helped to confirm him in the intention to educate me on a different plan from the prescriptive
one with which he had complied in the case of my elder
brother, already a tall youth at Eton. My brother was to be
his representative and successor; he must go to Eton and
Oxford, for the sake of making connections, of course: my
father was not a man to underrate the bearing of Latin satir-
ists or Greek dramatists on the attainment of an aristocratic
position. But, intrinsically, he had slight esteem for "those
dead but sceptred spirits;" having qualified himself for forming an independent opinion by reading Potter's "Æschylus,"
and dipping into Francis's "Horace." To this negative view
he added a positive one, derived from a recent connection with
mining speculations; namely, that a scientific education was
the really useful training for a younger son. Moreover, it was
clear that a shy, sensitive boy like me was not fit to encounter
the rough experience of a public school. Mr. Letherall had
said so very decidedly. Mr. Letherall was a large man in
spectacles, who one day took my small head between his large
hands, and pressed it here and there in an exploratory, suspicious manner — then placed each of his great thumbs on my
temples, and pushed me a little way from him, and stared at
me with glittering spectacles. The contemplation appeared to

displease him, for he frowned sternly, and said to my father, drawing his thumbs across my eyebrows —

" The deficiency is there, sir — there ; and here," he added, touching the upper sides of my head, " here is the excess. That must be brought out, sir, and this must be laid to sleep."

I was in a state of tremor, partly at the vague idea that I was the object of reprobation, partly in the agitation of my first hatred — hatred of this big, spectacled man, who pulled my head about as if he wanted to buy and cheapen it.

I am not aware how much Mr. Letherall had to do with the system afterwards adopted towards me, but it was presently clear that private tutors, natural history, science, and the modern languages, were the appliances by which the defects of my organization were to be remedied. I was very stupid about machines, so I was to be greatly occupied with them ; I had no memory for classification, so it was particularly necessary that I should study systematic zoology and botany ; I was hungry for human deeds and human emotions, so I was to be plentifully crammed with the mechanical powers, the elementary bodies, and the phenomena of electricity and magnetism. A better-constituted boy would certainly have profited under my intelligent tutors, with their scientific apparatus ; and would, doubtless, have found the phenomena of electricity and magnetism as fascinating as I was, every Thursday, assured they were. As it was, I could have paired off, for ignorance of whatever was taught me, with the worst Latin scholar that was ever turned out of a classical academy. I read Plutarch, and Shakespeare, and Don Quixote by the sly, and supplied myself in that way with wandering thoughts, while my tutor was assuring me that " an improved man, as distinguished from an ignorant one, was a man who knew the reason why water ran down-hill." I had no desire to be this improved man ; I was glad of the running water ; I could watch it and listen to it gurgling among the pebbles, and bathing the bright green water-plants, by the hour together. I did not want to know *why* it ran ; I had perfect confidence that there were good reasons for what was so very beautiful.

There is no need to dwell on this part of my life. I have

said enough to indicate that my nature was of the sensitive, unpractical order, and that it grew up in an uncongenial me- dium, which could never foster it into happy, healthy develop- ment. When I was sixteen I was sent to Geneva to complete my course of education; and the change was a very happy one to me, for the first sight of the Alps, with the setting sun on them, as we descended the Jura, seemed to me like an entrance into heaven; and the three years of my life there were spent in a perpetual sense of exaltation, as if from a draught of de- licious wine, at the presence of Nature in all her awful love- liness. You will think, perhaps, that I must have been a poet, from this early sensibility to Nature. But my lot was not so happy as that. A poet pours forth his song and *believes* in the listening ear and answering soul, to which his song will be floated sooner or later. But the poet's sensibility without his voice — the poet's sensibility that finds no vent but in silent tears on the sunny bank, when the noonday light sparkles on the water, or in an inward shudder at the sound of harsh hu- man tones, the sight of a cold human eye — this dumb passion brings with it a fatal solitude of soul in the society of one's fellow-men. My least solitary moments were those in which I pushed off in my boat, at evening, towards the centre of the lake; it seemed to me that the sky, and the glowing mountain- tops, and the wide blue water, surrounded me with a cherish- ing love such as no human face had shed on me since my mother's love had vanished out of my life. I used to do as Jean Jacques did — lie down in my boat and let it glide where it would, while I looked up at the departing glow leaving one mountain-top after the other, as if the prophet's chariot of fire were passing over them on its way to the home of light. Then, when the white summits were all sad and corpse-like, I had to push homeward, for I was under careful surveillance, and was allowed no late wanderings. This disposition of mine was not favorable to the formation of intimate friendships among the numerous youths of my own age who are always to be found studying at Geneva. Yet I made *one* such friend- ship; and, singularly enough, it was with a youth whose intel- lectual tendencies were the very reverse of my own. I shall call him Charles Meunier; his real surname — an English one, for he was of English extraction — having since become celebrated. He was an orphan, who lived on a miserable pittance while he pursued the medical studies for which he had a special genius. Strange! that with my vague mind, susceptible and unobservant, hating inquiry and given up to contemplation, I should have been drawn towards a youth whose strongest passion was science. But the bond was not an intellectual one; it came from a source that can happily blend the stupid with the brilliant, the dreamy with the practical: it came from community of feeling. Charles was poor and ugly, derided by Genevese *gamins*, and not acceptable in drawing-rooms. I saw that he was isolated, as I was, though from a different cause, and, stimulated by a sympathetic resentment, I made timid advances towards him. It is enough to say that there sprang up as much comradeship between us as our different habits would allow; and in Charles's rare holidays we went up the Salève together, or took the boat to Vevay, while I listened dreamily to the monologues in which he unfolded his bold conceptions of future experiment and discovery. I mingled them confusedly in my thought with glimpses of blue water and delicate floating cloud, with the notes of birds and the distant glitter of the glacier. He knew quite well that my mind was half absent, yet he liked to talk to me in this way; for don't we talk of our hopes and our projects even to dogs and birds, when they love us? I have mentioned this one friendship because of its connection with a strange and terrible scene which I shall have to narrate in my subsequent life.

This happier life at Geneva was put an end to by a severe illness, which is partly a blank to me, partly a time of dimly remembered suffering, with the presence of my father by my bed from time to time. Then came the languid monotony of convalescence, the days gradually breaking into variety and distinctness as my strength enabled me to take longer and longer drives. On one of these more vividly remembered days, my father said to me, as he sat beside my sofa —

"When you are quite well enough to travel, Latimer, I shall take you home with me. The journey will amuse you and do you good, for I shall go through the Tyrol and Austria, and you will see many new places. Our neighbors, the Fil-mores, are come; Alfred will join us at Basle, and we shall all go together to Vienna, and back by Prague — "

My father was called away before he had finished his sen-tence, and he left my mind resting on the word *Prague*, with a strange sense that a new and wondrous scene was breaking upon me : a city under the broad sunshine, that seemed to me as if it were the summer sunshine of a long-past century arrested in its course — unrefreshed for ages by the dews of night, or the rushing rain-cloud ; scorching the dusty, weary, time-eaten grandeur of a people doomed to live on in the stale repetition of memories, like deposed and superannuated kings in their regal gold-inwoven tatters. The city looked so thirsty that the broad river seemed to me a sheet of metal; and the blackened statues, as I passed under their blank gaze, along the unending bridge, with their ancient garments and their saintly crowns, seemed to me the real inhabitants and owners of this place, while the busy, trivial men and women, hurrying to and fro, were a swarm of ephemeral visitants infesting it for a day. It is such grim, stony beings as these, I thought, who are the fathers of ancient faded children, in those tanned time-fretted dwellings that crowd the steep before me ; who pay their court in the worn and crumbling pomp of the palace which stretches its monotonous length on the height; who worship wearily in the stifling air of the churches, urged by no fear or hope, but compelled by their doom to be ever old and undying, to live on in the rigidity of habit, as they live on in perpetual midday, without the repose of night or the new birth of morning.

A stunning clang of metal suddenly thrilled through me, and I became conscious of the objects in my room again : one of the fire-irons had fallen as Pierre opened the door to bring me my draught. My heart was palpitating violently, and I begged Pierre to leave my draught beside me ; I would take it presently.

As soon as I was alone again, I began to ask myself whether I had been sleeping. Was this a dream — this wonderfully

distinct vision — minute in its distinctness down to a patch of
rainbow light on the pavement, transmitted through a colored
lamp in the shape of a star — of a strange city, quite unfamiliar to my imagination ?   I had seen no picture of Prague : it
lay in my mind as a mere name, with vaguely remembered historical associations — ill-defined memories of imperial grandeur and religious wars.

Nothing of this sort had ever occurred in my dreaming experience before, for I had often been humiliated because my
dreams were only saved from being utterly disjointed and
commonplace by the frequent terrors of nightmare.   But I
could not believe that I had been asleep, for I remembered
distinctly the gradual breaking-in of the vision upon me, like
the new images in a dissolving view, or the growing distinctness of the landscape as the sun lifts up the veil of the morning mist.   And while I was conscious of this incipient vision,
I was also conscious that Pierre came to tell my father Mr.
Filmore was waiting for him, and that my father hurried out
of the room.   No, it was not a dream; was it — the thought
was full of tremulous exultation — was it the poet's nature in
me, hitherto only a troubled yearning sensibility, now manifesting itself suddenly as spontaneous creation ?   Surely it
was in this way that Homer saw the plain of Troy, that Dante
saw the abodes of the departed, that Milton saw the earthward
flight of the Tempter.   Was it that my illness had wrought
some happy change in my organization — given a firmer tension to my nerves — carried off some dull obstruction ?   I had
often read of such effects — in works of fiction at least.   Nay ;
in genuine biographies I had read of the subtilizing or exalting influence of some diseases on the mental powers.   Did not
Novalis feel his inspiration intensified under the progress of
consumption ?

When my mind had dwelt for some time on this blissful
idea, it seemed to me that I might perhaps test it by an exertion of my will.   The vision had begun when my father was
speaking of our going to Prague.   I did not for a moment
believe it was really a representation of that city ; I believed
— I hoped it was a picture that my newly liberated genius had

painted in fiery haste, with the colors snatched from lazy memory. Suppose I were to fix my mind on some other place — Venice, for example, which was far more familiar to my imagination than Prague: perhaps the same sort of result would follow. I concentrated my thoughts on Venice; I stimulated my imagination with poetic memories, and strove to feel myself present in Venice, as I had felt myself present in Prague. But in vain. I was only coloring the Canaletto engravings that hung in my old bedroom at home; the picture was a shifting one, my mind wandering uncertainly in search of more vivid images; I could see no accident of form or shadow without conscious labor after the necessary conditions. It was all prosaic effort, not rapt passivity, such as I had experienced half an hour before. I was discouraged: but I remembered that inspiration was fitful.

For several days I was in a state of excited expectation, watching for a recurrence of my new gift. I sent my thoughts ranging over my world of knowledge, in the hope that they would find some object which would send a reawakening vibration through my slumbering genius. But no; my world remained as dim as ever, and that flash of strange light refused to come again, though I watched for it with palpitating eagerness.

My father accompanied me every day in a drive, and a gradually lengthening walk as my powers of walking increased; and one evening he had agreed to come and fetch me at twelve the next day, that we might go together to select a musical box, and other purchases rigorously demanded of a rich Englishman visiting Geneva. He was one of the most punctual of men and bankers, and I was always nervously anxious to be quite ready for him at the appointed time. But, to my surprise, at a quarter past twelve he had not appeared. I felt all the impatience of a convalescent who has nothing particular to do, and who has just taken a tonic in the prospect of immediate exercise that would carry off the stimulus.

Unable to sit still and reserve my strength, I walked up and down the room, looking out on the current of the Rhone, just where it leaves the dark-blue lake ; but thinking all the while of the possible causes that could detain my father.

Suddenly I was conscious that my father was in the room, but not alone : there were two persons with him. Strange! I had heard no footstep, I had not seen the door open ; but I saw my father, and at his right hand our neighbor Mrs. Filmore, whom I remembered very well, though I had not seen her for five years. She was a commonplace middle-aged woman, in silk and cashmere ; but the lady on the left of my father was not more than twenty, a tall, slim, willowy figure, with luxuriant blond hair, arranged in cunning braids and folds that looked almost too massive for the slight figure and the small-featured, thin-lipped face they crowned. But the race had not a girlish expression : the features were sharp, the pale gray eyes at once acute, restless, and sarcastic. They were fixed on me in half-smiling curiosity, and I felt a painful sensation as if a sharp wind were cutting me. The pale-green dress, and the green leaves that seemed to form a border about her pale blond hair, made me think of a Water-Nixie, — for my mind was full of German lyrics, and this pale, fatal-eyed woman, with the green weeds, looked like a birth from some cold sedgy stream, the daughter of an aged river.

"Well, Latimer, you thought me long," my father said. . . .

But while the last word was in my ears, the whole group vanished, and there was nothing between me and the Chinese painted folding-screen that stood before the door. I was cold and trembling ; I could only totter forward and throw myself on the sofa. This strange new power had manifested itself again. . . . But *was* it a power ? Might it not rather be a disease — a sort of intermittent delirium, concentrating my energy of brain into moments of unhealthy activity, and leaving my saner hours all the more barren ? I felt a dizzy sense of unreality in what my eye rested on ; I grasped the bell convulsively, like one trying to free himself from nightmare, and rang it twice. Pierre came with a look of alarm in his face.

"Monsieur ne se trouve pas bien ? " he said, anxiously.

"I'm tired of waiting, Pierre," I said, as distinctly and emphatically as I could, like a man determined to be sober in spite of wine; "I'm afraid something has happened to my father — he's usually so punctual. Run to the Hôtel des Bergues and see if he is there."

Pierre left the room at once, with a soothing "Bien, Monsieur;" and I felt the better for this scene of simple, waking prose. Seeking to calm myself still further, I went into my bed-room, adjoining the *salon*, and opened a case of eau-de-Cologne; took out a bottle; went through the process of taking out the cork very neatly, and then rubbed the reviving spirit over my hands and forehead, and under my nostrils, drawing a new delight from the scent because I had procured it by slow details of labor, and by no strange sudden madness. Already I had begun to taste something of the horror that belongs to the lot of a human being whose nature is not adjusted to simple human conditions.

Still enjoying the scent, I returned to the *salon*, but it was not unoccupied, as it had been before I left it. In front of the Chinese folding-screen there was my father, with Mrs. Filmore on his right hand, and on his left — the slim blond-haired girl, with the keen face and the keen eyes fixed on me in half-smiling curiosity.

"Well, Latimer, you thought me long," my father said. . . .

I heard no more, felt no more, till I became conscious that I was lying with my head low on the sofa, Pierre and my father by my side. As soon as I was thoroughly revived, my father left the room, and presently returned, saying —

"I've been to tell the ladies how you are, Latimer. They were waiting in the next room. We shall put off our shopping expedition to-day."

Presently he said, "That young lady is Bertha Grant, Mrs. Filmore's orphan niece. Filmore has adopted her, and she lives with them, so you will have her for a neighbor when we go home — perhaps for a near relation; for there is a tenderness between her and Alfred, I suspect, and I should be gratified by the match, since Filmore means to provide for her in every way as if she were his daughter. It had not occurred to me that you knew nothing about her living with the Filmores."

He made no further allusion to the fact of my having fainted at the moment of seeing her, and I would not for the world have told him the reason: I shrank from the idea of disclosing to any one what might be regarded as a pitiable peculiarity, most of all from betraying it to my father, who would have suspected my sanity ever after.

I do not mean to dwell with particularity on the details of my experience. I have described these two cases at length, because they had definite, clearly traceable results in my after-lot.

Shortly after this last occurrence — I think the very next day — I began to be aware of a phase in my abnormal sensibility, to which, from the languid and slight nature of my intercourse with others since my illness, I had not been alive before. This was the obtrusion on my mind of the mental process going forward in first one person, and then another, with whom I happened to be in contact: the vagrant, frivolous ideas and emotions of some uninteresting acquaintance — Mrs. Filmore, for example — would force themselves on my consciousness like an importunate, ill-played musical instrument, or the loud activity of an imprisoned insect. But this unpleasant sensibility was fitful, and left me moments of rest, when the souls of my companions were once more shut out from me, and I felt a relief such as silence brings to wearied nerves. I might have believed this importunate insight to be merely a diseased activity of the imagination, but that my prevision of incalculable words and actions proved it to have a fixed relation to the mental process in other minds. But this superadded consciousness, wearying and annoying enough when it urged on me the trivial experience of indifferent people, became an intense pain and grief when it seemed to be opening to me the souls of those who were in a close relation to me — when the rational talk, the graceful attentions, the wittily turned phrases, and the kindly deeds, which used to make the web of their characters, were seen as if thrust asunder by a microscopic vision, that showed all the intermediate frivolities, all the suppressed egoism, all the struggling chaos of puerilities, meanness. vague capricious memories, and indolent make-shift thoughts, from which human words and deeds emerge like leaflets covering a fermenting heap.

At Basle we were joined by my brother Alfred, now a handsome self-confident man of six-and-twenty — a thorough contrast to my fragile, nervous, ineffectual self. I believe I was held to have a sort of half-womanish, half-ghostly beauty; for the portrait-painters, who are thick as weeds at Geneva, had often asked me to sit to them, and I had been the model of a dying minstrel in a fancy picture. But I thoroughly disliked my own *physique*, and nothing but the belief that it was a condition of poetic genius would have reconciled me to it. That brief hope was quite fled, and I saw in my face now nothing but the stamp of a morbid organization, framed for passive suffering — too feeble for the sublime resistance of poetic production. Alfred, from whom I had been almost constantly separated, and who, in his present stage of character and appearance, came before me as a perfect stranger, was bent on being extremely friendly and brother-like to me. He had the superficial kindness of a good-humored, self-satisfied nature, that fears no rivalry, and has encountered no contrarieties. I am not sure that my disposition was good enough for me to have been quite free from envy towards him, even if our desires had not clashed, and if I had been in the healthy human condition which admits of generous confidence and charitable construction. There must always have been an antipathy between our natures. As it was, he became in a few weeks an object of intense hatred to me; and when he entered the room, still more when he spoke, it was as if a sensation of grating metal had set my teeth on edge. My diseased consciousness was more intensely and continually occupied with his thoughts and emotions, than with those of any other person who came in my way. I was perpetually exasperated with the petty promptings of his conceit and his love of patronage, with his self-complacent belief in Bertha Grant's passion for him, with his half-pitying contempt for me — seen not in the ordinary indications of intonation and phrase and slight action, which an acute and suspicious mind is on the watch for, but in all their naked skinless complication.

For we were rivals, and our desires clashed, though he was not aware of it. I have said nothing yet of the effect Bertha Grant produced in me on a nearer acquaintance. That effect was chiefly determined by the fact that she made the only exception, among all the human beings about me, to my un-happy gift of insight. About Bertha I was always in a state of uncertainty: I could watch the expression of her face, and speculate on its meaning; I could ask for her opinion with the real interest of ignorance; I could listen for her words and watch for her smile with hope and fear: she had for me the fascination of an unravelled destiny. I say it was this fact that chiefly determined the strong effect she produced on me: for, in the abstract, no womanly character could seem to have less affinity for that of a shrinking, romantic, passionate youth than Bertha's. She was keen, sarcastic, unimaginative, pre-maturely cynical, remaining critical and unmoved in the most impressive scenes, inclined to dissect all my favorite poems, and especially contemptuous towards the German lyrics which were my pet literature at that time. To this moment I am unable to define my feeling towards her: it was not ordinary boyish admiration, for she was the very opposite, even to the color of her hair, of the ideal woman who still remained to me the type of loveliness; and she was without that enthusiasm for the great and good, which, even at the moment of her strongest dominion over me, I should have declared to be the highest element of character. But there is no tyranny more complete than that which a self-centred negative nature exercises over a morbidly sensitive nature perpetually craving sympathy and support. The most independent people feel the effect of a man's silence in heightening their value for his opinion — feel an additional triumph in conquering the rever-ence of a critic habitually captious and satirical: no wonder, then, that an enthusiastic self-distrusting youth should watch and wait before the closed secret of a sarcastic woman's face, as if it were the shrine of the doubtfully benignant deity who ruled his destiny. For a young enthusiast is unable to imagine the total negation in another mind of the emotions which are stirring his own: they may be feeble, latent, inactive, he thinks, but they are there — they may be called forth; sometimes, in moments of happy hallucination, he believes they may be there in all the greater strength because he sees no outward sign of them. And this effect, as I have intimated, was heightened to its utmost intensity in me, because Bertha was the only being who remained for me in the mysterious seclusion of soul that renders such youthful delusion possible. Doubtless there was another sort of fascination at work — that subtle physical attraction which delights in cheating our psychological predictions, and in compelling the men who paint sylphs, to fall in love with some *bonne et brave femme,* heavy-heeled and freckled.

Bertha's behavior towards me was such as to encourage all my illusions, to heighten my boyish passion, and make me more and more dependent on her smiles. Looking back with my present wretched knowledge, I conclude that her vanity and love of power were intensely gratified by the belief that I had fainted on first seeing her purely from the strong impression her person had produced on me. The most prosaic woman likes to believe herself the object of a violent, a poetic passion; and without a grain of romance in her, Bertha had that spirit of intrigue which gave piquancy to the idea that the brother of the man she meant to marry was dying with love and jealousy for her sake. That she meant to marry my brother, was what at that time I did not believe; for though he was assiduous in his attentions to her, and I knew well enough that both he and my father had made up their minds to this result, there was not yet an understood engagement — there had been no explicit declaration; and Bertha habitually, while she flirted with my brother, and accepted his homage in a way that implied to him a thorough recognition of its intention, made me believe, by the subtlest looks and phrases — feminine nothings which could never be quoted against her — that he was really the object of her secret ridicule; that she thought him, as I did, a coxcomb, whom she would have pleasure in disappointing. Me she openly petted in my brother's presence, as if I were too young and sickly ever to be thought of as a lover; and that was the view he took

of me. But I believe she must inwardly have delighted in
the tremors into which she threw me by the coaxing way in
which she patted my curls, while she laughed at my quotations. Such caresses were always given in the presence of
our friends; for when we were alone together, she affected
a much greater distance towards me, and now and then took
the opportunity, by words or slight actions, to stimulate my
foolish timid hope that she really preferred me. And why
should she not follow her inclination? I was not in so advantageous a position as my brother, but I had fortune, I was not
a year younger than she was, and she was an heiress, who
would soon be of age to decide for herself.

The fluctuations of hope and fear, confined to this one channel, made each day in her presence a delicious torment. There
was one deliberate act of hers which especially helped to intoxicate me. When we were at Vienna her twentieth birthday occurred, and as she was very fond of ornaments, we all
took the opportunity of the splendid jewellers' shops in that
Teutonic Paris to purchase her a birthday present of jewellery.
Mine, naturally, was the least expensive; it was an opal ring
— the opal was my favorite stone, because it seems to blush
and turn pale as if it had a soul. I told Bertha so when I
gave it her, and said that it was an emblem of the poetic nature,
changing with the changing light of heaven and of woman's
eyes. In the evening she appeared elegantly dressed, and
wearing conspicuously all the birthday presents except mine.
I looked eagerly at her fingers, but saw no opal. I had no
opportunity of noticing this to her during the evening; but
the next day, when I found her seated near the window alone,
after breakfast, I said, "You scorn to wear my poor opal. I
should have remembered that you despised poetic natures, and
should have given you coral, or turquoise, or some other
opaque unresponsive stone." "Do I despise it?" she answered,
taking hold of a delicate gold chain which she always wore
round her neck and drawing out the end from her bosom with
my ring hanging to it; "it hurts me a little, I can tell you,"
she said, with her usual dubious smile, "to wear it in that
secret place; and since your poetical nature is so stupid as

to prefer a more public position, I shall not endure the pain any longer."

She took off the ring from the chain and put it on her finger smiling still, while the blood rushed to my cheeks, and I could not trust myself to say a word of entreaty that she would keep the ring where it was before.

I was completely fooled by this, and for two days shut myself up in my own room whenever Bertha was absent, that I might intoxicate myself afresh with the thought of this scene and all it implied.

I should mention that during these two months — which seemed a long life to me from the novelty and intensity of the pleasures and pains I underwent — my diseased participation in other people's consciousness continued to torment me; now it was my father, and now my brother, now Mrs. Filmore or her husband, and now our German courier, whose stream of thought rushed upon me like a ringing in the ears not to be got rid of, though it allowed my own impulses and ideas to continue their uninterrupted course. It was like a preternaturally heightened sense of hearing, making audible to one a roar of sound where others find perfect stillness. The weariness and disgust of this involuntary intrusion into other souls was counteracted only by my ignorance of Bertha, and my growing passion for her; a passion enormously stimulated, if not produced, by that ignorance. She was my oasis of mystery in the dreary desert of knowledge. I had never allowed my diseased condition to betray itself, or to drive me into any unusual speech or action, except once, when, in a moment of peculiar bitterness against my brother, I had forestalled some words which I knew he was going to utter — a clever observation, which he had prepared beforehand. He had occasionally a slightly affected hesitation in his speech, and when he paused an instant after the second word, my impatience and jealousy impelled me to continue the speech for him, as if it were something we had both learned by rote. He colored and looked astonished, as well as annoyed; and the words had no sooner escaped my lips than I felt a shock of alarm lest such an anticipation of words —very far from being words of course, easy to divine — should have betrayed me as an exceptional being, a sort of quiet energumen, whom every one, Bertha above all, would shudder at and avoid. But I magnified, as usual, the impression any word or deed of mine could produce on others; for no one gave any sign of having noticed my interruption as more than a rudeness, to be forgiven me on the score of my feeble nervous condition.

While this superadded consciousness of the actual was almost constant with me, I had never had a recurrence of that distinct prevision which I have described in relation to my first interview with Bertha; and I was waiting with eager curiosity to know whether or not my vision of Prague would prove to have been an instance of the same kind. A few days after the incident of the opal ring, we were paying one of our frequent visits to the Lichtenberg Palace. I could never look at many pictures in succession; for pictures, when they are at all powerful, affect me so strongly that one or two exhaust all my capability of contemplation. This morning I had been looking at Giorgione's picture of the cruel-eyed woman, said to be a likeness of Lucrezia Borgia. I had stood long alone before it, fascinated by the terrible reality of that cunning, relentless face, till I felt a strange poisoned sensation, as if I had long been inhaling a fatal odor and was just beginning to be conscious of its effects. Perhaps even then I should not have moved away, if the rest of the party had not returned to this room, and announced that they were going to the Belvedere Gallery to settle a bet which had arisen between my brother and Mr. Filmore about a portrait. I followed them dreamily, and was hardly alive to what occurred till they had all gone up to the gallery, leaving me below; for I refused to come within sight of another picture that day. I made my way to the Grand Terrace, since it was agreed that we should saunter in the gardens when the dispute had been decided. I had been sitting here a short space, vaguely conscious of trim gardens, with a city and green hills in the distance, when, wishing to avoid the proximity of the sentinel, I rose and walked down the broad stone steps, intending to seat myself farther on in the gardens. Just as I reached the gravel-walk, I felt an arm slipped within mine, and a light hand gently pressing my wrist. In the same instant a strange intoxicating numbness passed over me, like the continuance or climax of the sensation I was still feeling from the gaze of Lucrezia Borgia. The gardens, the summer sky, the consciousness of Bertha's arm being within mine, all vanished, and I seemed to be suddenly in darkness, out of which there gradually broke a dim firelight, and I felt myself sitting in my father's leather chair in the library at home. I knew the fireplace — the dogs for the wood-fire — the black marble chimney-piece with the white marble medallion of the dying Cleopatra in the centre. Intense and hopeless misery was pressing on my soul; the light became stronger, for Bertha was entering with a candle in her hand — Bertha, my wife — with cruel eyes, with green jewels and green leaves on her white ball-dress; every hateful thought within her present to me. . . . "Madman, idiot! why don't you kill yourself, then?" It was a moment of hell. I saw into her pitiless soul — saw its barren worldliness, its scorching hate — and felt it clothe me round like an air I was obliged to breathe. She came with her candle and stood over me with a bitter smile of contempt; I saw the great emerald brooch on her bosom, a studded serpent with diamond eyes. I shuddered — I despised this woman with the barren soul and mean thoughts; but I felt helpless before her, as if she clutched my bleeding heart, and would clutch it till the last drop of life-blood ebbed away. She was my wife, and we hated each other. Gradually the hearth, the dim library, the candle-light disappeared — seemed to melt away into a background of light, the green serpent with the diamond eyes remaining a dark image on the retina. Then I had a sense of my eyelids quivering, and the living daylight broke in upon me; I saw gardens, and heard voices; I was seated on the steps of the Belvedere Terrace, and my friends were round me.

The tumult of mind into which I was thrown by this hideous vision made me ill for several days, and prolonged our stay at Vienna. I shuddered with horror as the scene recurred to me; and it recurred constantly, with all its minutiæ, as if they had been burnt into my memory; and yet, such is the madness of the human heart under the influence of its immediate desires. I felt a wild hell-braving joy that Bertha was to be mine; for the fulfilment of my former prevision concerning her first appearance before me, left me little hope that this last hideous glimpse of the future was the mere diseased play of my own mind, and had no relation to external realities. One thing alone I looked towards as a possible means of casting doubt on my terrible conviction — the discovery that my vision of Prague had been false — and Prague was the next city on our route.

Meanwhile, I was no sooner in Bertha's society again, than I was as completely under her sway as before. What if I saw into the heart of Bertha, the matured woman — Bertha, my wife ? Bertha, the *girl*, was a fascinating secret to me still: I trembled under her touch; I felt the witchery of her presence; I yearned to be assured of her love. The fear of poison is feeble against the sense of thirst. Nay, I was just as jealous of my brother as before — just as much irritated by his small patronizing ways; for my pride, my diseased sensibility, were there as they had always been, and winced as inevitably under every offence as my eye winced from an intruding mote. The future, even when brought within the compass of feeling by a vision that made me shudder, had still no more than the force of an idea, compared with the force of present emotion — of my love for Bertha, of my dislike and jealousy towards my brother.

It is an old story, that men sell themselves to the tempter, and sign a bond with their blood, because it is only to take effect at a distant day ; then rush on to snatch the cup their souls thirst after with an impulse not the less savage because there is a dark shadow beside them forevermore. There is no short cut, no patent tram-road to wisdom : after all the centuries of invention, the soul's path lies through the thorny wilderness which must be still trodden in solitude, with bleeding feet, with sobs for help, as it was trodden by them of old time.

My mind speculated eagerly on the means by which I should become my brother's successful rival, for I was still too timid,

in my ignorance of Bertha's actual feeling, to venture on any
step that would urge from her an avowal of it. I thought I
should gain confidence even for this, if my vision of Prague
proved to have been veracious; and yet, the horror of that
certitude! Behind the slim girl Bertha, whose words and
looks I watched for, whose touch was bliss, there stood continually that Bertha with the fuller form, the harder eyes, the
more rigid mouth, — with the barren selfish soul laid bare ; no
longer a fascinating secret, but a measured fact, urging itself
perpetually on my unwilling sight. Are you unable to give
me your sympathy — you who read this ? Are you unable to
imagine this double consciousness at work within me, flowing
on like two parallel streams which never mingle their waters
and blend into a common hue ? Yet you must have known
something of the presentiments that spring from an insight at
war with passion ; and my visions were only like presentiments intensified to horror. You have known the powerless-
ness of ideas before the might of impulse; and my visions,
when once they had passed into memory, were mere ideas —
pale shadows that beckoned in vain, while my hand was
grasped by the living and the loved.

In after days I thought with bitter regret that if I had fore-
seen something more or something different — if instead of
that hideous vision which poisoned the passion it could not
destroy, or if even along with it I could have had a foreshadow-
ing of that moment when I looked on my brother's face for
the last time, some softening influence would have been shed
over my feeling towards him : pride and hatred would surely
have been subdued into pity, and the record of those hidden
sins would have been shortened. But this is one of the vain
thoughts with which we men flatter ourselves. We try to
believe that the egoism within us would have easily been
melted, and that it was only the narrowness of our knowledge
which hemmed in our generosity, our awe, our human piety,
and hindered them from submerging our hard indifference to
the sensations and emotions of our fellow. Our tenderness
and self-renunciation seem strong when our egoism has had its
day — when, after our mean striving for a triumph that is to

be another's loss, the triumph comes suddenly, and we shudder at it, because it is held out by the chill hand of death.

Our arrival in Prague happened at night, and I was glad of this, for it seemed like a deferring of a terribly decisive moment, to be in the city for hours without seeing it. As we were not to remain long in Prague, but to go on speedily to Dresden, it was proposed that we should drive out the next morning and take a general view of the place, as well as visit some of its specially interesting spots, before the heat became oppressive — for we were in August, and the season was hot and dry. But it happened that the ladies were rather late at their morning toilet, and to my father's politely repressed but perceptible annoyance, we were not in the carriage till the morning was far advanced. I thought with a sense of relief, as we entered the Jews' quarter, where we were to visit the old synagogue, that we should be kept in this flat, shut-up part of the city, until we should all be too tired and too warm to go farther, and so we should return without seeing more than the streets through which we had already passed. That would give me another day's suspense — suspense, the only form in which a fearful spirit knows the solace of hope. But, as I stood under the blackened, groined arches of that old synagogue, made dimly visible by the seven thin candles in the sacred lamp, while our Jewish cicerone reached down the Book of the Law, and read to us in its ancient tongue, — I felt a shuddering impression that this strange building, with its shrunken lights, this surviving withered remnant of mediæval Judaism, was of a piece with my vision. Those darkened dusty Christian saints, with their loftier arches and their larger candles, needed the consolatory scorn with which they might point to a more shrivelled death-in-life than their own.

As I expected, when we left the Jews' quarter the elders of our party wished to return to the hotel. But now, instead of rejoicing in this, as I had done beforehand, I felt a sudden overpowering impulse to go on at once to the bridge, and put an end to the suspense I had been wishing to protract. I declared, with unusual decision, that I would get out of the carriage and walk on alone ; they might return without me. My father, thinking this merely a sample of my usual "poetic nonsense," objected that I should only do myself harm by walking in the heat; but when I persisted, he said angrily that I might follow my own absurd devices, but that Schmidt (our courier) must go with me. I assented to this, and set off with Schmidt towards the bridge. I had no sooner passed from under the archway of the grand old gate leading on to the bridge, than a trembling seized me, and I turned cold under the mid-day sun; yet I went on; I was in search of something — a small detail which I remembered with special intensity as part of my vision. There it was — the patch of rainbow light on the pavement transmitted through a lamp in the shape of a star.

CHAPTER II.

BEFORE the autumn was at an end, and while the brown leaves still stood thick on the beeches in our park, my brother and Bertha were engaged to each other, and it was understood that their marriage was to take place early in the next spring. In spite of the certainty I had felt from that moment on the bridge at Prague, that Bertha would one day be my wife, my constitutional timidity and distrust had continued to benumb me, and the words in which I had sometimes premeditated a confession of my love, had died away unuttered. The same conflict had gone on within me as before — the longing for an assurance of love from Bertha's lips, the dread lest a word of contempt and denial should fall upon me like a corrosive acid. What was the conviction of a distant necessity to me? I trembled under a present glance, I hungered after a present joy, I was clogged and chilled by a present fear. And so the days passed on : I witnessed Bertha's engagement and heard her marriage discussed as if I were under a conscious nightmare — knowing it was a dream that would vanish, but feeling stifled under the grasp of hard-clutching fingers.

When I was not in Bertha's presence — and I was with her very often, for she continued to treat me with a playful patronage that wakened no jealousy in my brother — I spent my time chiefly in wandering, in strolling, or taking long rides while the daylight lasted, and then shutting myself up with my unread books; for books had lost the power of chaining my attention. My self-consciousness was heightened to that pitch of intensity in which our own emotions take the form of a drama which urges itself imperatively on our contemplation, and we begin to weep, less under the sense of our suffering than at the thought of it. I felt a sort of pitying anguish over the pathos of my own lot : the lot of a being finely organized for pain, but with hardly any fibres that responded to pleasure — to whom the idea of future evil robbed the present of its joy, and for whom the idea of future good did not still the uneasiness of a present yearning or a present dread. I went dumbly through that stage of the poet's suffering, in which he feels the delicious pang of utterance, and makes an image of his sorrows.

I was left entirely without remonstrance concerning this dreamy wayward life : I knew my father's thought about me : "That lad will never be good for anything in life: he may waste his years in an insignificant way on the income that falls to him : I shall not trouble myself about a career for him."

One mild morning in the beginning of November, it happened that I was standing outside the portico patting lazy old Cæsar, a Newfoundland almost blind with age, the only dog that ever took any notice of me — for the very dogs shunned me, and fawned on the happier people about me — when the groom brought up my brother's horse which was to carry him to the hunt, and my brother himself appeared at the door, florid, broad-chested, and self-complacent, feeling what a good-natured fellow he was not to behave insolently to us all on the strength of his great advantages.

"Latimer, old boy," he said to me in a tone of compassionate cordiality, "what a pity it is you don't have a run with the hounds now and then ! The finest thing in the world for low spirits ! "

"Low spirits!" I thought bitterly, as he rode away; "that is the sort of phrase with which coarse, narrow natures like yours think to describe experience of which you can know nc more than your horse knows. It is to such as you that the good of this world falls: ready dulness, healthy selfishness, good-tempered conceit — these are the keys to happiness."

The quick thought came, that my selfishness was even stronger than his — it was only a suffering selfishness instead of an enjoying one. But then, again, my exasperating insight into Alfred's self-complacent soul, his freedom from all the doubts and fears, the unsatisfied yearnings, the exquisite tortures of sensitiveness, that had made the web of my life, seemed to absolve me from all bonds towards him. This man needed no pity, no love; those fine influences would have been as little felt by him as the delicate white mist is felt by the rock it caresses. There was no evil in store for *him:* if he was not to marry Bertha, it would be because he had found a lot pleasanter to himself.

Mr. Filmore's house lay not more than half a mile beyond our own gates, and whenever I knew my brother was gone in another direction, I went there for the chance of finding Bertha at home. Later on in the day I walked thither. By a rare accident she was alone, and we walked out in the grounds together, for she seldom went on foot beyond the trimly swept gravel-walks. I remember what a beautiful sylph she looked to me as the low November sun shone on her blond hair, and she tripped along teasing me with her usual light banter, to which I listened half fondly, half moodily; it was all the sign Bertha's mysterious inner self ever made to me. To-day perhaps the moodiness predominated, for I had not yet shaken off the access of jealous hate which my brother had raised in me by his parting patronage. Suddenly I interrupted and startled her by saying, almost fiercely, "Bertha, how can you love Alfred?"

She looked at me with surprise for a moment, but soon her light smile came again, and she answered sarcastically, "Why do you suppose I love him?"

"How can you ask that, Bertha?"

"What! your wisdom thinks I must love the man I'm going to marry? The most unpleasant thing in the world. I should quarrel with him; I should be jealous of him; our *ménage* would be conducted in a very ill-bred manner. A little quiet contempt contributes greatly to the elegance of life."

"Bertha, that is not your real feeling. Why do you delight in trying to deceive me by inventing such cynical speeches?"

"I need never take the trouble of invention in order to deceive you, my small Tasso" — (that was the mocking name she usually gave me). "The easiest way to deceive a poet is to tell him the truth."

She was testing the validity of her epigram in a daring way, and for a moment the shadow of my vision — the Bertha whose soul was no secret to me — passed between me and the radiant girl, the playful sylph whose feelings were a fascinating mystery. I suppose I must have shuddered, or betrayed in some other way my momentary chill of horror.

"Tasso!" she said, seizing my wrist, and peeping round into my face, "are you really beginning to discern what a heartless girl I am? Why, you are not half the poet I thought you were; you are actually capable of believing the truth about me."

The shadow passed from between us, and was no longer the object nearest to me. The girl whose light fingers grasped me, whose elfish charming face looked into mine — who, I thought, was betraying an interest in my feelings that she would not have directly avowed, — this warm-breathing presence again possessed my senses and imagination like a returning syren melody which had been overpowered for an instant by the roar of threatening waves. It was a moment as delicious to me as the waking up to a consciousness of youth after a dream of middle age. I forgot everything but my passion, and said with swimming eyes —

"Bertha, shall you love me when we are first married? I would n't mind if you really loved me only for a little while."

Her look of astonishment, as she loosed my hand and started away from me, recalled me to a sense of my strange, my criminal indiscretion.

"Forgive me," I said, hurriedly, as soon as I could speak again; "I did not know what I was saying."

"Ah, Tasso's mad fit has come on, I see," she answered quietly, for she had recovered herself sooner than I had. "Let him go home and keep his head cool. I must go in, for the sun is setting."

I left her — full of indignation against myself. I had let slip words which, if she reflected on them, might rouse in her a suspicion of my abnormal mental condition — a suspicion which of all things I dreaded. And besides that, I was ashamed of the apparent baseness I had committed in uttering them to my brother's betrothed wife. I wandered home slowly, entering our park through a private gate instead of by the lodges. As I approached the house, I saw a man dashing off at full speed from the stable-yard across the park. Had any accident happened at home? No; perhaps it was only one of my father's peremptory business errands that required this headlong haste. Nevertheless I quickened my pace without any distinct motive, and was soon at the house. I will not dwell on the scene I found there. My brother was dead — had been pitched from his horse, and killed on the spot by a concussion of the brain.

I went up to the room where he lay, and where my father was seated beside him with a look of rigid despair. I had shunned my father more than any one since our return home, for the radical antipathy between our natures made my insight into his inner self a constant affliction to me. But now, as I went up to him, and stood beside him in sad silence, I felt the presence of a new element that blended us as we had never been blent before. My father had been one of the most successful men in the money-getting world: he had had no sentimental sufferings, no illness. The heaviest trouble that had befallen him was the death of his first wife. But he married my mother soon after; and I remember he seemed exactly the same, to my keen childish observation, the week after her death as before. But now, at last, a sorrow had come — the sorrow of old age, which suffers the more from the crushing of its pride and its hopes, in proportion as the pride and hope are narrow and prosaic. His son was to have been married soon — would probably have stood for the borough at the next election. That son's existence was the best motive that could be alleged for making new purchases of land every year to round off the estate. It is a dreary thing to live on doing the same things year after year, without knowing why we do them. Perhaps the tragedy of disappointed youth and passion is less piteous than the tragedy of disappointed age and worldliness.

As I saw into the desolation of my father's heart, I felt a movement of deep pity towards him, which was the beginning of a new affection — an affection that grew and strengthened in spite of the strange bitterness with which he regarded me in the first month or two after my brother's death. If it had not been for the softening influence of my compassion for him — the first deep compassion I had ever felt — I should have been stung by the perception that my father transferred the inheritance of an eldest son to me with a mortified sense that fate had compelled him to the unwelcome course of caring for me as an important being. It was only in spite of himself that he began to think of me with anxious regard. There is hardly any neglected child for whom death has made vacant a more favored place, who will not understand what I mean.

Gradually, however, my new deference to his wishes, the effect of that patience which was born of my pity for him, won upon his affection, and he began to please himself with the endeavor to make me fill my brother's place as fully as my feebler personality would admit. I saw that the prospect which by-and-by presented itself of my becoming Bertha's husband was welcome to him, and he even contemplated in my case what he had not intended in my brother's — that his son and daughter-in-law should make one household with him. My softened feeling towards my father made this the happiest time I had known since childhood; — these last months in which I retained the delicious illusion of loving Bertha, of longing and doubting and hoping that she might love me. She behaved with a certain new consciousness and distance towards me after my brother's death; and I too was under a double constraint — that of delicacy towards my brother's memory, and of anxiety as to the impression my abrupt words had left on her mind. But the additional screen this mutual reserve erected between us only brought me more completely under her power: no matter how empty the adytum, so that the veil be thick enough. So absolute is our soul's need of something hidden and uncertain for the maintenance of that doubt and hope and effort which are the breath of its life, that if the whole future were laid bare to us beyond to-day, the interest of all mankind would be bent on the hours that lie between; we should pant after the uncertainties of our one morning and our one afternoon; we should rush fiercely to the Exchange for our last possibility of speculation, of success, of disappointment; we should have a glut of political prophets foretelling a crisis or a no-crisis within the only twenty-four hours left open to prophecy. Conceive the condition of the human mind if all propositions whatsoever were self-evident except one, which was to become self-evident at the close of a summer's day, but in the mean time might be the subject of question, of hypothesis, of debate. Art and philosophy, literature and science, would fasten like bees on that one proposition which had the honey of probability in it, and be the more eager because their enjoyment would end with sunset. Our impulses, our spiritual activities, no more adjust themselves to the idea of their future nullity, than the beating of our heart, or the irritability of our muscles.

Bertha, the slim, fair-haired girl, whose present thoughts and emotions were an enigma to me amidst the fatiguing obviousness of the other minds around me, was as absorbing to me as a single unknown to-day — as a single hypothetic proposition to remain problematic till sunset; and all the cramped, hemmed-in belief and disbelief, trust and distrust, of my nature, welled out in this one narrow channel.

And she made me believe that she loved me. Without ever quitting her tone of *badinage* and playful superiority, she intoxicated me with the sense that I was necessary to her, that she was never at ease unless I was near her, submitting to her playful tyranny. It costs a woman so little effort to besot us in this way! A half-repressed word, a moment's unexpected silence, even an easy fit of petulance on our account, will serve us as *hashish* for a long while. Out of the subtlest web of scarcely perceptible signs, she set me weaving the fancy that she had always unconsciously loved me better than Alfred, but that, with the ignorant fluttered sensibility of a young girl, she had been imposed on by the charm that lay for her in the distinction of being admired and chosen by a man who made so brilliant a figure in the world as my brother. She satirized herself in a very graceful way for her vanity and ambition. What was it to me that I had the light of my wretched prevision on the fact that now it was I who possessed at least all but the personal part of my brother's advantages? Our sweet illusions are half of them conscious illusions, like effects of color that we know to be made up of tinsel, broken glass, and rags.

We were married eighteen months after Alfred's death, one cold, clear morning in April, when there came hail and sunshine both together; and Bertha, in her white silk and palegreen leaves, and the pale hues of her hair and face, looked like the spirit of the morning. My father was happier than he had thought of being again : my marriage, he felt sure, would complete the desirable modification of my character, and make me practical and worldly enough to take my place in society among sane men. For he delighted in Bertha's tact and acuteness, and felt sure she would be mistress of me, and make me what she chose : I was only twenty-one, and madly in love with her. Poor father! He kept that hope a little while after our first year of marriage, and it was not quite extinct when paralysis came and saved him from utter disappointment.

I shall hurry through the rest of my story, not dwelling so much as I have hitherto done on my inward experience. When people are well known to each other, they talk rather of what befalls them externally, leaving their feelings and sentiments to be inferred.

We lived in a round of visits for some time after our return home, giving splendid dinner-parties, and making a sensation in our neighborhood by the new lustre of our equipage, for my father had reserved this display of his increased wealth for the period of his son's marriage; and we gave our acquaintances liberal opportunity for remarking that it was a pity I made so poor a figure as an heir and a bridegroom. The nervous fatigue of this existence, the insincerities and platitudes which I had to live through twice over — through my inner and outward sense — would have been maddening to me, if I had not had that sort of intoxicated callousness which came from the delights of a first passion. A bride and bridegroom, surrounded by all the appliances of wealth, hurried through the day by the whirl of society, filling their solitary moments with hastily snatched caresses, are prepared for their future life together as the novice is prepared for the cloister — by experiencing its utmost contrast.

Through all these crowded excited months, Bertha's inward self remained shrouded from me, and I still read her thoughts only through the language of her lips and demeanor: I had still the human interest of wondering whether what I did and said pleased her, of longing to hear a word of affection, of giving a delicious exaggeration of meaning to her smile. But I was conscious of a growing difference in her manner towards me; sometimes strong enough to be called haughty coldness, cutting and chilling me as the hail had done that came across the sunshine on our marriage morning; sometimes only perceptible in the dexterous avoidance of a *tête-à-tête* walk or dinner to which I had been looking forward. I had been deeply pained by this — had even felt a sort of crushing of the heart, from the sense that my brief day of happiness was near its setting; but still I remained dependent on Bertha, eager for the last rays of a bliss that would soon be gone forever, hoping and watching for some after-glow more beautiful from the impending night.

I remember — how should I not remember? — the time when that dependence and hope utterly left me, when the sadness I had felt in Bertha's growing estrangement became a joy that I looked back upon with longing, as a man might look back on the last pains in a paralyzed limb. It was just after the close of my father's last illness, which had necessarily withdrawn us from society and thrown us more upon each other. It was the evening of my father's death. On that evening the veil which had shrouded Bertha's soul from me — had made me find in her alone among my fellow-beings the blessed possibility of mystery, and doubt, and expectation — was first withdrawn. Perhaps it was the first day since the beginning of my passion for her, in which that passion was completely neutralized by the presence of an absorbing feeling of another kind. I had been watching by my father's death-bed : I had been witnessing the last fitful yearning glance his soul had cast back on the spent inheritance of life — the last faint consciousness of love he had gathered from the pressure of my hand. What are all our personal loves when we have been sharing in that supreme agony ? In the first moments when we come away from the presence of death, every other relation to the living is merged, to our feeling, in the great relation of a common nature and a common destiny.

In that state of mind I joined Bertha in her private sitting-room. She was seated in a leaning posture on a settee, with her back towards the door ; the great rich coils of her pale blond hair surmounting her small neck, visible above the back of the settee. I remember, as I closed the door behind me, a cold tremulousness seizing me, and a vague sense of being hated and lonely — vague and strong, like a presentiment. I know how I looked at that moment, for I saw myself in Bertha's thought as she lifted her cutting gray eyes, and looked at me : a miserable ghost-seer, surrounded by phantoms in the noonday, trembling under a breeze when the leaves were still, without appetite for the common objects of human desire, but pining after the moonbeams. We were front to front with each other, and judged each other. The terrible moment of complete illumination had come to me, and I saw that the darkness had hidden no landscape from me, but only a blank prosaic wall : from that evening forth, through the sickening years which followed, I saw all round the narrow room of this woman's soul — saw petty artifice and mere negation where I had delighted to believe in coy sensibilities and in wit at war with latent feeling — saw the light floating vanities of the girl defining themselves into the systematic coquetry, the scheming selfishness, of the woman — saw repulsion and antipathy harden into cruel hatred, giving pain only for the sake of wreaking itself.

For Bertha too, after her kind, felt the bitterness of disillusion. She had believed that my wild poet's passion for her would make me her slave; and that, being her slave, I should execute her will in all things. With the essential shallowness of a negative, unimaginative nature, she was unable to conceive the fact that sensibilities were anything else than weaknesses. She had thought my weaknesses would put me in her power, and she found them unmanageable forces. Our positions were reversed. Before marriage she had completely mastered my imagination, for she was a secret to me; and I created the unknown thought before which I trembled as if it were hers. But now that her soul was laid open to me, now that I was compelled to share the privacy of her motives, to follow all the petty devices that preceded her words and acts, she found herself powerless with me, except to produce in me the chill shudder of repulsion — powerless, because I could be acted on by no lever within her reach. I was dead to worldly ambitions, to social vanities, to all the incentives within the compass of her narrow imagination, and I lived under influences utterly invisible to her.

She was really pitiable to have such a husband, and so all the world thought. A graceful, brilliant woman, like Bertha, who smiled on morning callers, made a figure in ball-rooms, and was capable of that light repartee which, from such a woman, is accepted as wit, was secure of carrying off all sympathy from a husband who was sickly, abstracted, and, as some suspected, crack-brained. Even the servants in our house gave her the balance of their regard and pity. For there were no audible quarrels between us; our alienation, our repulsion from each other, lay within the silence of our own hearts; and if the mistress went out a great deal, and seemed to dislike the master's society, was it not natural, poor thing? The master was odd. I was kind and just to my dependants, but I excited in them a shrinking, half-contemptuous pity; for this class of men and women are but slightly determined in their estimate of others by general considerations, or even experience, of character. They judge of persons as they judge of coins, and value those who pass current at a high rate.

After a time I interfered so little with Bertha's habits, that it might seem wonderful how her hatred towards me could grow so intense and active as it did. But she had begun to suspect, by some involuntary betrayals of mine, that there was an abnormal power of penetration in me — that fitfully, at least, I was strangely cognizant of her thoughts and intentions, and she began to be haunted by a terror of me, which alternated every now and then with defiance. She meditated continually how the incubus could be shaken off her life — how she could be freed from this hateful bond to a being whom she at once despised as an imbecile, and dreaded as an inquisitor. For a long while she lived in the hope that my evident wretchedness would drive me to the commission of suicide; but suicide was not in my nature. I was too completely swayed by the sense that I was in the grasp of unknown forces, to believe in my power of self-release. Towards my own destiny I had become entirely passive; for my one ardent desire had spent itself, and impulse no longer predominated over knowledge. For this reason I never thought of taking any steps towards a complete separation, which would have made our alienation evident to the world. Why should I rush for help to a new course, when I was only suffering from the consequences of a deed which had been the act of my intensest will? That would have been the logic of one who had desires to gratify, and I had no desires. But Bertha and I lived more and more aloof from each other. The rich find it easy to live married and apart.

That course of our life which I have indicated in a few sentences filled the space of years. So much misery — so slow and hideous a growth of hatred and sin, may be compressed into a sentence! And men judge of each other's lives through this summary medium. They epitomize the experience of their fellow-mortal, and pronounce judgment on him in neat syntax, and feel themselves wise and virtuous — conquerors over the temptations they define in well-selected predicates. Seven years of wretchedness glide glibly over the lips of the man who has never counted them out in moments of chill disappointment, of head and heart throbbings, of dread and vain wrestling, of remorse and despair. We learn *words* by rote, but not their meaning; *that* must be paid for with our life-blood, and printed in the subtle fibres of our nerves.

But I will hasten to finish my story. Brevity is justified at once to those who readily understand, and to those who will never understand.

Some years after my father's death, I was sitting by the dim firelight in my library one January evening — sitting in the leather chair that used to be my father's — when Bertha appeared at the door, with a candle in her hand, and advanced towards me. I knew the ball-dress she had on — the white ball-dress, with the green jewels, shone upon by the light of the wax candle which lit up the medallion of the dying Cleopatra on the mantel-piece. Why did she come to me before going out? I had not seen her in the library, which was my habitual place, for months. Why did she stand before me with the candle in her hand, with her cruel contemptuous eyes fixed on me, and the glittering serpent, like a familiar demon, on her breast? For a moment I thought this fulfil-ment of my vision at Vienna marked some dreadful crisis in my fate, but I saw nothing in Bertha's mind, as she stood before me, except scorn for the look of overwhelming misery with which I sat before her. . . . "Fool, idiot, why don't you kill yourself, then?" — that was her thought. But at length her thoughts reverted to her errand, and she spoke aloud. The apparently indifferent nature of the errand seemed to make a ridiculous anticlimax to my prevision and my agitation.

"I have had to hire a new maid. Fletcher is going to be married, and she wants me to ask you to let her husband have the public-house and farm at Molton. I wish him to have it. You must give the promise now, because Fletcher is going to-morrow morning — and quickly, because I'm in a hurry."

"Very well; you may promise her," I said, indifferently, and Bertha swept out of the library again.

I always shrank from the sight of a new person, and all the more when it was a person whose mental life was likely to weary my reluctant insight with worldly ignorant trivialities. But I shrank especially from the sight of this new maid, because her advent had been announced to me at a moment to which I could not cease to attach some fatality: I had a vague dread that I should find her mixed up with the dreary drama of my life — that some new sickening vision would reveal her to me as an evil genius. When at last I did unavoidably meet her, the vague dread was changed into definite disgust. She was a tall, wiry, dark-eyed woman, this Mrs. Archer, with a face handsome enough to give her coarse hard nature the odious finish of bold, self-confident coquetry. That was enough to make me avoid her, quite apart from the contemptuous feeling with which she contemplated me. I seldom saw her; but I perceived that she rapidly became a favorite with her mistress, and, after the lapse of eight or nine months, I began to be aware that there had arisen in Bertha's mind towards this woman a mingled feeling of fear and dependence, and that this feeling was associated with ill-defined images of candle-light scenes in her dressing-room, and the locking up of something in Bertha's cabinet. My interviews with my wife had become so brief and so rarely solitary, that I had no opportunity of perceiving these images in her mind with more definiteness. The recollections of the past become contracted in the rapidity of thought till they sometimes bear hardly a more distinct resemblance to the external reality than the forms of an oriental alphabet to the objects that suggested them.

Besides, for the last year or more a modification had been going forward in my mental condition, and was growing more and more marked. My insight into the minds of those around me was becoming dimmer and more fitful, and the ideas that

crowded my double consciousness became less and less dependent on any personal contact. All that was personal in me
seemed to be suffering a gradual death, so that I was losing
the organ through which the personal agitations and projects
of others could affect me. But along with this relief from
wearisome insight, there was a new development of what I
concluded — as I have since found rightly — to be a prevision
of external scenes. It was as if the relation between me and
my fellow-men was more and more deadened, and my relation
to what we call the inanimate was quickened into new life.
The more I lived apart from society, and in proportion as my
wretchedness subsided from the violent throb of agonized
passion into the dulness of habitual pain, the more frequent
and vivid became such visions as that I had had of Prague —
of strange cities, of sandy plains, of gigantic ruins, of midnight
skies with strange bright constellations, of mountain-passes,
of grassy nooks flecked with the afternoon sunshine through
the boughs : I was in the midst of such scenes, and in all of
them one presence seemed to weigh on me in all these mighty
shapes — the presence of something unknown and pitiless.
For continual suffering had annihilated religious faith within
me : to the utterly miserable — the unloving and the unloved
— there is no religion possible, no worship but a worship of
devils. And beyond all these, and continually recurring, was
the vision of my death — the pangs, the suffocation, the last
struggle, when life would be grasped at in vain.

Things were in this state near the end of the seventh year.
I had become entirely free from insight, from my abnormal
cognizance of any other consciousness than my own, and instead of intruding involuntarily into the world of other minds,
was living continually in my own solitary future. Bertha was
aware that I was greatly changed. To my surprise she had of
late seemed to seek opportunities of remaining in my society,
and had cultivated that kind of distant yet familiar talk which
is customary between a husband and wife who live in polite
and irrevocable alienation. I bore this with languid submission, and without feeling enough interest in her motives to be
roused into keen observation ; yet I could not help perceiving

something triumphant and excited in her carriage and the expression of her face — something too subtle to express itself in words or tones, but giving one the idea that she lived in a state of expectation or hopeful suspense. My chief feeling was satisfaction that her inner self was once more shut out from me ; and I almost revelled for the moment in the absent melancholy that made me answer her at cross purposes, and betray utter ignorance of what she had been saying. I remember well the look and the smile with which she one day said, after a mistake of this kind on my part: "I used to think you were a clairvoyant, and that was the reason why you were so bitter against other clairvoyants, wanting to keep your monopoly ; but I see now you have become rather duller than the rest of the world."

I said nothing in reply. It occurred to me that her recent obtrusion of herself upon me might have been prompted by the wish to test my power of detecting some of her secrets ; but I let the thought drop again at once : her motives and her deeds had no interest for me, and whatever pleasures she might be seeking, I had no wish to balk her. There was still pity in my soul for every living thing, and Bertha was living — was surrounded with possibilities of misery.

Just at this time there occurred an event which roused me somewhat from my inertia, and gave me an interest in the passing moment that I had thought impossible for me. It was a visit from Charles Meunier, who had written me word that he was coming to England for relaxation from too strenuous labor, and would like to see me. Meunier had now a European reputation ; but his letter to me expressed that keen remembrance of an early regard, an early debt of sympathy, which is inseparable from nobility of character : and I too felt as if his presence would be to me like a transient resurrection into a happier pre-existence.

He came, and as far as possible, I renewed our old pleasure of making *tête-à-tête* excursions, though, instead of mountains and glaciers and the wide blue lake, we had to content ourselves with mere slopes and ponds and artificial plantations. The years had changed us both, but with what different result !

Meunier was now a brilliant figure in society, to whom elegant women pretended to listen, and whose acquaintance was boasted of by noblemen ambitious of brains. He repressed with the utmost delicacy all betrayal of the shock which I am sure he must have received from our meeting, or of a desire to penetrate into my condition and circumstances, and sought by the utmost exertion of his charming social powers to make our reunion agreeable. Bertha was much struck by the unexpected fascinations of a visitor whom she had expected to find presentable only on the score of his celebrity, and put forth all her coquetries and accomplishments. Apparently she succeeded in attracting his admiration, for his manner towards her was attentive and flattering. The effect of his presence on me was so benignant, especially in those renewals of our old *tête-à-tête* wanderings, when he poured forth to me wonderful narratives of his professional experience, that more than once, when his talk turned on the psychological relations of disease, the thought crossed my mind that, if his stay with me were long enough, I might possibly bring myself to tell this man the secrets of my lot. Might there not lie some remedy for *me*, too, in his science? Might there not at least lie some comprehension and sympathy ready for me in his large and susceptible mind? But the thought only flickered feebly now and then, and died out before it could become a wish. The horror I had of again breaking in on the privacy of another soul, made me, by an irrational instinct, draw the shroud of concealment more closely around my own, as we automatically perform the gesture we feel to be wanting in another.

When Meunier's visit was approaching its conclusion, there happened an event which caused some excitement in our household, owing to the surprisingly strong effect it appeared to produce on Bertha — on Bertha, the self-possessed, who usually seemed inaccessible to feminine agitations, and did even her hate in a self-restrained hygienic manner. This event was the sudden severe illness of her maid, Mrs. Archer. I have reserved to this moment the mention of a circumstance which had forced itself on my notice shortly before Meunier's

arrival, namely, that there had been some quarrel between
Bertha and this maid, apparently during a visit to a distant
family, in which she had accompanied her mistress. I had
overheard Archer speaking in a tone of bitter insolence, which
I should have thought an adequate reason for immediate
dismissal. No dismissal followed; on the contrary, Bertha
seemed to be silently putting up with personal inconveniences
from the exhibitions of this woman's temper. I was the more
astonished to observe that her illness seemed a cause of strong
solicitude to Bertha; that she was at the bedside night and
day, and would allow no one else to officiate as head-nurse.
It happened that our family doctor was out on a holiday, an
accident which made Meunier's presence in the house doubly
welcome, and he apparently entered into the case with an interest which seemed so much stronger than the ordinary professional feeling, that one day when he had fallen into a long
fit of silence after visiting her, I said to him —

"Is this a very peculiar case of disease, Meunier?"

"No," he answered, "it is an attack of peritonitis, which
will be fatal, but which does not differ physically from many
other cases that have come under my observation. But I'll
tell you what I have on my mind. I want to make an experiment on this woman, if you will give me permission. It can
do her no harm — will give her no pain — for I shall not make
it until life is extinct to all purposes of sensation. I want to
try the effect of transfusing blood into her arteries after the
heart has ceased to beat for some minutes. I have tried the
experiment again and again with animals that have died of
this disease, with astounding results, and I want to try it on
a human subject. I have the small tubes necessary, in a case
I have with me, and the rest of the apparatus could be prepared readily. I should use my own blood — take it from my
own arm. This woman won't live through the night, I'm convinced, and I want you to promise me your assistance in making the experiment. I can't do without another hand, but it
would perhaps not be well to call in a medical assistant from
among your provincial doctors. A disagreeable foolish version
of the thing might get abroad."

"Have you spoken to my wife on the subject?" I said, "because she appears to be peculiarly sensitive about this woman: she has been a favorite maid."

"To tell you the truth," said Meunier, "I don't want her to know about it. There are always insuperable difficulties with women in these matters, and the effect on the supposed dead body may be startling. You and I will sit up together, and be in readiness. When certain symptoms appear I shall take you in, and at the right moment we must manage to get every one else out of the room."

I need not give our farther conversation on the subject. He entered very fully into the details, and overcame my repulsion from them, by exciting in me a mingled awe and curiosity concerning the possible results of his experiment.

We prepared everything, and he instructed me in my part as assistant. He had not told Bertha of his absolute conviction that Archer would not survive through the night, and endeavored to persuade her to leave the patient and take a night's rest. But she was obstinate, suspecting the fact that death was at hand, and supposing that he wished merely to save her nerves. She refused to leave the sick-room. Meunier and I sat up together in the library, he making frequent visits to the sick-room, and returning with the information that the case was taking precisely the course he expected. Once he said to me, "Can you imagine any cause of ill feeling this woman has against her mistress, who is so devoted to her?"

"I think there was some misunderstanding between them before her illness. Why do you ask?"

"Because I have observed for the last five or six hours — since, I fancy, she has lost all hope of recovery — there seems a strange prompting in her to say something which pain and failing strength forbid her to utter; and there is a look of hideous meaning in her eyes, which she turns continually towards her mistress. In this disease the mind often remains singularly clear to the last."

"I am not surprised at an indication of malevolent feeling in her," I said. "She is a woman who has always inspired me with distrust and dislike, but she managed to insinuate herself into her mistress's favor." He was silent after this, looking at the fire with an air of absorption, till he went up-stairs again. He stayed away longer than usual, and on returning, said to me quietly, "Come now."

I followed him to the chamber where death was hovering. The dark hangings of the large bed made a background that gave a strong relief to Bertha's pale face as I entered. She started forward as she saw me enter, and then looked at Meunier with an expression of angry inquiry; but he lifted up his hand as if to impose silence, while he fixed his glance on the dying woman and felt her pulse. The face was pinched and ghastly, a cold perspiration was on the forehead, and the eyelids were lowered so as almost to conceal the large dark eyes. After a minute or two, Meunier walked round to the other side of the bed where Bertha stood, and with his usual air of gentle politeness towards her begged her to leave the patient under our care — everything should be done for her — she was no longer in a state to be conscious of an affectionate presence. Bertha was hesitating, apparently almost willing to believe his assurance and to comply. She looked round at the ghastly dying face, as if to read the confirmation of that assurance, when for a moment the lowered eyelids were raised again, and it seemed as if the eyes were looking towards Bertha, but blankly. A shudder passed through Bertha's frame, and she returned to her station near the pillow, tacitly imply-ing that she would not leave the room.

The eyelids were lifted no more. Once I looked at Bertha as she watched the face of the dying one. She wore a rich *peignoir*, and her blond hair was half covered by a lace cap: in her attire she was, as always, an elegant woman, fit to figure in a picture of modern aristocratic life: but I asked myself how that face of hers could ever have seemed to me the face of a woman born of woman, with memories of child-hood, capable of pain, needing to be fondled? The features at that moment seemed so preternaturally sharp, the eyes were so hard and eager — she looked like a cruel immortal, finding her spiritual feast in the agonies of a dying race. For across those hard features there came something like a flash when the last hour had been breathed out, and we all felt that the dark veil had completely fallen. What secret was there between Bertha and this woman? I turned my eyes from her with a horrible dread lest my insight should return, and I should be obliged to see what had been breeding about two unloving women's hearts. I felt that Bertha had been watching for the moment of death as the sealing of her secret: I thanked Heaven it could remain sealed for me.

Meunier said quietly, "She is gone." He then gave his arm to Bertha, and she submitted to be led out of the room.

I suppose it was at her order that two female attendants came into the room, and dismissed the younger one who had been present before. When they entered, Meunier had already opened the artery in the long thin neck that lay rigid on the pillow, and I dismissed them, ordering them to remain at a distance till we rang: the doctor, I said, had an operation to perform — he was not sure about the death. For the next twenty minutes I forgot everything but Meunier and the experiment in which he was so absorbed, that I think his senses would have been closed against all sounds or sights which had no relation to it. It was my task at first to keep up the artificial respiration in the body after the transfusion had been effected, but presently Meunier relieved me, and I could see the wondrous slow return of life; the breast began to heave, the inspirations became stronger, the eyelids quivered, and the soul seemed to have returned beneath them. The artificial respiration was withdrawn: still the breathing continued, and there was a movement of the lips.

Just then I heard the handle of the door moving: I suppose Bertha had heard from the women that they had been dismissed: probably a vague fear had arisen in her mind, for she entered with a look of alarm. She came to the foot of the bed and gave a stifled cry.

The dead woman's eyes were wide open, and met hers in full recognition — the recognition of hate. With a sudden strong effort, the hand that Bertha had thought forever still was pointed towards her, and the haggard face moved. The gasping eager voice said —

"You mean to poison your husband . . . the poison is in the black cabinet . . . I got it for you . . . you laughed at me, and told lies about me behind my back, to make me disgusting . . . because you were jealous . . . are you sorry . . . now ? "

The lips continued to murmur, but the sounds were no longer distinct. Soon there was no sound — only a slight movement : the flame had leaped out, and was being extinguished the faster. The wretched woman's heart-strings had been set to hatred and vengeance ; the spirit of life had swept the chords for an instant, and was gone again forever. Great God ! Is this what it is to live again . . . to wake up with our unstilled thirst upon us, with our unuttered curses rising to our lips, with our muscles ready to act out their half-committed sins ?

Bertha stood pale at the foot of the bed, quivering and helpless, despairing of devices, like a cunning animal whose hiding-places are surrounded by swift-advancing flame. Even Meunier looked paralyzed ; life for that moment ceased to be a scientific problem to him. As for me, this scene seemed of one texture with the rest of my existence : horror was my familiar, and this new revelation was only like an old pain recurring with new circumstances.

. . . .

Since then Bertha and I have lived apart — she in her own neighborhood, the mistress of half our wealth, I as a wanderer in foreign countries, until I came to this Devonshire nest to die. Bertha lives pitied and admired ; for what had I against that charming woman, whom every one but myself could have been happy with ? There had been no witness of the scene in the dying room except Meunier, and while Meunier lived his lips were sealed by a promise to me.

Once or twice, weary of wandering, I rested in a favorite spot, and my heart went out towards the men and women and children whose faces were becoming familiar to me ; but I was driven away again in terror at the approach of my old insight — driven away to live continually with the one Unknown Presence revealed and yet hidden by the moving curtain of the earth and sky. Till at last disease took hold of me and forced me to rest here — forced me to live in dependence on my servants. And then the curse of insight — of my double consciousness, came again, and has never left me. I know all their narrow thoughts, their feeble regard, their half-wearied pity.

.   .   .   .

It is the 20th of September, 1850. I know these figures I have just written, as if they were a long familiar inscription. I have seen them on this page in my desk unnumbered times, when the scene of my dying struggle has opened upon me. . . .

BROTHER JACOB.

Trompeurs, c'est pour vous que j'écris,
Attendez vous à la pareille.

La Fontaine.

BROTHER JACOB.

CHAPTER I.

AMONG the many fatalities attending the bloom of young desire, that of blindly taking to the confectionery line has not, perhaps, been sufficiently considered. How is the son of a British yeoman, who has been fed principally on salt pork and yeast dumplings, to know that there is satiety for the human stomach even in a paradise of glass jars full of sugared almonds and pink lozenges, and that the tedium of life can reach a pitch where plum-buns at discretion cease to offer the slightest enticement? Or how, at the tender age when a confectioner seems to him a very prince whom all the world must envy, — who breakfasts on macaroons, dines on marengs, sups on twelfth-cake, and fills up the intermediate hours with sugar-candy or peppermint, — how is he to foresee the day of sad wisdom, when he will discern that the confectioner's calling is not socially influential, or favorable to a soaring ambition? I have known a man who turned out to have a metaphysical genius, incautiously, in the period of youthful buoyancy, commence his career as a dancing-master; and you may imagine the use that was made of this initial mistake by opponents who felt themselves bound to warn the public against his doctrine of the Inconceivable. He could not give up his dancing-lessons, because he made his bread by them, and metaphysics would not have found him in so much as salt to his bread. It was really the same with Mr. David Faux and the confectionery business. His uncle, the butler at the great house close by Brigford, had made a pet of him in his early boyhood, and it was on a visit to this uncle that the confectioners' shops in that brilliant town had, on a single day, fired his tender imagination. He carried home the pleasing illusion that a confectioner must be at once the happiest and the foremost of men, since the things he made were not only the most beautiful to behold, but the very best eating, and such as the Lord Mayor must always order largely for his private recreation ; so that when his father declared he must be put to a trade, David chose his line without a moment's hesitation ; and, with a rashness inspired by a sweet tooth, wedded himself irrevocably to confectionery. Soon, however, the tooth lost its relish and fell into blank indifference ; and all the while, his mind expanded, his ambition took new shapes, which could hardly be satisfied within the sphere his youthful ardor had chosen. But what was he to do ? He was a young man of much mental activity, and, above all, gifted with a spirit of contrivance ; but then, his faculties would not tell with great effect in any other medium than that of candied sugars, conserves, and pastry. Say what you will about the identity of the reasoning process in all branches of thought, or about the advantage of coming to subjects with a fresh mind, the adjustment of butter to flour, and of heat to pastry, is *not* the best preparation for the office of prime minister ; besides, in the present imperfectly organized state of society, there are social barriers. David could invent delightful things in the way of drop-cakes, and he had the widest views of the sugar department ; but in other directions he certainly felt hampered by the want of knowledge and practical skill ; and the world is so inconveniently constituted, that the vague consciousness of being a fine fellow is no guarantee of success in any line of business.

This difficulty pressed with some severity on Mr. David Faux, even before his apprenticeship was ended. His soul swelled with an impatient sense that he ought to become something very remarkable — that it was quite out of the question for him to put up with a narrow lot as other men did : he scorned the idea that he could accept an average. He was sure there was nothing average about him : even such a person as Mrs. Tibbits, the washerwoman, perceived it, and probably had a preference for his linen. At that particular period he was weighing out gingerbread-nuts; but such an anomaly could not continue. No position could be suited to Mr. David Faux that was not in the highest degree easy to the flesh and flattering to the spirit. If he had fallen on the present times, and enjoyed the advantages of a Mechanics' Institute, he would certainly have taken to literature and have written reviews; but his education had not been liberal. He had read some novels from the adjoining circulating library, and had even bought the story of "Inkle and Yarico," which had made him feel very sorry for poor Mr. Inkle; so that his ideas might not have been below a certain mark of the literary calling; but his spelling and diction were too unconventional.

When a man is not adequately appreciated or comfortably placed in his own country, his thoughts naturally turn towards foreign climes; and David's imagination circled round and round the utmost limits of his geographical knowledge, in search of a country where a young gentleman of pasty visage, lipless mouth, and stumpy hair, would be likely to be received with the hospitable enthusiasm which he had a right to expect. Having a general idea of America as a country where the population was chiefly black, it appeared to him the most propitious destination for an emigrant who, to begin with, had the broad and easily recognizable merit of whiteness; and this idea gradually took such strong possession of him that Satan seized the opportunity of suggesting to him that he might emigrate under easier circumstances, if he supplied himself with a little money from his master's till. But that evil spirit, whose understanding, I am convinced, has been much overrated, quite wasted his time on this occasion. David would certainly have liked well to have some of his master's money in his pocket, if he had been sure his master would have been the only man to suffer for it; but he was a cautious youth, and quite determined to run no risks on his own account. So he stayed out his apprenticeship, and committed no act of dishonesty that was at all likely to be discovered, reserving his plan of emigration for a future opportunity. And the circumstances under which he carried it

out were in this wise. Having been at home a week or two
partaking of the family beans, he had used his leisure in as-
certaining a fact which was of considerable importance to
him, namely, that his mother had a small sum in guineas
painfully saved from her maiden perquisites, and kept in the
corner of a drawer where her baby-linen had reposed for the
last twenty years — ever since her son David had taken to his
feet, with a slight promise of bow-legs which had not been
altogether unfulfilled. Mr. Faux, senior, had told his son
very frankly, that he must not look to being set up in business
by *him :* with seven sons, and one of them a very healthy and
well-developed idiot, who consumed a dumpling about eight
inches in diameter every day, it was pretty well if they got
a hundred apiece at his death. Under these circumstances,
what was David to do ? It was certainly hard that he should
take his mother's money ; but he saw no other ready means
of getting any, and it was not to be expected that a young
man of his merit should put up with inconveniences that
could be avoided. Besides, it is not robbery to take property
belonging to your mother : she does n't prosecute you. And
David was very well behaved to his mother ; he comforted
her by speaking highly of himself to her, and assuring her
that he never fell into the vices he saw practised by other
youths of his own age, and that he was particularly fond of
honesty If his mother would have given him her twenty
guineas as a reward of this noble disposition, he really would
not have stolen them from her, and it would have been more
agreeable to his feelings. Nevertheless, to an active mind
like David's, ingenuity is not without its pleasures : it was
rather an interesting occupation to become stealthily acquainted with the wards of his mother's simple key (not in
the least like Chubb's patent), and to get one that would do
its work equally well ; and also to arrange a little drama by
which he would escape suspicion, and run no risk of forfeiting
the prospective hundred at his father's death, which would
be convenient in the improbable case of his *not* making a large
fortune in the " Indies."

First, he spoke freely of his intention to start shortly for

Liverpool and take ship for America; a resolution which cost his good mother some pain, for, after Jacob the idiot, there was not one of her sons to whom her heart clung more than to her youngest-born, David. Next, it appeared to him that Sunday afternoon, when everybody was gone to church except Jacob and the cow-boy, was so singularly favorable an opportunity for sons who wanted to appropriate their mothers' guineas, that he half thought it must have been kindly intended by Providence for such purposes. Especially the third Sunday in Lent; because Jacob had been out on one of his occasional wanderings for the last two days; and David, being a timid young man, had a considerable dread and hatred of Jacob, as of a large personage who went about habitually with a pitchfork in his hand.

Nothing could be easier, then, than for David on this Sunday afternoon to decline going to church, on the ground that he was going to tea at Mr. Lunn's, whose pretty daughter Sally had been an early flame of his, and, when the church-goers were at a safe distance, to abstract the guineas from their wooden box and slip them into a small canvas bag — nothing easier than to call to the cow-boy that he was going, and tell him to keep an eye on the house for fear of Sunday tramps. David thought it would be easy, too, to get to a small thicket and bury his bag in a hole he had already made and covered up under the roots of an old hollow ash, and he had, in fact, found the hole without a moment's difficulty, had uncovered it, and was about gently to drop the bag into it, when the sound of a large body rustling towards him with something like a bellow was such a surprise to David, who, as a gentleman gifted with much contrivance, was naturally only prepared for what he expected, that instead of dropping the bag gently he let it fall so as to make it untwist and vomit forth the shining guineas. In the same moment he looked up and saw his dear brother Jacob close upon him, holding the pitchfork so that the bright smooth prongs were a yard in advance of his own body, and about a foot off David's. (A learned friend, to whom I once narrated this history, observed that it was David's guilt which made these prongs formidable, and that the *mens nil conscia sibi* strips a pitchfork of all terrors. I thought this idea so valuable, that I obtained his leave to use it on condition of suppressing his name.) Nevertheless, David did not entirely lose his presence of mind ; for in that case he would have sunk on the earth or started backward; whereas he kept his ground and smiled at Jacob, who nodded his head up and down, and said, "Hoich, Zavy !" in a painfully equivocal manner. David's heart was beating audibly, and if he had had any lips they would have been pale ; but his mental activity, instead of being paralyzed, was stimulated. While he was inwardly praying (he always prayed when he was much frightened), — "Oh, save me this once, and I 'll never get into danger again ! " — he was thrusting his hand into his pocket in search of a box of yellow lozenges, which he had brought with him from Brigford among other delicacies of the same portable kind, as a means of conciliating proud beauty, and more particularly the beauty of Miss Sarah Lunn. Not one of these delicacies had he ever offered to poor Jacob, for David was not a young man to waste his jujubes and barley-sugar in giving pleasure to people from whom he expected nothing. But an idiot with equivocal intentions and a pitchfork is as well worth flattering and cajoling as if he were Louis Napoleon. So David, with a promptitude equal to the occasion, drew out his box of yellow lozenges, lifted the lid, and performed a pantomime with his mouth and fingers, which was meant to imply that he was delighted to see his dear brother Jacob, and seized the opportunity of making him a small present, which he would find particularly agreeable to the taste. Jacob, you understand, was not an intense idiot, but within a certain limited range knew how to choose the good and reject the evil : he took one lozenge, by way of test, and sucked it as if he had been a philosopher ; then, in as great an ecstasy at its new and complex savor as Caliban at the taste of Trinculo's wine, chuckled and stroked this suddenly beneficent brother, and held out his hand for more ; for, except in fits of anger, Jacob was not ferocious or needlessly predatory. David's courage half returned, and he left off praying ; pouring a dozen lozenges into Jacob's palm, and trying to look very fond of him. He congratulated himself that he had formed the plan of going to see Miss Sally Lunn this afternoon, and that, as a consequence, he had brought with him these propitiatory delicacies : he was certainly a lucky fellow ; indeed, it was always likely Providence should be fonder of him than of other apprentices, and since he *was* to be interrupted, why, an idiot was preferable to any other sort of witness. For the first time in his life, David thought he saw the advantage of idiots.

As for Jacob, he had thrust his pitchfork into the ground, and had thrown himself down beside it, in thorough abandonment to the unprecedented pleasure of having five lozenges in his mouth at once, blinking meanwhile, and making inarticulate sounds of gustative content. He had not yet given any sign of noticing the guineas, but in seating himself he had laid his broad right hand on them, and unconsciously kept it in that position, absorbed in the sensations of his palate. If he could only be kept so occupied with the lozenges as not to see the guineas before David could manage to cover them ! That was David's best hope of safety ; for Jacob knew his mother's guineas ; it had been part of their common experience as boys to be allowed to look at these handsome coins, and rattle them in their box on high days and holidays, and among all Jacob's narrow experiences as to money, this was likely to be the most memorable.

" Here, Jacob," said David, in an insinuating tone, handing the box to him, " I 'll give 'em all to you. Run ! — make haste ! — else somebody 'll come and take 'em."

David, not having studied the psychology of idiots, was not aware that they are not to be wrought upon by imaginative fears. Jacob took the box with his left hand, but saw no necessity for running away. Was ever a promising young man wishing to lay the foundation of his fortune by appropriating his mother's guineas obstructed by such a day-mare as this ? But the moment must come when Jacob would move his right hand to draw off the lid of the tin box, and then David would sweep the guineas into the hole with the utmost address and swiftness, and immediately seat himself upon them. Ah, no ! It 's of no use to have foresight when you are dealing with an idiot: he is not to be calculated upon. Jacob's right hand was given to vague clutching and throwing; it suddenly clutched the guineas as if they had been so many pebbles, and was raised in an attitude which promised to scatter them like seed over a distant bramble, when, from some prompting or other — probably of an unwonted sensation — it paused, descended to Jacob's knee, and opened slowly under the inspection of Jacob's dull eyes. David began to pray again, but immediately desisted — another resource having occurred to him.

"Mother! zinnies!" exclaimed the innocent Jacob. Then, looking at David, he said, interrogatively, "Box?"

"Hush! hush!" said David, summoning all his ingenuity in this severe strait. "See, Jacob!" He took the tin box from his brother's hand, and emptied it of the lozenges, returning half of them to Jacob, but secretly keeping the rest in his own hand. Then he held out the empty box, and said, "Here's the box, Jacob! The box for the guineas!" gently sweeping them from Jacob's palm into the box.

This procedure was not objectionable to Jacob; on the contrary, the guineas clinked so pleasantly as they fell, that he wished for a repetition of the sound, and seizing the box, began to rattle it very gleefully. David, seizing the opportunity, deposited his reserve of lozenges in the ground and hastily swept some earth over them. "Look, Jacob!" he said, at last. Jacob paused from his clinking, and looked into the hole, while David began to scratch away the earth, as if in doubtful expectation. When the lozenges were laid bare, he took them out one by one, and gave them to Jacob.

"Hush!" he said, in a loud whisper, "Tell nobody — all for Jacob — hush—sh—sh! Put guineas in the hole — they'll come out like this!" To make the lesson more complete, he took a guinea, and lowering it into the hole, said, "Put in *so*." Then, as he took the last lozenge out, he said, "Come out *so*," and put the lozenge into Jacob's hospitable mouth.

Jacob turned his head on one side, looked first at his brother and then at the hole, like a reflective monkey, and, finally, laid the box of guineas in the hole with much decision. David made haste to add every one of the stray coins, put on the lid, and covered it well with earth, saying in his most coaxing tone —

"Take'm out to-morrow, Jacob; all for Jacob! Hush—sh —sh!"

Jacob, to whom this once indifferent brother had all at once become a sort of sweet-tasted fetish, stroked David's best coat with his adhesive fingers, and then hugged him with an accompaniment of that mingled chuckling and gurgling by which he was accustomed to express the milder passions. But if he had chosen to bite a small morsel out of his beneficent brother's cheek, David would have been obliged to bear it.

And here I must pause, to point out to you the short-sighted-ness of human contrivance. This ingenious young man, Mr. David Faux, thought he had achieved a triumph of cunning when he had associated himself in his brother's rudimentary mind with the flavor of yellow lozenges. But he had yet to learn that it is a dreadful thing to make an idiot fond of you, when you yourself are not of an affectionate disposition: especially an idiot with a pitchfork — obviously a difficult friend to shake off by rough usage.

It may seem to you rather a blundering contrivance for a clever young man to bury the guineas. But, if everything had turned out as David had calculated, you would have seen that his plan was worthy of his talents. The guineas would have lain safely in the earth while the theft was discovered, and David, with the calm of conscious innocence, would have lingered at home, reluctant to say good-by to his dear mother while she was in grief about her guineas; till at length, on the eve of his departure, he would have disinterred them in the strictest privacy, and carried them on his own person without inconvenience. But David, you perceive, had reckoned with-out his host, or, to speak more precisely, without his idiot brother — an item of so uncertain and fluctuating a character, that I doubt whether he would not have puzzled the astute heroes of M. de Balzac, whose foresight is so remarkably at home in the future.

It was clear to David now that he had only one alternative

before him : he must either renounce the guineas, by quietly putting them back in his mother's drawer (a course not un-attended with difficulty); or he must leave more than a suspicion behind him, by departing early the next morning without giving notice, and with the guineas in his pocket. For if he gave notice that he was going, his mother, he knew, would insist on fetching from her box of guineas the three she had always promised him as his share; indeed, in his original plan, he had counted on this as a means by which the theft would be discovered under circumstances that would themselves speak for his innocence; but now, as I need hardly explain, that well-combined plan was completely frustrated. Even if David could have bribed Jacob with perpetual lozenges, an idiot's secrecy is itself betrayal. He dared not even go to tea at Mr. Lunn's, for in that case he would have lost sight of Jacob, who, in his impatience for the crop of lozenges, might scratch up the box again while he was absent, and carry it home — depriving him at once of reputation and guineas. No! he must think of nothing all the rest of this day, but of coaxing Jacob and keeping him out of mischief. It was a fatiguing and anxious evening to David; nevertheless, he dared not go to sleep without tying a piece of string to his thumb and great toe, to secure his frequent waking; for he meant to be up with the first peep of dawn, and be far out of reach before breakfast-time. His father, he thought, would certainly cut him off with a shilling; but what then? Such a striking young man as he would be sure to be well received in the West Indies : in foreign countries there are always openings — even for cats. It was probable that some Princess Yarico would want him to marry her, and make him presents of very large jewels beforehand; after which, he need n't marry her unless he liked. David had made up his mind not to steal any more, even from people who were fond of him : it was an unpleasant way of making your fortune in a world where you were likely to be surprised in the act by brothers. Such alarms did not agree with David's constitu-tion, and he had felt so much nausea this evening that no doubt his liver was affected. Besides, he would have been greatly

hurt not to be thought well of in the world: he always meant
to make a figure, and be thought worthy of the best seats and
the best morsels.

Ruminating to this effect on the brilliant future in reserve
for him, David by the help of his check-string kept himself on
the alert to seize the time of earliest dawn for his rising and
departure.   His brothers, of course, were early risers, but he
should anticipate them by at least an hour and a half, and the
little room which he had to himself as only an occasional visitor, had its window over the horse-block, so that he could slip
out through the window without the least difficulty.   Jacob,
the horrible Jacob, had an awkward trick of getting up before
everybody else, to stem his hunger by emptying the milk-bowl
that was "duly set" for him; but of late he had taken to
sleeping in the hay-loft, and if he came into the house, it
would be on the opposite side to that from which David was
making his exit.   There was no need to think of Jacob; yet
David was liberal enough to bestow a curse on him — it was
the only thing he ever did bestow gratuitously.   His small
bundle of clothes was ready packed, and he was soon treading
lightly on the steps of the horse-block, soon walking at a smart
pace across the fields towards the thicket.   It would take him
no more than two minutes to get out the box; he could make
out the tree it was under by the pale strip where the bark was
off, although the dawning light was rather dimmer in the
thicket.   But what, in the name of — burnt pastry — was that
large body with a staff planted beside it, close at the foot of
the ash-tree ?   David paused, not to make up his mind as to
the nature of the apparition — he had not the happiness of
doubting for a moment that the staff was Jacob's pitchfork —
but to gather the self-command necessary for addressing his
brother with a sufficiently honeyed accent.   Jacob was absorbed in scratching up the earth, and had not heard David's
approach.

"I say, Jacob," said David in a loud whisper, just as the
tin box was lifted out of the hole.

Jacob looked up, and discerning his sweet-flavored brother,
nodded and grinned in the dim light in a way that made him

seem to David like a triumphant demon. If he had been of
an impetuous disposition, he would have snatched the pitchfork from the ground and impaled this fraternal demon. But
David was by no means impetuous; he was a young man
greatly given to calculate consequences, a habit which has
been held to be the foundation of virtue. But somehow it had
not precisely that effect in David: he calculated whether an
action would harm himself, or whether it would only harm
other people. In the former case he was very timid about
satisfying his immediate desires, but in the latter he would
risk the result with much courage.

"Give it *me*, Jacob," he said, stooping down and patting his
brother. "Let us see."

Jacob, finding the lid rather tight, gave the box to his
brother in perfect faith. David raised the lid, and shook his
head, while Jacob put his finger in and took out a guinea to
taste whether the metamorphosis into lozenges was complete
and satisfactory.

"No, Jacob; too soon, too soon," said David, when the
guinea had been tasted. "Give it me; we'll go and bury it
somewhere else; we'll put it in yonder," he added, pointing
vaguely toward the distance.

David screwed on the lid, while Jacob, looking grave, rose
and grasped his pitchfork. Then, seeing David's bundle, he
snatched it, like a too officious Newfoundland, stuck his pitchfork into it and carried it over his shoulder in triumph as he
accompanied David and the box out of the thicket.

What on earth was David to do? It would have been easy
to frown at Jacob, and kick him, and order him to get away;
but David dared as soon have kicked the bull. Jacob was
quiet as long as he was treated indulgently; but on the slightest show of anger, he became unmanageable, and was liable to
fits of fury which would have made him formidable even without his pitchfork. There was no mastery to be obtained over
him except by kindness or guile. David tried guile.

"Go, Jacob," he said, when they were out of the thicket —
pointing towards the house as he spoke; "go and fetch me a
spade — a spade. But give *me* the bundle," he added, trying

to reach it from the fork, where it hung high above Jacob's tall shoulder.

But Jacob showed as much alacrity in obeying as a wasp shows in leaving a sugar-basin. Near David, he felt himself in the vicinity of lozenges: he chuckled and rubbed his brother's back, brandishing the bundle higher out of reach. David, with an inward groan, changed his tactics, and walked on as fast as he could. It was not safe to linger. Jacob would get tired of following him, or, at all events, could be eluded. If they could once get to the distant highroad, a coach would overtake them, David would mount it, having previously by some ingenious means secured his bundle, and then Jacob might howl and flourish his pitchfork as much as he liked. Meanwhile he was under the fatal necessity of being very kind to this ogre, and of providing a large breakfast for him when they stopped at a roadside inn. It was already three hours since they had started, and David was tired. Would no coach be coming up soon? he inquired. No coach for the next two hours. But there was a carrier's cart to come immediately, on its way to the next town. If he could slip out, even leaving his bundle behind, and get into the cart without Jacob! But there was a new obstacle. Jacob had recently discovered a remnant of sugar-candy in one of his brother's tail-pockets; and, since then, had cautiously kept his hold on that limb of the garment, perhaps with an expectation that there would be a further development of sugar-candy after a longer or shorter interval. Now every one who has worn a coat will understand the sensibilities that must keep a man from starting away in a hurry when there is a grasp on his coat-tail. David looked forward to being well received among strangers, but it might make a difference if he had only one tail to his coat.

He felt himself in a cold perspiration. He could walk no more: he must get into the cart and let Jacob get in with him. Presently a cheering idea occurred to him: after so large a breakfast, Jacob would be sure to go to sleep in the cart; you see at once that David meant to seize his bundle, jump out, and be free. His expectation was partly fulfilled.

Jacob did go to sleep in the cart, but it was in a peculiar attitude — it was with his arms tightly fastened round his dear brother's body; and if ever David attempted to move, the grasp tightened with the force of an affectionate boa-constrictor.

"Th' innicent's fond on you," observed the carrier, thinking that David was probably an amiable brother, and wishing to pay him a compliment.

David groaned. The ways of thieving were not ways of pleasantness. Oh, why had he an idiot brother? Or why, in general, was the world so constituted that a man could not take his mother's guineas comfortably? David became grimly speculative.

Copious dinner at noon for Jacob; but little dinner, because little appetite, for David. Instead of eating, he plied Jacob with beer; for through this liberality he descried a hope. Jacob fell into a dead sleep, at last, *without* having his arms round David, who paid the reckoning, took his bundle, and walked off. In another half-hour he was on the coach on his way to Liverpool, smiling the smile of the triumphant wicked. He was rid of Jacob — he was bound for the Indies, where a gullible princess awaited him. He would never steal any more, but there would be no need; he would show himself so deserving, that people would make him presents freely. He must give up the notion of his father's legacy; but it was not likely he would ever want that trifle; and even if he did — why, it was a compensation to think that in being forever divided from his family he was divided from Jacob, more terrible than Gorgon or Demogorgon to David's timid green eyes. Thank heaven, he should never see Jacob any more!

CHAPTER II.

IT was nearly six years after the departure of Mr. David Faux for the West Indies, that the vacant shop in the market-place at Grimworth was understood to have been let to the stranger with a sallow complexion and a buff cravat, whose first appearance had caused some excitement in the bar of the Woolpack, where he had called to wait for the coach.

Grimworth, to a discerning eye, was a good place to set up shopkeeping in. There was no competition in it at present; the Church-people had their own grocer and draper; the Dissenters had theirs; and the two or three butchers found a ready market for their joints without strict reference to religious persuasion — except that the rector's wife had given a general order for the veal sweet-breads and the mutton kidneys, while Mr. Rodd, the Baptist minister, had requested that, so far as was compatible with the fair accommodation of other customers, the sheep's trotters might be reserved for him. And it was likely to be a growing place, for the trustees of Mr. Zephaniah Crypt's Charity, under the stimulus of a late visitation by commissioners, were beginning to apply long-accumulating funds to the rebuilding of the Yellow Coat School, which was henceforth to be carried forward on a greatly extended scale, the testator having left no restrictions concerning the curriculum, but only concerning the coat.

The shopkeepers at Grimworth were by no means unanimous as to the advantages promised by this prospect of increased population and trading, being substantial men, who liked doing a quiet business in which they were sure of their customers, and could calculate their returns to a nicety. Hitherto, it had been held a point of honor by the families in Grimworth parish, to buy their sugar and their flannel at the shops where their fathers and mothers had bought before them; but, if new-comers were to bring in the system of neck-

and-neck trading, and solicit feminine eyes by gown-pieces laid in fan-like folds, and surmounted by artificial flowers, giving them a factitious charm (for on what human figure would a gown sit like a fan, or what female head was like a bunch of China-asters ?), or, if new grocers were to fill their windows with mountains of currants and sugar, made seductive by contrast and tickets, — what security was there for Grimworth, that a vagrant spirit in shopping, once introduced, would not in the end carry the most important families to the larger market town of Cattelton, where, business being done on a system of small profits and quick returns, the fashions were of the freshest, and goods of all kinds might be bought at an advantage ?

With this view of the times predominant among the tradespeople at Grimworth, their uncertainty concerning the nature of the business which the sallow-complexioned stranger was about to set up in the vacant shop, naturally gave some additional strength to the fears of the less sanguine. If he was going to sell drapery, it was probable that a pale-faced fellow like that would deal in showy and inferior articles — printed cottons and muslins which would leave their dye in the washtub, jobbed linen full of knots, and flannel that would soon look like gauze. If grocery, then it was to be hoped that no mother of a family would trust the teas of an untried grocer. Such things had been known in some parishes as tradesmen going about canvassing for custom with cards in their pockets : when people came from nobody knew where, there was no knowing what they might do. It was a thousand pities that Mr. Moffat, the auctioneer and broker, had died without leaving anybody to follow him in the business, and Mrs. Cleve's trustee ought to have known better than to let a shop to a stranger. Even the discovery that ovens were being put up on the premises, and that the shop was, in fact, being fitted up for a confectioner and pastry-cook's business, hitherto unknown in Grimworth, did not quite suffice to turn the scale in the new-comer's favor, though the landlady at the Woolpack defended him warmly, said he seemed to be a very clever young man, and from what she could make out, came of a very good family; indeed, was most likely a good many people's betters.

It certainly made a blaze of light and color, almost as if a rainbow had suddenly descended into the market-place, when, one fine morning, the shutters were taken down from the new shop, and the two windows displayed their decorations. On one side, there were the variegated tints of collared and marbled meats, set off by bright green leaves, the pale brown of glazed pies, the rich tones of sauces and bottled fruits enclosed in their veil of glass — altogether a sight to bring tears into the eyes of a Dutch painter; and on the other, there was a predominance of the more delicate hues of pink, and white, and yellow, and buff, in the abundant lozenges, candies, sweet biscuits and icings, which to the eyes of a bilious person might easily have been blended into a faëry landscape in Turner's latest style. What a sight to dawn upon the eyes of Grimworth children! They almost forgot to go to their dinner that day, their appetites being preoccupied with imaginary sugar-plums; and I think even Punch, setting up his tabernacle in the market-place, would not have succeeded in drawing them away from those shop-windows, where they stood according to gradations of size and strength, the biggest and strongest being nearest the window, and the little ones in the outermost rows lifting wide-open eyes and mouths towards the upper tier of jars, like small birds at meal-time.

The elder inhabitants pished and pshawed a little at the folly of the new shopkeeper in venturing on such an outlay in goods that would not keep; to be sure, Christmas was coming, but what housewife in Grimworth would not think shame to furnish forth her table with articles that were not home-cooked? No, no. Mr. Edward Freely, as he called himself, was deceived, if he thought Grimworth money was to flow into his pockets on such terms.

Edward Freely was the name that shone in gilt letters on a mazarine ground over the doorplace of the new shop — a generous-sounding name, that might have belonged to the open-hearted, improvident hero of an old comedy, who would have delighted in raining sugared almonds, like a new manna-gift, among that small generation outside the windows. But Mr. Edward Freely was a man whose impulses were kept in due subordination: he held that the desire for sweets and pastry must only be satisfied in a direct ratio with the power of paying for them. If the smallest child in Grimworth would go to him with a halfpenny in its tiny fist, he would, after ringing the halfpenny, deliver a just equivalent in "rock." He was not a man to cheat even the smallest child — he often said so, observing at the same time that he loved honesty, and also that he was very tender-hearted, though he did n't show his feelings as some people did.

Either in reward of such virtue, or according to some more hidden law of sequence, Mr. Freely's business, in spite of prejudice, started under favorable auspices. For Mrs. Chaloner, the rector's wife, was among the earliest customers at the shop, thinking it only right to encourage a new parishioner who had made a decorous appearance at church; and she found Mr. Freely a most civil, obliging young man, and intelligent to a surprising degree for a confectioner; well-principled, too, for in giving her useful hints about choosing sugars he had thrown much light on the dishonesty of other tradesmen. Moreover, he had been in the West Indies, and had seen the very estate which had been her poor grandfather's property; and he said the missionaries were the only cause of the negro's discontent — an observing young man, evidently. Mrs. Chaloner ordered wine-biscuits and olives, and gave Mr. Freely to understand that she should find his shop a great convenience. So did the doctor's wife, and so did Mrs. Gate, at the large carding-mill, who, having high connections frequently visiting her, might be expected to have a large consumption of ratafias and macaroons.

The less aristocratic matrons of Grimworth seemed likely at first to justify their husbands' confidence that they would never pay a percentage of profits on drop-cakes, instead of making their own, or get up a hollow show of liberal housekeeping by purchasing slices of collared meat when a neighbor came in for supper. But it is my task to narrate the gradual corruption of Grimworth manners from their primitive sim-

plicity — a melancholy task, if it were not cheered by the prospect of the fine peripateia or downfall by which the progress
of the corruption was ultimately checked.

It was young Mrs. Steene, the veterinary surgeon's wife,
who first gave way to temptation. I fear she had been rather
over-educated for her station in life, for she knew by heart
many passages in "Lalla Rookh," the "Corsair," and the
"Siege of Corinth," which had given her a distaste for domestic
occupations, and caused her a withering disappointment at the
discovery that Mr. Steene, since his marriage, had lost all interest in the "bulbul," openly preferred discussing the nature
of spavin with a coarse neighbor, and was angry if the pud-
ding turned out watery — indeed, was simply a top-booted
"vet.," who came in hungry at dinner-time; and not in the
least like a nobleman turned Corsair out of pure scorn for his
race, or like a renegade with a turban and crescent, unless it
were in the irritability of his temper. And scorn is such a
very different thing in top-boots !

This brutal man had invited a supper-party for Christmas
eve, when he would expect to see mince-pies on the table.
Mrs. Steene had prepared her mince-meat, and had devoted
much butter, fine flour, and labor, to the making of a batch of
pies in the morning; but they proved to be so very heavy
when they came out of the oven, that she could only think
with trembling of the moment when her husband should catch
sight of them on the supper-table. He would storm at her,
she was certain; and before all the company; and then she
should never help crying : it was so dreadful to think she had
come to that, after the bulbul and everything ! Suddenly the
thought darted through her mind that *this once* she might send
for a dish of mince-pies from Freely's : she knew he had some.
But what was to become of the eighteen heavy mince-pies ?
Oh, it was of no use thinking about that; it was very expensive — indeed, making mince-pies at all was a great expense,
when they were not sure to turn out well : it would be much
better to buy them ready-made. You paid a little more for
them, but there was no risk of waste.

Such was the sophistry with which this misguided young

woman — enough. Mrs. Steene sent for the mince-pies, and, I am grieved to add, garbled her household accounts in order to conceal the fact from her husband. This was the second step in a downward course, all owing to a young woman's being out of harmony with her circumstances, yearning after renegades and bulbuls, and being subject to claims from a veterinary surgeon fond of mince-pies. The third step was to harden herself by telling the fact of the bought mince-pies to her intimate friend Mrs. Mole, who had already guessed it, and who subsequently encouraged herself in buying a mould of jelly, instead of exerting her own skill, by the reflection that "other people" did the same sort of thing. The infection spread; soon there was a party or clique in Grimworth on the side of "buying at Freely's;" and many husbands, kept for some time in the dark on this point, innocently swallowed at two mouthfuls a tart on which they were paying a profit of a hundred per cent, and as innocently encouraged a fatal disingenuousness in the partners of their bosoms by praising the pastry. Others, more keen-sighted, winked at the too frequent presentation on washing-days, and at impromptu suppers, of superior spiced-beef, which flattered their palates more than the cold remnants they had formerly been contented with. Every housewife who had once "bought at Freely's" felt a secret joy when she detected a similar perversion in her neighbor's practice, and soon only two or three old-fashioned mistresses of families held out in the protest against the growing demoralization, saying to their neighbors who came to sup with them, "I can't offer you Freely's beef, or Freely's cheese-cakes; everything in our house is home-made; I'm afraid you'll hardly have any appetite for our plain pastry." The doctor, whose cook was not satisfactory, the curate, who kept no cook, and the mining agent, who was a great *bon vivant,* even began to rely on Freely for the greater part of their dinner, when they wished to give an entertainment of some brilliancy. In short, the business of manufacturing the more fanciful viands was fast passing out of the hands of maids and matrons in private families, and was becoming the work of a special commercial organ.

I am not ignorant that this sort of thing is called the inevitable course of civilization, division of labor, and so forth, and that the maids and matrons may be said to have had their hands set free from cookery to add to the wealth of society in some other way. Only it happened at Grimworth, which, to be sure, was a low place, that the maids and matrons could do nothing with their hands at all better than cooking; not even those who had always made heavy cakes and leathery pastry. And so it came to pass, that the progress of civilization at Grimworth was not otherwise apparent than in the impoverishment of men, the gossiping idleness of women, and the heightening prosperity of Mr. Edward Freely.

The Yellow Coat School was a double source of profit to the calculating confectioner; for he opened an eating-room for the superior workmen employed on the new school, and he accommodated the pupils at the old school by giving great attention to the fancy-sugar department. When I think of the sweet-tasted swans and other ingenious white shapes crunched by the small teeth of that rising generation, I am glad to remember that a certain amount of calcareous food has been held good for young creatures whose bones are not quite formed; for I have observed these delicacies to have an inorganic flavor which would have recommended them greatly to that young lady of the "Spectator's" acquaintance who habitually made her dessert on the stems of tobacco-pipes.

As for the confectioner himself, he made his way gradually into Grimworth homes, as his commodities did, in spite of some initial repugnance. Somehow or other, his reception as a guest seemed a thing that required justifying, like the purchasing of his pastry. In the first place, he was a stranger, and therefore open to suspicion; secondly, the confectionery business was so entirely new at Grimworth, that its place in the scale of rank had not been distinctly ascertained. There was no doubt about drapers and grocers, when they came of good old Grimworth families, like Mr. Luff and Mr. Prettyman: they visited with the Palfreys, who farmed their own land, played many a game at whist with the doctor, and condescended a little towards the timber-merchant, who had lately taken to the coal-trade also, and had got new furniture; but whether a confectioner should be admitted to this higher level of respectability, or should be understood to find his associates among butchers and bakers, was a new question on which tradition threw no light. His being a bachelor was in his favor, and would perhaps have been enough to turn the scale, even if Mr. Edward Freely's other personal pretensions had been of an entirely insignificant cast. But so far from this, it very soon appeared that he was a remarkable young man, who had been in the West Indies, and had seen many wonders by sea and land, so that he could charm the ears of Grimworth Desdemonas with stories of strange fishes, especially sharks, which he had stabbed in the nick of time by bravely plunging overboard just as the monster was turning on his side to devour the cook's mate; of terrible fevers which he had undergone in a land where the wind blows from all quarters at once; of rounds of toast cut straight from the bread-fruit trees; of toes bitten off by land-crabs; of large honors that had been offered to him as a man who knew what was what, and was therefore particularly needed in a tropical climate; and of a Creole heiress who had wept bitterly at his departure. Such conversational talents as these, we know, will overcome disadvantages of complexion; and young Towers, whose cheeks were of the finest pink, set off by a fringe of dark whisker, was quite eclipsed by the presence of the sallow Mr. Freely. So exceptional a confectioner elevated his business, and might well begin to make disengaged hearts flutter a little.

Fathers and mothers were naturally more slow and cautious in their recognition of the new-comer's merits.

"He's an amusing fellow," said Mr. Prettyman, the highly respectable grocer. (Mrs. Prettyman was a Miss Fothergill, and her sister had married a London mercer.) "He's an amusing fellow; and I've no objection to his making one at the Oyster Club; but he's a bit too fond of riding the high horse. He's uncommonly knowing, I'll allow; but how came he to go to the Indies? I should like that answered. It's unnatural in a confectioner. I'm not fond of people that have been beyond seas, if they can't give a good account how they happened to go. When folks go so far off, it's because they've got little credit nearer home — that's my opinion. However, he's got some good rum; but I don't want to be hand and glove with him, for all that."

It was this kind of dim suspicion which beclouded the view of Mr. Freely's qualities in the maturer minds of Grimworth through the early months of his residence there. But when the confectioner ceased to be a novelty, the suspicions also ceased to be novel, and people got tired of hinting at them, especially as they seemed to be refuted by his advancing prosperity and importance. Mr. Freely was becoming a person of influence in the parish; he was found useful as an overseer of the poor, having great firmness in enduring other people's pain, which firmness, he said, was due to his great benevolence; he always did what was good for people in the end. Mr. Chaloner had even selected him as clergyman's churchwarden, for he was a very handy man, and much more of Mr. Chaloner's opinion in everything about church business than the older parishioners. Mr. Freely was a very regular churchman, but at the Oyster Club he was sometimes a little free in his conversation, more than hinting at a life of Sultanic self-indulgence which he had passed in the West Indies, shaking his head now and then and smiling rather bitterly, as men are wont to do when they intimate that they have become a little too wise to be instructed about a world which has long been flat and stale to them.

For some time he was quite general in his attentions to the fair sex, combining the gallantries of a lady's man with a severity of criticism on the person and manners of absent belles, which tended rather to stimulate in the feminine breast the desire to conquer the approval of so fastidious a judge. Nothing short of the very best in the department of female charms and virtues could suffice to kindle the ardor of Mr. Edward Freely, who had become familiar with the most luxuriant and dazzling beauty in the West Indies. It may seem incredible that a confectioner should have ideas and conversation so much resembling those to be met with in a higher walk of life, but it must be remembered that he had not merely travelled, he had also bow-legs and a sallow, small-featured visage, so that nature herself had stamped him for a fastidious connoisseur of the fair sex.

As last, however, it seemed clear that Cupid had found a sharper arrow than usual, and that Mr. Freely's heart was pierced. It was the general talk among the young people at Grimworth. But was it really love? and not rather ambition? Miss Fullilove, the timber-merchant's daughter, was quite sure that if *she* were Miss Penny Palfrey, she would be cautious; it was not a good sign when men looked so much above themselves for a wife. For it was no less a person than Miss Penelope Palfrey, second daughter of the Mr. Palfrey who farmed his own land, that had attracted Mr. Freely's peculiar regard, and conquered his fastidiousness; and no wonder; for the Ideal, as exhibited in the finest waxwork, was perhaps never so closely approached by the Real as in the person of the pretty Penelope. Her yellowish flaxen hair did not curl naturally, I admit, but its bright crisp ringlets were such smooth, perfect miniature tubes, that you would have longed to pass your little finger through them, and feel their soft elasticity. She wore them in a crop, for in those days, when society was in a healthier state, young ladies wore crops long after they were twenty, and Penelope was not yet nineteen. Like the waxen ideal, she had round blue eyes, and round nostrils in her little nose, and teeth such as the ideal would be seen to have, if it ever showed them. Altogether, she was a small, round thing, as neat as a pink and white double daisy, and as guileless; for I hope it does not argue guile in a pretty damsel of nineteen, to think that she should like to have a beau and be " engaged," when her elder sister had already been in that position a year and a half. To be sure, there was young Towers always coming to the house; but Penny felt convinced he only came to see her brother, for he never had anything to say to her, and never offered her his arm, and was as awkward and silent as possible.

It is not unlikely that Mr. Freely had early been smitten by Penny's charms, as brought under his observation at church, but he had to make his way in society a little before he could come into nearer contact with them; and even after he was well received in Grimworth families, it was a long while before he could converse with Penny otherwise than in an incidental meeting at Mr. Luff's. It was not so easy to get invited to Long Meadows, the residence of the Palfreys; for though Mr Palfrey had been losing money of late years, not being able quite to recover his feet after the terrible murrain which forced him to borrow, his family were far from considering themselves on the same level even as the old-established tradespeople with whom they visited. The greatest people, even kings and queens, must visit with somebody, and the equals of the great are scarce. They were especially scarce at Grimworth, which, as I have before observed, was a low parish, mentioned with the most scornful brevity in gazetteers. Even the great people there were far behind those of their own standing in other parts of this realm. Mr. Palfrey's farmyard doors had the paint all worn off them, and the front garden walks had long been merged in a general weediness. Still, his father had been called Squire Palfrey, and had been respected by the last Grimworth generation as a man who could afford to drink too much in his own house.

Pretty Penny was not blind to the fact that Mr. Freely admired her, and she felt sure that it was he who had sent her a beautiful valentine; but her sister seemed to think so lightly of him (all young ladies think lightly of the gentlemen to whom they are not engaged), that Penny never dared mention him, and trembled and blushed whenever they met him, thinking of the valentine, which was very strong in its expressions, and which she felt guilty of knowing by heart. A man who had been to the Indies, and knew the sea so well, seemed to her a sort of public character, almost like Robinson Crusoe or Captain Cook; and Penny had always wished her husband to be a remarkable personage, likely to be put in Mangnall's Questions, with which register of the immortals she had become acquainted during her one year at a boarding-school. Only it seemed strange that a remarkable man should be a confectioner and pastry-cook, and this anomaly quite disturbed Penny's dreams. Her brothers, she knew, laughed at men

who could n't sit on horseback well, and called them tailors;
but her brothers were very rough, and were quite without that
power of anecdote which made Mr. Freely such a delightful
companion. He was a very good man, she thought, for she
had heard him say at Mr. Luff's, one day, that he always
wished to do his duty in whatever state of life he might be
placed ; and he knew a great deal of poetry, for one day he
had repeated a verse of a song. She wondered if he had made
the words of the valentine ! — it ended in this way : —

> " Without thee, it is pain to live,
> But with thee, it were sweet to die."

Poor Mr. Freely ! her father would very likely object —
she felt sure he would, for he always called Mr. Freely " that
sugar-plum fellow." Oh, it was very cruel, when true love
was crossed in that way, and all because Mr. Freely was a
confectioner : well, Penny would be true to him, for all that,
and since his being a confectioner gave her an opportunity of
showing her faithfulness, she was glad of it. Edward Freely
was a pretty name, much better than John Towers. Young
Towers had offered her a rose out of his button-hole the other
day, blushing very much ; but she refused it, and thought with
delight how much Mr. Freely would be comforted if he knew
her firmness of mind.

Poor little Penny ! the days were so very long among the
daisies on a grazing farm, and thought is so active — how was
it possible that the inward drama should not get the start of
the outward ? I have known young ladies, much better educated, and with an outward world diversified by instructive
lectures, to say nothing of literature and highly developed
fancy-work, who have spun a cocoon of visionary joys and
sorrows for themselves, just as Penny did. Her elder sister
Letitia, who had a prouder style of beauty, and a more worldly
ambition, was engaged to a wool-factor, who came all the way
from Cattelton to see her ; and everybody knows that a wool
factor takes a very high rank, sometimes driving a double-
bodied gig. Letty's notions got higher every day, and Penny
never dared to speak of her cherished griefs to her lofty sister

—never dared to propose that they should call at Mr. Freely's to buy liquorice, though she had prepared for such an incident by mentioning a slight sore throat. So she had to pass the shop on the other side of the market-place, and reflect, with a suppressed sigh, that behind those pink and white jars somebody was thinking of her tenderly, unconscious of the small space that divided her from him.

And it was quite true that, when business permitted, Mr. Freely thought a great deal of Penny. He thought her prettiness comparable to the loveliest things in confectionery; he judged her to be of submissive temper — likely to wait upon him as well as if she had been a negress, and to be silently terrified when his liver made him irritable; and he considered the Palfrey family quite the best in the parish possessing marriageable daughters. On the whole, he thought her worthy to become Mrs. Edward Freely, and all the more so, because it would probably require some ingenuity to win her. Mr. Palfrey was capable of horse-whipping a too rash pretender to his daughter's hand; and, moreover, he had three tall sons: it was clear that a suitor would be at a disadvantage with such a family, unless travel and natural acumen had given him a countervailing power of contrivance. And the first idea that occurred to him in the matter was, that Mr. Palfrey would object less if he knew that the Freelys were a much higher family than his own. It had been foolish modesty in him hitherto to conceal the fact that a branch of the Freelys held a manor in Yorkshire, and to shut up the portrait of his great-uncle the admiral, instead of hanging it up where a family portrait should be hung — over the mantel-piece in the parlor. Admiral Freely, K.C.B., once placed in this conspicuous position, was seen to have had one arm only, and one eye, — in these points resembling the heroic Nelson, — while a certain pallid insignificance of feature confirmed the relationship between himself and his grand-nephew.

Next, Mr. Freely was seized with an irrepressible ambition to possess Mrs. Palfrey's receipt for brawn, hers being pronounced on all hands to be superior to his own — as he informed her in a very flattering letter carried by his errand-boy.

Now Mrs. Palfrey, like other geniuses, wrought by instinct rather than by rule, and possessed no receipts, — indeed, despised all people who used them, observing that people who pickled by book, must pickle by weights and measures, and such nonsense; as for herself, her weights and measures were the tip of her finger and the tip of her tongue, and if you went nearer, why, of course, for dry goods like flour and spice, you went by handfuls and pinches, and for wet, there was a middle-sized jug — quite the best thing whether for much or little, because you might know how much a teacupful was if you 'd got any use of your senses, and you might be sure it would take five middle-sized jugs to make a gallon. Knowledge of this kind is like Titian's coloring, difficult to communicate; and as Mrs. Palfrey, once remarkably handsome, had now become rather stout and asthmatical, and scarcely ever left home, her oral teaching could hardly be given anywhere except at Long Meadows. Even a matron is not insusceptible to flattery, and the prospect of a visitor whose great object would be to listen to her conversation, was not without its charms to Mrs. Palfrey. Since there was no receipt to be sent in reply to Mr. Freely's humble request, she called on her more docile daughter, Penny, to write a note, telling him that her mother would be glad to see him and talk with him on brawn, any day that he could call at Long Meadows. Penny obeyed with a trembling hand, thinking how wonderfully things came about in this world.

In this way, Mr. Freely got himself introduced into the home of the Palfreys, and notwithstanding a tendency in the male part of the family to jeer at him a little as " peaky " and bow-legged, he presently established his position as an accepted and frequent guest. Young Towers looked at him with increasing disgust when they met at the house on a Sunday, and secretly longed to try his ferret upon him, as a piece of vermin which that valuable animal would be likely to tackle with unhesitating vigor. But — so blind sometimes are parents — neither Mr. nor Mrs. Palfrey suspected that Penny would have anything to say to a tradesman of questionable rank whose youthful bloom was much withered. Young

ad an eye to her, and *that* was likely
some day; but Penny was a child at
while Penny was imagining the circum-
Mr. Freely would make her an offer:
row of damson-trees, when they were
tea; perhaps by letter — in which case,
begin? "Dearest Penelope?" or "My
" or straight off, without dear anything,
natural when people were embarrassed?
ght make the offer, she would not accept
r's consent: she would always be true to
would not disobey her father. For Penny
h some of her female friends were after-
poke ill for her not to have felt an
Freely.

ished to be quite sure of the
marriage were not entirely
d with considerations of
his position, as if he
on his education.
lace; and so,
or of the
Palfrey
eing

of in a mixed circle — especially conce[
from his uncle in Jamaica, who had n[
his nephew Edward better than any on[
though he had been so hurt at his leaving[
threatened to cut him off with a shillin[
since written to state his full forgivenes[
an eccentric old gentleman and could no[
money during his life, Mr. Edward Free[
Palfrey the letter which declared, plainly[
be the affectionate uncle's heir. Mr. Palfr[
letter, and could not help admiring the s[
who declared that such brilliant hopes as t[
ence to his conduct; he should work a[
and make his modest fortune at it[
maica estate was to come to hi[
nothing very surprising for on[
an estate left him, considerin[
sessed in time gone by[
umberland branch. [
of rum ? and als[
counts ? M[
virtues, a[
men wo[
    W[

inclined to sneer than to sympathize. Grimworth rang with the news. All men extolled Mr. Freely's good fortune; while the women, with the tender solicitude characteristic of the sex, wished the marriage might turn out well.

While affairs were at this triumphant juncture, Mr. Freely one morning observed that a stone-carver who had been break-fasting in the eating-room had left a newspaper behind. It was the "X——shire Gazette," and X——shire being a county not unknown to Mr. Freely, he felt some curiosity to glance over it, and especially over the advertisements. A slight flush came over his face as he read. It was produced by the following announcement: "If David Faux, son of Jona-than Faux, late of Gilsbrook, will apply at the office of Mr. Strutt, attorney, of Rodham, he will hear of something to his advantage."

"Father's dead!" exclaimed Mr. Freely, involuntarily. "Can he have left me a legacy?"

———◆———

CHAPTER III.

PERHAPS it was a result quite different from your expecta-tions, that Mr. David Faux should have returned from the West Indies only a few years after his arrival there, and have set up in his old business, like any plain man who had never travelled. But these cases do occur in life. Since, as we know, men change their skies and see new constellations with-out changing their souls, it will follow sometimes that they don't change their business under those novel circumstances.

Certainly, this result was contrary to David's own expecta-tions. He had looked forward, you are aware, to a brilliant career among "the blacks;" but, either because they had already seen too many white men, or for some other reason, they did not at once recognize him as a superior order of human being; besides, there were no princesses among them.

Nobody in Jamaica was anxious to maintain David for the mere pleasure of his society; and those hidden merits of a man which are so well known to himself were as little recognized there as they notoriously are in the effete society of the Old World. So that in the dark hints that David threw out at the Oyster Club about that life of Sultanic self-indulgence spent by him in the luxurious Indies, I really think he was doing himself a wrong; I believe he worked for his bread, and, in fact, took to cooking again, as, after all, the only department in which he could offer skilled labor. He had formed several ingenious plans by which he meant to circumvent people of large fortune and small faculty; but then he never met with exactly the right people under exactly the right circumstances. David's devices for getting rich without work had apparently no direct relation with the world outside him, as his confectionery receipts had. It is possible to pass a great many bad halfpennies and bad half-crowns, but I believe there has no instance been known of passing a halfpenny or a half-crown as a sovereign. A sharper can drive a brisk trade in this world: it is undeniable that there may be a fine career for him, if he will dare consequences; but David was too timid to be a sharper, or venture in any way among the man-traps of the law. He dared rob nobody but his mother. And so he had to fall back on the genuine value there was in him — to be content to pass as a good halfpenny, or, to speak more accurately, as a good confectioner. For in spite of some additional reading and observation, there was nothing else he could make so much money by; nay, he found in himself even a capability of extending his skill in this direction, and embracing all forms of cookery; while, in other branches of human labor, he began to see that it was not possible for him to shine. Fate was too strong for him; he had thought to master her inclination and had fled over the seas to that end; but she caught him, tied an apron round him, and snatching him from all other devices, made him devise cakes and patties in a kitchen at Kingstown. He was getting submissive to her, since she paid him with tolerable gains; but fevers and prickly heat, and other evils incidental to cooks in ardent climates, made him long for his native land; so he took ship once more, carrying his six years' savings, and seeing distinctly, this time, what were Fate's intentions as to his career. If you question me closely as to whether all the money with which he set up at Grimworth consisted of pure and simple earnings, I am obliged to confess that he got a sum or two for charitably abstaining from mentioning some other people's misdemeanors. Altogether, since no prospects were attached to his family name, and since a new christening seemed a suitable com: mencement of a new life, Mr. David Faux thought it as well to call himself Mr. Edward Freely.

But lo! now, in opposition to all calculable probability, some benefit appeared to be attached to the name of David Faux. Should he neglect it, as beneath the attention of a prosperous tradesman? It might bring him into contact with his family again, and he felt no yearnings in that direction: moreover, he had small belief that the "something to his advantage" could be anything considerable. On the other hand, even a small gain is pleasant, and the promise of it in this instance was so surprising, that David felt his curiosity awakened. The scale dipped at last on the side of writing to the lawyer, and, to be brief, the correspondence ended in an appointment for a meeting between David and his eldest brother at Mr. Strutt's, the vague "something" having been defined as a legacy from his father of eighty-two pounds three shillings.

David, you know, had expected to be disinherited; and so he would have been, if he had not, like some other indifferent sons, come of excellent parents, whose conscience made them scrupulous where much more highly instructed people often feel themselves warranted in following the bent of their indignation. Good Mrs. Faux could never forget that she had brought this ill-conditioned son into the world when he was in that entirely helpless state which excluded the smallest choice on his part; and, somehow or other, she felt that his going wrong would be his father's and mother's fault, if they failed in one tittle of their parental duty. Her notion of parental duty was not of a high and subtle kind, but it included giving him his due share of the family property; for when a

man had got a little honest money of his own, was he so likely
to steal? To cut the delinquent son off with a shilling, was
like delivering him over to his evil propensities. No; let the
sum of twenty guineas which he had stolen be deducted from
his share, and then let the sum of three guineas be put back
from it, seeing that his mother had always considered three of
the twenty guineas as his; and, though he had run away, and
was, perhaps, gone across the sea, let the money be left to him
all the same, and be kept in reserve for his possible return.
Mr. Faux agreed to his wife's views, and made a codicil to
his will accordingly, in time to die with a clear conscience.
But for some time his family thought it likely that David
would never reappear; and the eldest son, who had the charge
of Jacob on his hands, often thought it a little hard that David
might perhaps be dead, and yet, for want of certitude on that
point, his legacy could not fall to his legal heir. But in this
state of things the opposite certitude — namely, that David
was still alive and in England — seemed to be brought by the
testimony of a neighbor, who, having been on a journey to
Cattelton, was pretty sure he had seen David in a gig, with
a stout man driving by his side. He could "swear it was
David," though he could "give no account why, for he had
no marks on him; but no more had a white dog, and that
did n't hinder folks from knowing a white dog." It was this
incident which had led to the advertisement.

The legacy was paid, of course, after a few preliminary disclosures as to Mr. David's actual position. He begged to send
his love to his mother, and to say that he hoped to pay her a
dutiful visit by-and-by; but, at present, his business and near
prospect of marriage made it difficult for him to leave home.
His brother replied with much frankness.

"My mother may do as she likes about having you to see
her, but, for my part, I don't want to catch sight of you on the
premises again. When folks have taken a new name, they'd
better keep to their new 'quinetance."

David pocketed the insult along with the eighty-two pounds
three, and travelled home again in some triumph at the ease
of a transaction which had enriched him to this extent. He

had no intention of offending his brother by further claims on his fraternal recognition, and relapsed with full contentment into the character of Mr. Edward Freely, the orphan, scion of a great but reduced family, with an eccentric uncle in the West Indies. (I have already hinted that he had some acquaintance with imaginative literature; and being of a practical turn, he had, you perceive, applied even this form of knowledge to practical purposes.)

It was little more than a week after the return from his fruitful journey, that the day of his marriage with Penny having been fixed, it was agreed that Mrs. Palfrey should overcome her reluctance to move from home, and that she and her husband should bring their two daughters to inspect little Penny's future abode and decide on the new arrangements to be made for the reception of the bride. Mr. Freely meant her to have a house so pretty and comfortable that she need not envy even a wool-factor's wife. Of course, the upper room over the shop was to be the best sitting-room; but also the parlor behind the shop was to be made a suitable bower for the lovely Penny, who would naturally wish to be near her husband, though Mr. Freely declared his resolution never to allow *his* wife to wait in the shop. The decisions about the parlor furniture were left till last, because the party was to take tea there; and, about five o'clock, they were all seated there with the best muffins and buttered buns before them, little Penny blushing and smiling, with her "crop" in the best order, and a blue frock showing her little white shoulders, while her opinion was being always asked and never given. She secretly wished to have a particular sort of chimney ornaments, but she could not have brought herself to mention it. Seated by the side of her yellow and rather withered lover, who, though he had not reached his thirtieth year, had already crow's-feet about his eyes, she was quite tremulous at the greatness of her lot in being married to a man who had travelled so much — and before her sister Letty! The handsome Letitia looked rather proud and contemptuous, thought her future brother-in-law an odious person, and was vexed with her father and mother for letting Penny marry him. Dear little

Penny! She certainly did look like a fresh white-heart cherry
going to be bitten off the stem by that lipless mouth. Would
no deliverer come to make a slip between that cherry and that
mouth without a lip?

"Quite a family likeness between the admiral and you, Mr.
Freely," observed Mrs. Palfrey, who was looking at the family
portrait for the first time. "It's wonderful! and only a grand-
uncle. Do you feature the rest of your family, as you know
of?"

"I can't say," said Mr. Freely, with a sigh. "My family
have mostly thought themselves too high to take any notice
of me."

At this moment an extraordinary disturbance was heard in
the shop, as of a heavy animal stamping about and making
angry noises, and then of a glass vessel falling in shivers,
while the voice of the apprentice was heard calling "Master"
in great alarm.

Mr. Freely rose in anxious astonishment, and hastened into
the shop, followed by the four Palfreys, who made a group at
the parlor-door, transfixed with wonder at seeing a large man
in a smock-frock, with a pitchfork in his hand, rush up to
Mr. Freely and hug him, crying out, — "Zavy, Zavy, b'other
Zavy!"

It was Jacob, and for some moments David lost all presence
of mind. He felt arrested for having stolen his mother's
guineas. He turned cold, and trembled in his brother's grasp.

"Why, how's this?" said Mr. Palfrey, advancing from the
door. "Who is he?"

Jacob supplied the answer by saying over and over again, —
"I'se Zacob, b'other Zacob. Come 'o zee Zavy" — till hunger prompted him to relax his grasp, and to seize a large
raised pie, which he lifted to his mouth.

By this time David's power of device had begun to return,
but it was a very hard task for his prudence to master his
rage and hatred towards poor Jacob.

"I don't know who he is; he must be drunk," he said, in
a low tone to Mr. Palfrey. "But he's dangerous with that
pitchfork. He'll never let it go." Then checking himself

on the point of betraying too great an intimacy with Jacob's habits, he added, " *You* watch him, while I run for the constable." And he hurried out of the shop.

" Why, where do you come from, my man ? " said Mr. Palfrey, speaking to Jacob in a conciliatory tone. Jacob was eating his pie by large mouthfuls, and looking round at the other good things in the shop, while he embraced his pitchfork with his left arm and laid his left hand on some Bath buns. He was in the rare position of a person who recovers a long absent friend and finds him richer than ever in the characteristics that won his heart.

" I 's Zacob — b'other Zacob — 't home. I love Zavy — b'other Zavy," he said, as soon as Mr. Palfrey had drawn his attention. "Zavy come back from z' Indies — got mother's zinnies. Where 's Zavy ? " he added, looking round and then turning to the others with a questioning air, puzzled by David's disappearance.

" It 's very odd," observed Mr. Palfrey to his wife and daughters. "He seems to say Freely 's his brother come back from th' Indies."

" What a pleasant relation for us ! " said Letitia, sarcastically. "I think he 's a good deal like Mr. Freely. He 's got just the same sort of nose, and his eyes are the same color."

Poor Penny was ready to cry.

But now Mr. Freely re-entered the shop without the constable. During his walk of a few yards he had had time and calmness enough to widen his view of consequences, and he saw that to get Jacob taken to the workhouse or to the lockup house as an offensive stranger, might have awkward effects if his family took the trouble of inquiring after him. He must resign himself to more patient measures.

" On second thoughts," he said, beckoning to Mr. Palfrey and whispering to him while Jacob's back was turned, " he 's a poor half-witted fellow. Perhaps his friends will come after him. I don't mind giving him something to eat, and letting him lie down for the night. He 's got it into his head that he knows me — they do get these fancies, idiots do. He 'll perhaps go away again in an hour or two, and make no more ado.

I 'm a kind-hearted man *myself* — I should n't like to have the poor fellow ill-used."

"Why, he 'll eat a sovereign's worth in no time," said Mr. Palfrey, thinking Mr. Freely a little too magnificent in his generosity.

"Eh, Zavy, come back?" exclaimed Jacob, giving his dear brother another hug, which crushed Mr. Freely's features inconveniently against the stale of the pitchfork.

"Ay, ay," said Mr. Freely, smiling, with every capability of murder in his mind, except the courage to commit it. He wished the Bath buns might by chance have arsenic in them.

"Mother's zinnies?" said Jacob, pointing to a glass jar of yellow lozenges that stood in the window. "Zive 'em me."

David dared not do otherwise than reach down the glass jar and give Jacob a handful. He received them in his smock-frock, which he held out for more.

"They 'll keep him quiet a bit, at any rate," thought David, and emptied the jar. Jacob grinned and mowed with delight.

"You 're very good to this stranger, Mr. Freely," said Letitia; and then spitefully, as David joined the party at the parlor-door, "I think you could hardly treat him better, if he was really your brother."

"I 've always thought it a duty to be good to idiots," said Mr. Freely, striving after the most moral view of the subject. "We might have been idiots ourselves — everybody might have been born idiots, instead of having their right senses."

"I don't know where there 'd ha' been victual for us all then," observed Mrs. Palfrey, regarding the matter in a house-wifely light.

"But let us sit down again and finish our tea," said Mr. Freely. "Let us leave the poor creature to himself."

They walked into the parlor again; but Jacob, not apparently appreciating the kindness of leaving him to himself, immediately followed his brother, and seated himself, pitchfork grounded, at the table.

"Well," said Miss Letitia, rising, "I don't know whether *you* mean to stay, mother; but I shall go home."

"Oh, me too," said Penny, frightened to death at Jacob, who had begun to nod and grin at her.

"Well, I think we *had* better be going, Mr. Palfrey," said the mother, rising more slowly.

Mr. Freely, whose complexion had become decidedly yellower during the last half-hour, did not resist this proposition. He hoped they should meet again "under happier circumstances."

"It's my belief the man is his brother," said Letitia, when they were all on their way home.

"Letty, it's very ill-natured of *you*," said Penny, beginning to cry.

"Nonsense!" said Mr. Palfrey. "Freely's got no brother — he's said so many and many a time; he's an orphan; he's got nothing but uncles — leastwise, one. What's it matter what an idiot says? What call had Freely to tell lies?"

Letitia tossed her head and was silent.

Mr. Freely, left alone with his affectionate brother Jacob, brooded over the possibility of luring him out of the town early the next morning, and getting him conveyed to Gilsbrook without further betrayals. But the thing was difficult. He saw clearly that if he took Jacob away himself, his absence, conjoined with the disappearance of the stranger, would either cause the conviction that he was really a relative, or would oblige him to the dangerous course of inventing a story to account for his disappearance, and his own absence at the same time. David groaned. There come occasions when falsehood is felt to be inconvenient. It would, perhaps, have been a longer-headed device, if he had never told any of those clever fibs about his uncles, grand and otherwise; for the Palfreys were simple people, and shared the popular prejudice against lying. Even if he could get Jacob away this time, what security was there that he would not come again, having once found the way? O guineas! O lozenges! what enviable people those were who had never robbed their mothers, and had never told fibs! David spent a sleepless night, while Jacob was snoring close by. Was this the upshot of travelling to the Indies, and acquiring experience combined with anecdote?

He rose at break of day, as he had once before done when he was in fear of Jacob, and took all gentle means to rouse this fatal brother from his deep sleep ; he dared not be loud, because his apprentice was in the house, and would report everything. But Jacob was not to be roused. He fought out with his fist at the unknown cause of disturbance, turned over, and snored again. He must be left to wake as he would, David, with a cold perspiration on his brow, confessed to him self that Jacob could not be got away that day.

Mr. Palfrey came over to Grimworth before noon, with a natural curiosity to see how his future son-in-law got on with the stranger to whom he was so benevolently inclined. He found a crowd round the shop. All Grimworth by this time had heard how Freely had been fastened on by an idiot, who called him " Brother Zavy ; " and the younger population seemed to find the singular stranger an unwearying source of fascination, while the householders dropped in one by one to inquire into the incident.

" Why don't you send him to the workhouse ? " said Mr. Prettyman. " You 'll have a row with him and the children presently, and he 'll eat you up. The workhouse is the proper place for him ; let his kin claim him, if he 's got any."

" Those may be *your* feelings, Mr. Prettyman," said David, his mind quite enfeebled by the torture of his position.

" What ! *is* he your brother, then ? " said Mr. Prettyman, looking at his neighbor Freely rather sharply.

" All men are our brothers, and idiots particular so," said Mr. Freely, who, like many other travelled men, was not master of the English language.

" Come, come, if he 's your brother, tell the truth, man," said Mr. Prettyman, with growing suspicion. " Don't be ashamed of your own flesh and blood."

Mr. Palfrey was present, and also had his eye on Freely. It is difficult for a man to believe in the advantage of a truth which will disclose him to have been a liar. In this critical moment, David shrank from this immediate disgrace in the eyes of his future father-in-law.

" Mr. Prettyman," he said, " I take your observations as an

insult. I 've no reason to be otherwise than proud of my own flesh and blood. If this poor man was my brother more than all men are, I should say so."

A tall figure darkened the door, and David, lifting his eyes in that direction, saw his eldest brother, Jonathan, on the door-sill.

"I 'll stay wi' Zavy," shouted Jacob, as he, too, caught sight of his eldest brother; and, running behind the counter, he clutched David hard.

"What, he *is* here ? " said Jonathan Faux, coming forward. "My mother would have no nay, as he 'd been away so long, but I must see after him. And it struck me he was very like come after you, because we 'd been talking of you o' late, and where you lived."

David saw there was no escape ; he smiled a ghastly smile.

"What ! is this a relation of yours, sir ? " said Mr. Palfrey to Jonathan.

"Ay, it 's my innicent of a brother, sure enough," said honest Jonathan. "A fine trouble and cost he is to us, in th' eating and other things, but we must bear what 's laid on us."

"And your name 's Freely, is it ? " said Mr. Prettyman.

"Nay, nay, my name 's Faux, I know nothing o' Freelys," said Jonathan, curtly. "Come," he added, turning to David, "I must take some news to mother about Jacob. Shall I take him with me, or will you undertake to send him back ? "

"Take him, if you can make him loose his hold of me," said David, feebly.

"Is this gentleman here in the confectionery line your brother, then, sir ? " said Mr. Prettyman, feeling that it was an occasion on which formal language must be used.

"*I* don't want to own him," said Jonathan, unable to resist a movement of indignation that had never been allowed to satisfy itself. "He run away from home with good reasons in his pocket years ago : he did n't want to be owned again, I reckon."

Mr. Palfrey left the shop ; he felt his own pride too severely wounded by the sense that he had let himself be fooled, to

feel curiosity for further details. The most pressing business
was to go home and tell his daughter that Freely was a
poor sneak, probably a rascal, and that her engagement was
broken off.

Mr. Prettyman stayed, with some internal self-gratulation
that *he* had never given in to Freely, and that Mr. Chaloner
would see now what sort of fellow it was that he had put over
the heads of older parishioners. He considered it due from
him (Mr. Prettyman) that, for the interests of the parish, he
should know all that was to be known about this "interloper."
Grimworth would have people coming from Botany Bay to
settle in it, if things went on in this way.

It soon appeared that Jacob could not be made to quit his
dear brother David except by force. He understood, with a
clearness equal to that of the most intelligent mind, that
Jonathan would take him back to skimmed milk, apple-
dumpling, broad-beans, and pork. And he had found a paradise in his brother's shop. It was a difficult matter to use
force with Jacob, for he wore heavy nailed boots ; and if his
pitchfork had been mastered, he would have resorted without
hesitation to kicks. Nothing short of using guile to bind him
hand and foot would have made all parties safe.

"Let him stay," said David, with desperate resignation,
frightened above all things at the idea of further disturbances
in his shop, which would make his exposure all the more conspicuous. " *You* go away again, and to-morrow I can, perhaps,
get him to go to Gilsbrook with me. He 'll follow me fast
enough, I dare say," he added, with a half-groan.

"Very well," said Jonathan, gruffly. " I don't see why *you*
should n't have some trouble and expense with him as well as
the rest of us. But mind you bring him back safe and soon,
else mother 'll never rest."

On this arrangement being concluded, Mr. Prettyman begged
Mr. Jonathan Faux to go and take a snack with him, an invitation which was quite acceptable ; and as honest Jonathan
had nothing to be ashamed of, it is probable that he was very
frank in his communications to the civil draper, who, pursuing
the benefit of the parish, hastened to make all the informa-

tion he could gather about Freely common parochial property. You may imagine that the meeting of the Club at the Wool-pack that evening was unusually lively. Every member was anxious to prove that he had never liked Freely, as he called himself. Faux was his name, was it? Fox would have been more suitable. The majority expressed a desire to see him hooted out of the town.

Mr. Freely did not venture over his door-sill that day, for he knew Jacob would keep at his side, and there was every probability that they would have a train of juvenile followers. He sent to engage the Woolpack gig for an early hour the next morning; but this order was not kept religiously a secret by the landlord. Mr. Freely was informed that he could not have the gig till seven; and the Grimworth people were early risers. Perhaps they were more alert than usual on this par-ticular morning; for when Jacob, with a bag of sweets in his hand, was induced to mount the gig with his brother David, the inhabitants of the market-place were looking out of their doors and windows, and at the turning of the street there was even a muster of apprentices and schoolboys, who shouted as they passed in what Jacob took to be a very merry and friendly way, nodding and grinning in return. "Huzzay, David Faux! how's your uncle?" was their morning's greeting. Like other pointed things, it was not altogether impromptu.

Even this public derision was not so crushing to David as the horrible thought that though he might succeed now in getting Jacob home again there would never be any security against his coming back, like a wasp to the honey-pot. As long as David lived at Grimworth, Jacob's return would be hanging over him. But could he go on living at Grimworth —an object of ridicule, discarded by the Palfreys, after having revelled in the consciousness that he was an envied and prosperous confectioner? David liked to be envied; he minded less about being loved.

His doubts on this point were soon settled. The mind of Grimworth became obstinately set against him and his viands, and the new school being finished, the eating-room was closed. If there had been no other reason, sympathy with the Palfreys, that respectable family who had lived in the parish time out or mind, would have determined all well-to-do people to decline Freely's goods. Besides, he had absconded with his mother's guineas: who knew what else he had done, in Jamaica or elsewhere, before he came to Grimworth, worming himself into families under false pretences? Females shuddered. Dreadful suspicions gathered round him: his green eyes, his bow-legs, had a criminal aspect. The rector disliked the sight of a man who had imposed upon him; and all boys who could not afford to purchase, hooted "David Faux" as they passed his shop. Certainly no man now would pay anything for the "good-will" of Mr. Freely's business, and he would be obliged to quit it without a peculium so desirable towards defraying the expense of moving.

In a few months the shop in the market-place was again to let, and Mr. David Faux, *alias* Mr. Edward Freely, had gone — nobody at Grimworth knew whither. In this way the demoralization of Grimworth women was checked. Young Mrs. Steene renewed her efforts to make light mince-pies, and having at last made a batch so excellent that Mr. Steene looked at her with complacency as he ate them, and said they were the best he had ever eaten in his life, she thought less of bul-buls and renegades ever after. The secrets of the finer cookery were revived in the breasts of matronly housewives, and daughters were again anxious to be initiated in them.

You will further, I hope, be glad to hear, that some purchases of drapery made by pretty Penny, in preparation for her marriage with Mr. Freely, came in quite as well for her wedding with young Towers as if they had been made expressly for the latter occasion. For Penny's complexion had not altered, and blue always became it best.

Here ends the story of Mr. David Faux, confectioner, and his brother Jacob. And we see in it, I think, an admirable instance of the unexpected forms in which the great Nemesis hides herself.